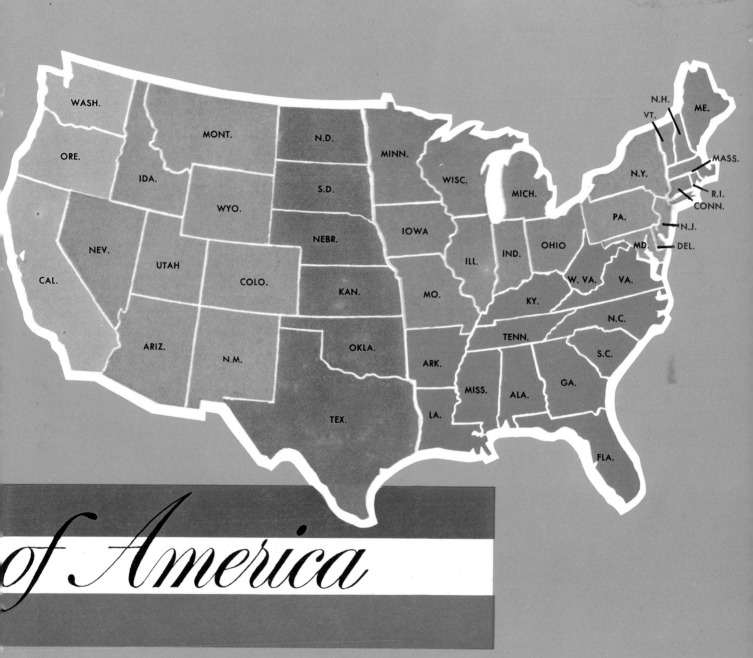

of America

OUR
FIFTY STATES

By EARL SCHENCK MIERS

Illustrated by ELEANOR MILL
Maps by LEONARD DARWIN

GROSSET & DUNLAP · Publishers · NEW YORK

Contents

State Maps

Regional Maps

New England

MASSACHUSETTS
"The Bay State"

MASSACHUSETTS is a combination of three Algonquin words — *adchu* (mountain or hill), *set* (location near or in the vicinity of), and *massu* (great). The name means "near the great mountain."

The first white man to land on the shores of Massachusetts may have been Leif Ericsson, son of Eric the Red, whose Norsemen visited North America in the year 1000. Then for almost five hundred years, the region "near the great mountain" remained the undisturbed domain of the red man. Beginning in 1497, a procession of explorers appeared during the next

century — John and Sebastian Cabot under the flag of Britain, Verrazano flying the *fleur de lis* of France, Gomez for Spain.

In 1578 Queen Elizabeth gave Sir Humphrey Gilbert a patent to establish a permanent English settlement in the New World. Before Sir Humphrey could achieve this goal he died on the storm-tossed Atlantic, shouting, "We are as near to heaven by sea as by land." Gilbert's patent legally passed to his half brother, Sir Walter Raleigh, but others attempted settlements despite Raleigh's claim. In 1602 Bartholomew Gosnold sailed into Massachu-

The
Bay State

setts Bay, named Cape Cod, and landed on the nearby Elizabeth Islands. Although an ill-fated colony was started at the mouth of the Kennebec River in 1607, not for another thirteen years would the real story of Massachusetts begin. Then, on September 16, 1620, a little ship, the *Mayflower,* sailed from Plymouth in England's Devonshire.

Voyage of the Mayflower

Among the 102 passengers of the *Mayflower* were strong-willed Separatists, or Pilgrims, who were seeking in the New World a haven where they could worship God according to the dictates of their consciences. Soon gales swept the ocean. The little ship tossed wildly and sprang a leak in its upper section. Next, one of the main beams amidships cracked. Some passengers talked of turning back, but the stouthearted among them pointed out that the under parts of the vessel remained tight and sturdy. So the *Mayflower* sailed on — through gale and calm and gale again. Scurvy made many too weak to walk. New storms arose, bouncing the *Mayflower* upon the great waves like a toy boat, yet only one Pilgrim, young William Butten, died at sea.

After sixty-five days the highlands of Cape Cod were sighted on November 21, 1620. Sailing into Provincetown harbor, the Pilgrims shuddered at a country "full of woods and thickets" that presented "a wild and savage view." Passengers and crew assembled on the deck and agreed to the Mayflower Compact, the first written plan for self-government in America founded upon a belief in "just and

equal laws." Then the Pilgrims sailed on, searching for a more hospitable-appearing shore. On the day after Christmas they settled on Plymouth harbor.

In a land that still turned upon them "a weather-beaten face," they built their first common house. The Indians befriended them and, when spring came, taught the colonists how to plant corn and beans — with such success that by autumn they realized God had delivered them from hunger and exposure, and Governor William Bradford proclaimed the first Thanksgiving Day.

The Great Migration

Other settlers — chiefly traders, fishermen and indentured servants — came to Massachusetts, among them the followers of Thomas Morton, who were found dancing around the Maypole and otherwise "frisking together like so many fairies or furies." Horrified Pilgrims sent an armed force under Captain Miles Standish to put down such frivolity. A new group of growing influence in Massachusetts became known as the Puritans, who wanted to purify society from within rather than by separating from the Established Church, as the Pilgrims had done.

A royal grant gave the Puritans all the land from sea to sea between a point three miles south of the Charles River and three miles north of the Merrimack River. This grant created the Massachusetts Bay Colony, which was to be run by two general courts. One court was to be composed of stockholders or freemen, a provision that laid the basis for representative government in

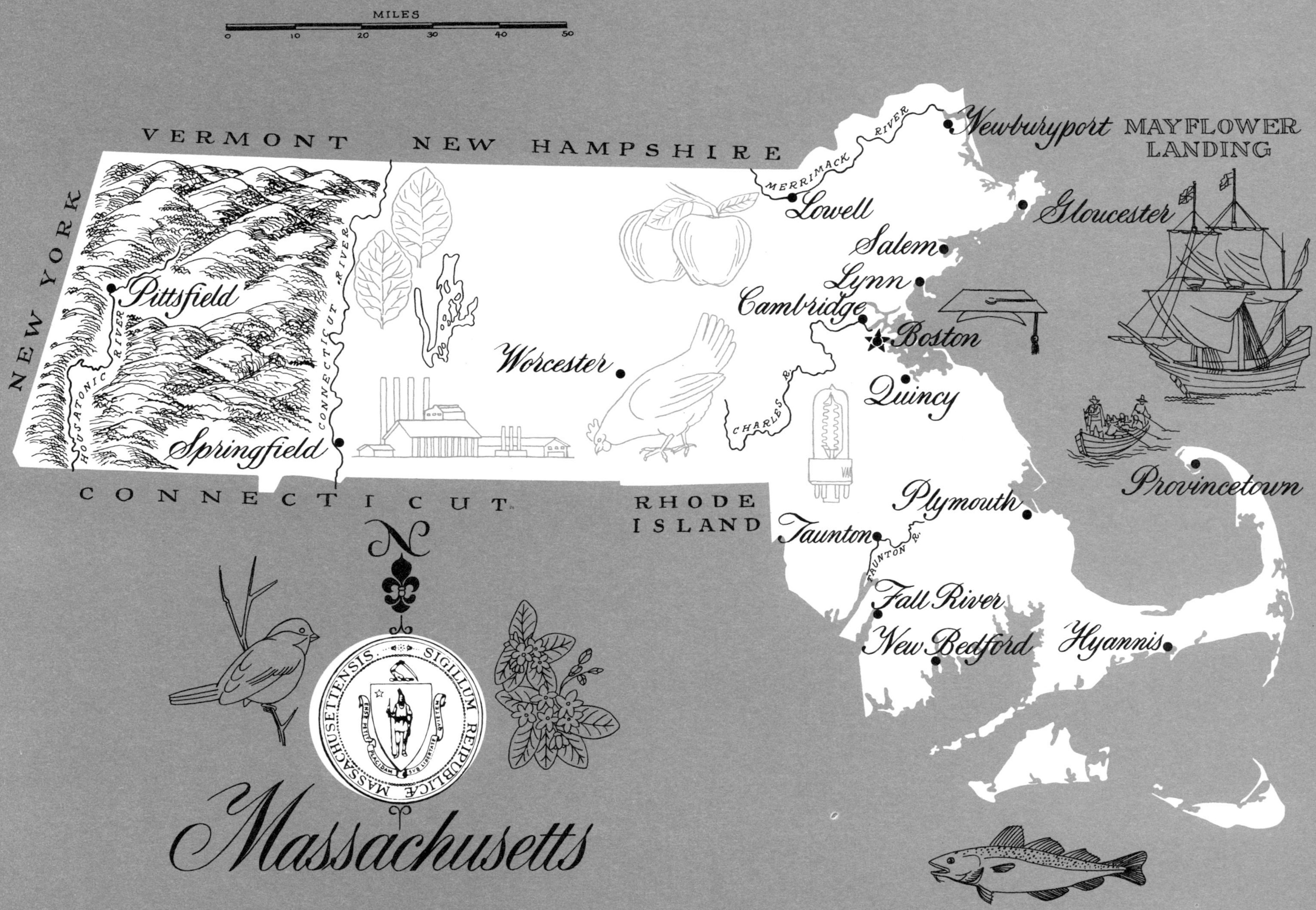

NEWBURYPORT MAYFLOWER LANDING

Gloucester

Provincetown

Hyannis

Newburyport

Salem

Lynn

Lowell

Cambridge

Boston

Quincy

Plymouth

Fall River

New Bedford

MERRIMACK RIVER

CHARLES

TAUNTON R.

Taunton

Worcester

NEW HAMPSHIRE

VERMONT

RHODE ISLAND

CONNECTICUT

CONNECTICUT RIVER

Springfield

Pittsfield

HOUSATONIC RIVER

NEW YORK

MILES

50
40
30
20
10
0

SIGILLUM REIPUBLICÆ MASSACHUSETTENSIS
ENSE PETIT PLACIDAM SVB LIBERTATE QVIETEM

Massachusetts

*The
Bay State*

Massachusetts. Insofar as the charter failed to stipulate that the meetings of the court must be held in England, the colony was left to develop its destiny in an atmosphere of independence.

By 1640, ten years of the "Great Migration" brought 16,000 people into Massachusetts. On the south shore, settlements existed at Duxbury, Scituate, Hingham, Barnstable, Yarmouth and Marshfield, and on the north shore, at Saugus (Lynn), Ipswich, Marblehead, Newbury, Rowley and Salisbury. Westward the traveler journeyed through Cambridge, Dedham, Braintree, Concord, Sudbury. Whereas the early settlers of Massachusetts wished freedom to worship God according to their own beliefs, both Pilgrim and Puritan were severely intolerant of other dissenters and soon the Bay Colony became crisscrossed with the trails of leaders and their followers seeking their own brand of freedom. Thomas Hooker led his band into Connecticut. Roger Williams sought refuge in Rhode Island. John Wheelwright went to New Hampshire.

The New England "Spirit"

Hostility between settlers also seemed to breed trouble between red man and white, resulting finally in the frightful bloodshed of King Philip's War. An experiment in 1684 created the Dominion of New England under Sir Edmund Andros, and for a time this single governmental unit embraced Massachusetts, Rhode Island, Connecticut, New Hampshire, Maine, New York and New Jersey. Andros' tyrannical

acts led to his undoing and the Puritans set up a provisional government for Massachusetts until William and Mary granted a new charter in 1691.

Despite the bad tempers of the Puritans that could lead them, for example, to drive away Quakers seeking refuge in the Bay Colony, Massachusetts achieved a miracle in evolving the New England town. This snug community, built around the town square and the church, produced a spirit that greatly influenced American life. The long winter evenings brought the New Englander an opportunity to develop many skills — as a harnessmaker, blower of glass, cabinetmaker, silversmith — and his reputation as a jack-of-all-trades grew into a tradition.

Although the church prescribed how a self-respecting New Englander must act, talk and dress—thus giving America its first blue laws — the church also encouraged education. As early as 1636, John Harvard gave America its first college, and a law in 1647 requiring elementary schools in towns of fifty families and secondary schools in towns double that size began the movement of popular education. The town meeting, where any citizen could speak out, brought democratic government to a high peak — often in spite of Puritan and Pilgrim.

And yet the essential fact was that there grew in the people an increasing attitude of "live and let live." By the 1700's sports and games in Colonial Massachusetts included an Indian dice game called "hubbub," shuffleboard, bowling, horse racing, hog races. The Boston *Gazette* announced in its issue for May 22-29, 1721: "There will be a Pig Run for by Boys, at 9 in the morning. The Boy who takes the Pig and fairly holds it by the Tail, wins the Prize."

"Chasing the Redcoats Down the Lane"

The part played by Massachusetts in the events leading up to the Revolution supplies a thrilling chapter in the nation's history. The Boston Massacre of 1770, where the first blood was spilled, and the Boston Tea Party of 1773 were forerunners of those fateful April days of 1775 at Lexington and Concord when the Minutemen clashed with the British Regimentals. As Henry Wadsworth Longfellow told it:

*How the farmers gave them ball
  for ball,
From behind each fence and
  farmyard wall,
Chasing the redcoats down the lane,
Then crossing the fields to
  emerge again
Under the trees at the turn of
  the road,
And only pausing to fire and load.*

*The
Bay State*

An economic depression, following the Revolution, especially hurt the farmers of Massachusetts, and under old Daniel Shays they threatened to capture Boston before Shays's Rebellion was put down in 1787. These same farmers distrusted the United States Constitution, believing it was more favorable to trade and finance than to agriculture, but the influence of John

*The
Bay State*

Hancock prevailed and in 1788 Massachusetts became the sixth state to ratify the document. A period of prosperity followed, but was ended all too quickly by the War of 1812, as a poet of the day explained:

*Our ships all in motion once
    whitened the ocean,
They sailed and returned with
    a cargo;
Now doomed to decay, they have
    fallen a prey
To Jefferson — worms — and
    embargo.*

Yankee Trade and Traders

Yet the Yankee jack-of-all-trades could not be long subdued. The sewing machine of Elias Howe and the telephone of Alexander Graham Bell would be but two of his inventions. From his shipyards would come whaling vessels that circled the globe. Not only was the Massachusetts man willing to make, sell and deliver almost any article of merchandise, but he was also ingenious in advertising his trade as this Boston manufacturer of Byam's matches demonstrated in 1848:

*For quickness and sureness the
    public will find,
These matches will leave all
    others behind:
Without further remarks we
    invite you to try 'em,
Remember all goods that are
    signed by — E. Byam.*

As the home of William Lloyd Garrison and his militantly antislavery newspaper, *The Liberator,* and as the state of that unwavering spokesman for the Union, Daniel Webster, Massachusetts could not avoid a deep involvement in the causes and events of the American Civil War. But in time those tragic years ended and Massachusetts once more concentrated on fulfilling its role as one of our nation's greatest industrial states. Factories turning out boots and shoes would be responsible in no small measure for that success, along with the textile mills powered by the waters of the Merrimack and Fall rivers. Cotton and woolen goods, felt goods, rugs, silk, cordage and twine, paper, books, machinery, clocks and watches were other products keeping the hum in Massachusetts factories.

In addition, the state has a prosperous agriculture. Its Cape Cod fisherman is second to none, and mountains and beaches and the islands of Martha's Vineyard and Nantucket make the Bay State a favorite vacation retreat.

But Massachusetts pride — the heritage it has bestowed upon America — cannot be measured in material terms. Longfellow, Thoreau, Emerson, Whittier, Hawthorne, Melville, Louisa May Alcott, Amy Lowell, Emily Dickinson, among others — in such great men and women of literature does Massachusetts count its gifts to the nation. Birthplace of Benjamin Franklin, home of the remarkable Adams family that sent two Presidents to the White House, of President John F. Kennedy, of artists like John Singleton Copley and educators like Horace Mann — here, too, is symbolized the spirit of Massachusetts, the truth of its motto: "By the sword we seek peace, but peace only under liberty."

RHODE ISLAND
"Little Rhody"

ALTHOUGH more than 480 states the size of Rhode Island could be carved from Alaska, our largest state, "Little Rhody" has no need to take second place to any member of the Union.

The smallest of the thirteen original colonies, Rhode Island was the first to declare her independence from Britain — a reflection of Little Rhody's flair for often being "firstest with the mostest." The first white girl born in New England howled her welcome to the world in Rhode Island. The nation's oldest military organization, the Newport Artillery Company, was chartered in 1741, and the first street in America to be lighted by gas was Pelham Street in Newport (1806). The three oldest houses of religious worship in the United States — one Quaker, one Seventh Day Baptist, one Jewish — are located in Rhode Island. The first automobile driver to draw a jail sentence for speeding (1904) stood before

a Rhode Island judge. To Little Rhody goes the credit for beginning in Pawtucket the nation's textile industry, and to Betsey Metcalf of Providence, who was then twelve years old, goes the credit for making America's first straw bonnet (1798).

But that's only a sampling. What, above all else, sets Little Rhody apart in the American pageant is the fact that here religious freedom first flowered and flourished in New England.

White Men and Red

Navigators of many nations explored the coast of Rhode Island. Probably the first to reach these shores was Miguel Côrte-Real of Portugal in 1501 or 1502. Some years later, in 1524, a Florentine navigator employed by France, Giovanni da Verrazano, entered Narragansett Bay, and tradition insists that Verrazano was so struck by the resemblance between this region and the Isle of Rhodos (Island of

Little Rhody

Roses) in the Mediterranean that he named the land Rhode Island. Next of importance to sail this coast was a Dutchman, Captain Adriaen Block, who appeared in 1614.

In the century between Corte-Real and Block, Rhode Island remained the homeland of five tribes of Algonquins — the Narragansetts, Niantics, Nipmucks, Pequots and Wampanoags — a strong-willed people who lived by a strict tribal code. If, for example, these Indians killed a deer on soil belonging to another tribe, part of the slain animal always was sent to the sachem ruling the territory. By using grains of corn they devised a system for counting from 1 to 100,000. They coined money (or wampum) from shells, using the inner shell of the periwinkle and the shell of the quahog (clam). Their houses were made of upright poles, arranged in a circle and covered with bark or skins.

The Indians of Rhode Island developed many skills. From stones they made axes, chisels, arrowheads, pestles and mortars. Baked earthenware supplied their dishes and cooking utensils. They hunted and trapped and plowed the ground with sharp sticks. They were splendid weavers of baskets and nets and they hollowed out logs for their canoes. A bread made of crushed strawberries and meal was a favorite delicacy, and they valued tobacco as a cure for toothache and a preventative against rheumatism. A Rhode Island Indian, at his fanciest, usually appeared before his admiring onlookers in a coat of turkey feathers — a proud man, willing to fight for his rights.

Roger Williams, Colonial Rebel

Roger Williams, often called the father of Rhode Island, never offered the least offense to the Indians, and had others been as wise as he, the colony would have escaped the Indian wars that were soon to terrorize it. But few men in Colonial America thought or acted like Roger Williams, whose patron in England, the great lawyer Sir Edward Coke, also loved justice. Williams reached Boston in 1631 and within two years his liberal views had brought him to a breaking point with the Puritan leaders of Massachusetts.

What did Williams say that threw the Bay Colony into an uproar?

He denied that a civil court had the right to punish a person for breaches of religious discipline, insisting that in matters of conscience "man is responsible to God alone!" He denied that the King of England had a right to give away land belonging to the Indians!

Not surprisingly, Roger Williams was banished from the Bay Colony. In 1636 he followed the "narrow Indian path" out of Salem that brought him ultimately to that spot which, in gratitude to "God's providence," he called Providence. Other settlements at Portsmouth, Newport and Warwick were formed in 1644 into a union called "Providence Plantations," and in 1663 Charles II granted the charter of "Rhode Island and Providence Plantation." It stipulated that "no person . . . at any time" could be molested or punished "for any differences in matters of religion" as long as that person behaved "peaceably and quietly."

Nathanael Greene

*Little
Rhody*

Our First Free Republic

Among the Indians, young chiefs came to power who were neither bound in affection to moderate leaders like Roger Williams, nor inclined to stand in awe of the white man. A series of violent uprisings swept Rhode Island. There was, during King Philip's War, an especially bloody December day in 1675 when, in the Great Swamp Fight near Kingston, the Indians were burned out of their winter encampment. Other raids, fires, scalpings and murders followed, yet Rhode Island continued to grow — in farms, towns, ships, commerce and independence of spirit. Today Rhode Island calls itself the "New World's first free republic," basing its claim on the events of May 4, 1776, when, two months before the thirteen colonies broke with Britain, the General Assembly of the Colony of Rhode Island declared its independence from the mother country.

Insofar as Rhode Island had been carrying on a private war for a dozen years with the British, the action should have surprised no one. The Stamp Act found sailors of *H.M.S. Squirrel* and citizens of Newport battling with cutlasses and clubs as early as July 9, 1764. The following year, when Patrick Henry spoke out in the Virginia Legislature against the Stamp Act, papers in Williamsburg, Philadelphia and New York hesitated to print his remarks, but the Newport *Mercury* gave the speech wide circulation. In 1765 Newporters returned to their private war, burning the longboats of the sloop-of-war *Liberty*.

Little Rhody's rebellion against Britain shifted next to Providence, where the citizens not only organized their own tea-dumping party, but also, one night in 1772, sent a party of merchants and sailors to board a British revenue vessel, the *Gaspee*. The crew was captured and torches soon left the ship a mass of flames. This act of defiance against unjust laws stirred all the colonies, and in Williamsburg, Virginia, George Washington helped pay for a fireworks display to celebrate the event!

War, Slavery, Statehood

Truthfully, one could say that Rhode Island fought as much of the American Revolution before as after war was declared. In October, 1776, the British frigate *Rose* bombarded Bristol and from December 8, 1776 to October 25, 1779 the British occupied Newport. French aid under Count Rochambeau

Little
Rhody

ultimately forced the British out of Rhode Island. Meanwhile, one of Little Rhody's citizens, General Nathanael Greene, was fighting a brilliant campaign against the British in the Carolinas, and another of Little Rhody's citizens, Esek Hopkins, was winning honors as first admiral of the Continental Navy. In the midst of war, Rhode Island pressed ahead with a program of progressive legislation begun in 1774 when it prohibited the slave trade. Measures for the gradual emancipation of slaves were enacted in 1784.

Perhaps it was within the character of Rhode Island that, jealous of any outside interference, the state was last among the thirteen original colonies to ratify the United States Constitution. But Little Rhody wanted assurance that the rights of the smaller states would be protected, and its consent, given in 1790, was bestowed somewhat grudgingly — 34 ayes, 32 nays!

All Manner of Heroes

Cotton manufacturing by water power, introduced in Providence that same year, started Rhode Island's rapid industrial growth. Today, in cities like Providence, Pawtucket, Central Falls and Woonsocket, the textile mills of Rhode Island turn out woolens and worsted, cottons, silk, rayon and lace goods. Little Rhody's silverware and jewelry factories owe their start to two brothers in Providence, Nehemiah and Seril Dodge, who, in 1790, discovered a method for covering a cheaper metal with a more precious metal. Other industries that make Little Rhody economically strong are machinery, rubber goods, machine tools, optical and electrical supplies, paper and boat-building. The chief mineral resources of the state are granite and limestone, and its fisheries are noted for lobsters, crabs, oysters, clams, scallops, mussels, mackerel, eel, flounder, scup and striped bass. Narragansett Bay comprises one-sixth the area of the state.

Once a prosperous sheep-raising state, then renowned for a breed of saddle horse known as the Narragansett Pacer (actually developed for export to Virginia and the West Indies), Little Rhody's enduring fame in agriculture stems from the development, in 1854, of a new breed of chicken called the Rhode Island Red. A monument, unique in America, stands at Adamsville, commemorating the contribution of Rhode Island Red to America's poultry raisers!

Little Rhody's famous sons are many — Commodore Oliver Hazard Perry, hero of the battle of Lake Erie; General Ambrose E. Burnside of Civil War fame; Captain Robert Gray, discoverer of the Columbia River and the first navigator to carry the American flag around the world; Thomas Willett, the first English-speaking mayor of New York (1665-67); and George M. Cohan, one of America's best-loved composers of popular songs. Others could be added but care has to be taken in such matters, or one is likely to be reminded that a famous American poet, William Cullen Bryant, wrote:

Rogue's Island once — but when the
rogues were dead,
Rhode Island was the name it took
instead.

MASS.

Woonsocket

BLACKSTONE R.

Pawtucket

Providence

PAWTUXET R.

CONNECTICUT

Newport

ROGER WILLIAMS

N

SEAL OF THE STATE OF RHODE ISLAND AND PROVIDENCE PLANTATIONS · HOPE · 1636

Rhode Island

MILES
0 2 4 6 8 10

CONNECTICUT
"Home of the Yankee Peddler"

THE PATTISON brothers, Edward and William, makers of tinware in Berlin, Connecticut, started about 1740 selling their goods from door to door to become the first "Yankee Peddlers." Soon they employed other salesmen to travel a route covering fifteen hundred miles. Pack on back, these hardy peddlers tramped wilderness trails to Cape Cod, to the shores of Lake Erie, to Detroit and Canada, to Kentucky and the sleepy bayou country around New Orleans.

To the stocks of tinware were added the products of other Connecticut craftsmen — clocks from Plymouth, combs from Ivoryton, galluses (suspenders) from Middletown, needles, pins and buttons from the Naugatuck Valley. Sometimes the Yankee peddler saw himself mimicked on the stage as "Sam Slick." Likely he grinned, for in the wilderness he could find many a

cabin without chair or table that still owned a Connecticut clock!

Connecticut has many nicknames. It has been called "The Constitution State" and "The Nutmeg State." George Washington, grateful for the state's support during the Revolution, referred to Connecticut as "The Provision State." Today, residents speak of Connecticut as the "Land of Steady Habits," but in the story of America, Connecticut must always endure as the birthplace and home of the Yankee peddler!

"By the Great Tidal River"

The history of Connecticut — an Indian word meaning "by the great tidal river" — begins in 1614 when, on a voyage from Manhattan Island, the Dutch navigator, Captain Adriaen Block, sailed up the Connecticut River as far as the Enfield Rapids. Although

Block traded with the Indians, nearly twenty years passed before the Dutch built a trading post and fort near present-day Hartford. Meanwhile, in Massachusetts, the English heard from the Indians glowing accounts of the fertility of the soil in Connecticut, and in 1632 Edward Winslow, governor of Plymouth Colony, visited the Connecticut Valley. That same year a royal grant gave to Lord Say-and-Sele, Lord Brooke and eleven others all the land between Narragansett Bay and the Pacific Ocean.

British interest suddenly awakened Wouter Van Twiller, governor of New Netherlands, to the forgotten empire which Adriaen Block had claimed. Van Twiller hurried a party to the mouth of the Connecticut River, bought some land from the Indians, and nailed the Dutch coat of arms to a tree.

The English were not impressed. In September, 1633, a small group from Plymouth Colony under William Holmes settled at Windsor. The following year John Oldham brought a band of colonists from Watertown, Massachusetts, to Wethersfield. In 1635 the dissenters from New Town (Cambridge), who followed John Steel and Thomas Hooker, reached Hartford, and other settlers under John Winthrop, Jr. erected a fort at Saybrook.

On the Warpath

The English, pushing the Dutch into their lone trading post and fort, made no secret of the fact that the British had come to Connecticut to stay. In 1636 they established the General Court, in which all the "towns" of Connecticut were represented so that they could act in concert. Sooner than they expected came a need for unity of action when the Pequot Indians — nudged by the Dutch — took to the warpath.

Tensions quickened. Two Englishmen, Captains Stone and Norton, journeying up the Connecticut on a trading mission, were murdered. Then John Oldham, father of the Wethersfield settlement, was killed off Block Island. The fall and winter of 1636-37 brought raids and massacres at Saybrook and Wethersfield. On May 1, 1637, the General Court of Hartford acted — the settlers would raise an army under Captain John Mason and fight the Pequots.

Not counting Mohegan and Narragansett guides and allies, the little Connecticut army of seventy-seven advanced on the morning of May 26 upon the chief Indian fort at Pequot Hill, West Mystic. Here in a circular area covering several acres were about seventy wigwams. Mason, a good soldier, had caught the Pequots flat-footed — indeed, many were asleep. Torches were put to the camp and a rising wind quickly spread the flames. What followed was not a pretty business for many Pequots. A swamp fight at Fairfield in July finished off the last remnant of Pequot resistance and the English held Connecticut by right of settlement and conquest!

Some Very Blue Laws

In April, 1638, about 250 men, women and children under Theophilus Eaton, Edward Hopkins and the Reverend John Davenport settled at New Haven. That June an earthquake shook

Home of the Yankee Peddler

*Home
of the
Yankee
Peddler*

southern Connecticut, but this frightening trick of nature could not compare to the terrible consequences awaiting those who disobeyed the Blue Laws adopted by the New Haven Colony. Here are a few samples recalled by the Reverend Samuel Peters:

"No one shall cross a river on Sunday but an authorized clergyman."

"No woman shall kiss her child on the Sabbath or fasting day."

"Every male shall have his hair cut round according to a cap."

"No one shall read common prayer, keep Christmas or saint days, make minced pies, dance, play cards, or play on any instrument of music, except the drum, trumpet, and jew's-harp."

"No one shall be a freeman or have a vote, unless he is converted and a member of one of the churches allowed in the dominion."

And Some Very Good Laws

A sermon by Thomas Hooker in 1638

inspired Roger Ludlow to draw up the Fundamental Orders, which were adopted by the settlements of Windsor, Wethersfield and Hartford in order to establish "one publike State or Commonwealth." The Fundamental Orders, which advanced the radical principle that "the foundation of authority is in the free consent of the people," served as Connecticut's first written constitution. In 1662, under a charter from Charles II, all the settlements from Massachusetts to Long Island Sound and from Narragansett Bay to the Pacific Ocean were consolidated. Twice, Sir Edmund Andros, as governor of the short-lived Dominion of New England, tried to wrest authority, but when he demanded the surrender of the Connecticut Charter, the colonists at Hartford hid it inside an oak tree — Connecticut's immortal Charter Oak!

During the Revolution, the British burned Danbury (1777) and raided New Haven (1779), and in 1781 Bene-

RHODE ISLAND

THAMES R.

Connecticut

SIGILLUM REIPUBLICÆ CONNECTICUTENSIS

CONNECTICUT RIVER

Hartford

New Haven

MILES

0   5   10   15

Waterbury

NAUGATUCK R.

HOUSATONIC RIVER

Bridgeport

NEW YORK

GEN. PUTNAM

*Home
of the
Yankee
Peddler*

dict Arnold captured Fort Griswold and Fort Trumbull. The spirit with which Connecticut supported the young nation was reflected in the state's willingness, in 1786, to surrender to the United States all rights in western land except the Western Reserve (now Ohio). For a time the War of 1812 somewhat strained that spirit, resulting in the Hartford Convention, where members of the Federalist Party sought to obtain guarantees of stronger states' rights.

Connecticut's future, however, was being decided in other areas — in New Britain, for example, where James North and Joseph Shipman started manufacturing sleigh bells, and in Bristol where Seth Thomas established his clock factory. Off trudged the Yankee peddler, pack on back, to bring fame and fortune to Connecticut.

Modern Connecticut

Modern Connecticut, with her great shipyards at New London where atomic submarines are built, sometimes boasts that she is a central bulwark in the "Arsenal of Democracy." Certainly her industrial strength is what one should expect, for the records of the United States Patent Office show more patents issued to Connecticut residents, in proportion to population, than for any other state. Among Connecticut's chief industries, in addition to shipbuilding, are brass and other alloys, electrical appliances, power-transmission equipment, hardware, hats, cottons, woolens and worsteds, clocks and watches, and the "notions" that once filled so large a part of the Yankee peddler's pack.

Hartford is known as the insurance capital of America. Connecticut farms provide dairy products, eggs, hay, tobacco, chickens, potatoes, fruits and vegetables. With three chief ports — Bridgeport, New Haven and New London (home of the United States Coast Guard Academy) — Connecticut's fisheries prosper. Among the state's mineral resources are traprock, clay, feldspar, mica, limestone, granite, kaolin, silica and garnets.

Of distinguished sons and daughters, Connecticut can claim her proud share — Moses Austin, pioneer settler who played a vital role in the history of Texas; P. T. Barnum, the great showman; Samuel Colt, inventor of the revolving-breech pistol; John Fitch, pioneer builder of steamboats; Nathan Hale, patriot of the Revolution who, hanged by the British, is said to have uttered on the gallows, "I only regret that I have but one life to lose for my country"; Harriet Beecher Stowe, whose novel, *Uncle Tom's Cabin,* helped start a war — or so, reputedly, Lincoln once said; Noah Webster, who gave America its dictionary; and Eli Whitney, inventor of the cotton gin.

"Heaven is no larger than Connecticut," wrote Bliss Carman, obviously stretching a point. In almost as reverent a mood a famous French visitor to our shores, Alexis de Tocqueville, once told an audience in Paris: "Connecticut [is] the little yellow spot [on the map] that makes the clock-peddler, the schoolmaster, and the senator. The first gives you time; the second tells you what to do with it; and the third makes your law and your civilization."

VERMONT
"The Green Mountain State"

We give them the best the Kingdom
provides;
They have everything here that they
want,
But not a Vermonter in Heaven abides;
A very brief period here he resides,
Then hikes his way back to Vermont.

THESE LINES by Ernest Fenwick Johnstone do not overstate the case, by a Vermonter's estimate. Nor is there the least thought of giving offense, for, as everyone knows, Heaven is a very fine place.

But so is Vermont.

Since mountains dominate the state, perhaps it comes naturally to the Vermonter to live with a high heart and broad horizon. His beloved Green Mountains, extending from Massachusetts to Canada, divide the state east and west. To the southwest are the Taconic Mountains, another scenic mar-

vel. East of the Green Mountains, running from about mid-state to Canada, are the Granite Hills, and along the edge of Lake Champlain are the Red Sandrock Hills. At the surface of Lake Champlain the elevation is ninety-five feet. Mount Mansfield, the highest point in the Green Mountains, rises 4,393 feet.

People who live in mountains become known, usually, for their self-reliance, a cussed streak that can be called independence or stubbornness, their refusal to be kicked around. The history of Vermont is tied together by these three traits.

"White Man's Lightning"

Before the white man appeared, Vermont served the Indians as a hunting ground, but no evidence remains that an Indian settlement of any consequence ever existed in this region. Some

The Green Mountain State

time before the white men came, the Iroquois battled the Algonquins for control of the territory and that bitter war went about as one should have expected — victory for the Iroquois, with their vastly superior intelligence.

Probably the first white man to visit Vermont was Samuel de Champlain, the French explorer who, in 1609, discovered the fine lake that bears his name. Champlain had come down from Canada, planning to help the Algonquins against the Iroquois, but about all he achieved was to make implacable enemies for France, since the Iroquois, a proud people, never forgot who first turned the "white man's lightning" upon them. A French post — part military, part a shrine to Sainte Anne — founded in 1666 by Captain La Mothe, was the first white settlement in present-day Vermont, but the post did not last long. Thereafter, for half a century, Vermont could best be described as the highway from Canada used by the French and Indians seeking to raid English settlements to the south and west.

Fort Dummer, established in 1724 near present-day Brattleboro, offered the first protection to the western settlements. The French built a fort at Crown Point seven years later, but there was no real French will to settle the region, and by treaty in 1763, France yielded all her claims to Great Britain.

"The New Hampshire Grants"

A fine mix-up followed when the British monarch and the royal governors of New Hampshire and New York each had his own idea of who should deed the land in the "New Hampshire Grants," as Vermont was then called. Soon settlers who came into the territory under grants secured through the governor of New Hampshire found process servers arriving from New York to oust them from their farms.

Fists began to fly, and more than one sheriff's posse made tracks for home with its process notices unserved, especially in the western district of Vermont. There, Ethan Allen, Seth Warner and Remember Baker organized the "Green Mountain Boys" for the express purpose of hastening the "Yorkers" on their way. With the outbreak of the American Revolution, however, Vermonters put aside their quarrel with the province of New York. Less than a month after the Minutemen fired on the Redcoats at Lexington and Concord, Ethan Allen — with help from Benedict Arnold — crossed Lake Champlain, fell upon a sleeping British garrison and demanded the surrender of Fort Ticonderoga "in the name of the Great Jehovah and the Continental Congress." Two days later a force under Seth Warner seized the fort at Crown Point — the same Seth Warner whose stubborn delaying action against Burgoyne's army in 1777 gave the Americans time to gather forces for the victory at Bennington that stopped British land operations in the north.

"New Connecticut"

The notion that the "New Hampshire Grants" should become a separate

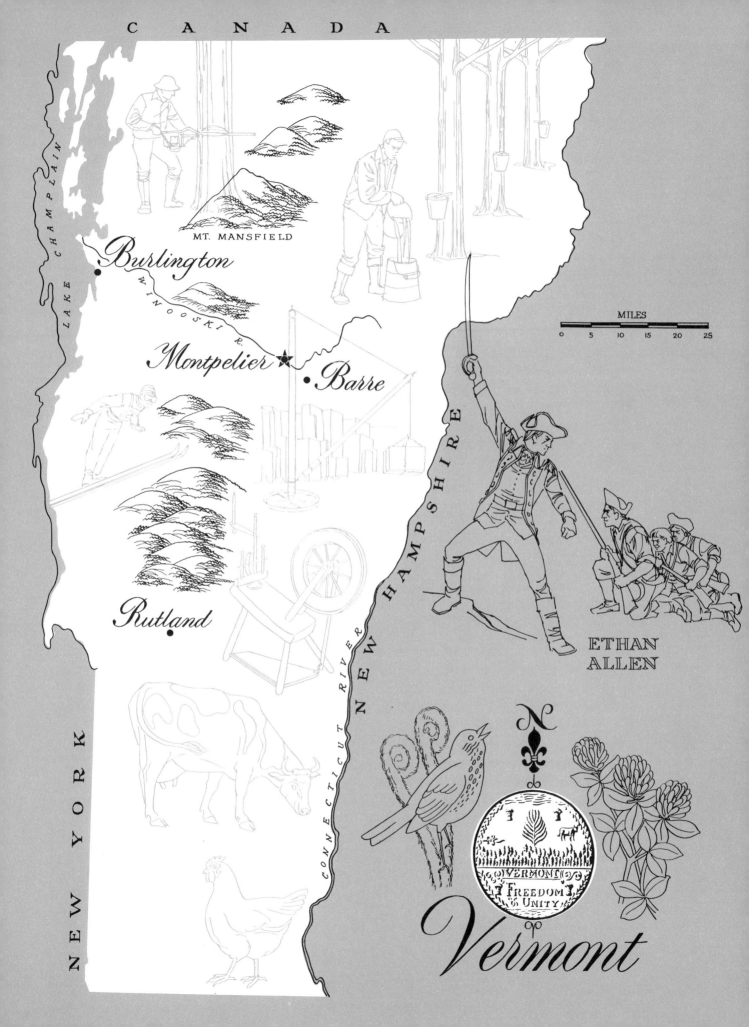

C A N A D A

LAKE CHAMPLAIN

NEW YORK

MT. MANSFIELD

Burlington

WINOOSKI R.

Montpelier ★ •*Barre*

Rutland •

CONNECTICUT RIVER

NEW HAMPSHIRE

MILES
0 5 10 15 20 25

ETHAN ALLEN

N

VERMONT
FREEDOM & UNITY

Vermont

The Green Mountain State

state had taken root before the outbreak of the war, and the Declaration of Independence strengthened this conviction. Settlers now began speaking of themselves as "inhabitants of Vermont," taking the name from the French words *vert mont,* meaning *green mountain*. In January, 1777, Vermont declared its independence and adopted a Constitution which stipulated that no one of legal age "ought to be holden by law to serve any person as a servant, slave, or apprentice" — history's first constitutional prohibition against human slavery in any form. Whereas elsewhere in America a person had to own or rent property or possess a specified yearly income in order to vote, Vermont became the first state to provide for universal manhood suffrage.

From July 8, 1777 to March 4, 1791 Vermont existed as a completely independent republic, and some called the place "New Connecticut." The little "country" issued its own bills of credit, coined money, regulated weights and measures, established post offices, naturalized citizens from other states and countries, and entered into diplomatic correspondence with foreign governments! In 1783 President George Washington considered sending an armed force to conquer Vermont, but in 1790, with a payment of $30,000, Vermont settled its grievances with New York, opening the way for Congress to admit Vermont to the Union as our fourteenth state.

Quickly Vermont took its place as a productive partner in the life of the nation. Its troops played a decisive part during the War of 1812 in the battles of Plattsburg, Chippewa and Lundy's Lane. In the shipyards at Vergennes, during the winter of 1813-14, were built the vessels — of Vermont timber — that gave America control of Lake Champlain and ended the threat of British occupation of Vermont. Then came the bitter time of 1816 — "the famine year" — when snow was drifting three feet deep in June, and snow flurries in July and August were followed by a heavy frost in early September. Crops failed, cattle perished, and the suffering drove many settlers westward (especially into Ohio) in search of a happier homeland.

Raiders From the South

Those who stayed, after that hard year, possessed the rugged quality of independence which has become a Vermonter's birthright. As the slavery question began to divide the Union, certainly no one had any reason ever to doubt where Vermont stood. Although Stephen A. Douglas, the Democratic nominee for President, had been born and raised in Vermont, the state gave its vote to Abraham Lincoln by a plurality of four to one. Unexpectedly, in October, 1864, the war itself came to Vermont when about twenty Confederate raiders crossed the Canadian border and attacked the town of St. Albans.

The raiders herded the citizens into the town square. In a businesslike manner, the Rebs emptied the banks of their money and set fire to hotels and buildings. From the windows of dwellings citizen-snipers pegged away at the Rebs, seriously wounding three. A brisk skirmish followed and one Vermonter was killed. Federal soldiers, appearing in the square, gave a new turn to the affair. Off dashed the Rebs on stolen horses and after them in buggies and on horseback came a determined posse of citizens. The Rebs recrossed the border before they were overtaken, and the refusal of Canadian authorities to permit the raiders to be carried back to St. Albans for trial was an act deeply resented. It should not have come as a surprise, therefore, that when, in 1866, an Irish group called the Fenians tried to free Canada from British rule, their base of military operations was St. Albans!

On the Glory Road

In 1880, when Chester A. Arthur became President upon the death of James A. Garfield, Vermont saw its first native son reach the White House. And when, in the Spanish-American War, another son of Vermont, Commodore George Dewey, sailed off in "the conflict between the town of Montpelier and the Kingdom of Spain," no Vermonter doubted for a moment but that Montpelier would win — gloriously! As expected, in a single short morning's battle, without losing an American, Dewey smashed the Spanish fleet in Manila Bay and opened the way for the United States to acquire the Philippine Islands. Equally dramatic and significant was the feat of Captain Charles Clark, native of Bradford, Vermont. In sixty days he sailed the *Oregon,* pride of the American fleet, from San Francisco to Santiago, Cuba, arriving in the nick of time to

participate in the destruction of another Spanish fleet. Deep down, Vermont always has thought that it practically won that war single-handed! Again, Vermont pride soared when another native son, Calvin Coolidge, became President of the United States in 1923.

Since that day in 1761 when Samuel Robinson of Bennington started boiling down the sap from his trees, Vermont maple sugar has become famous the world over. So, too, have its mineral resources — asbestos, granite, lime, limestone, marble, slate and talc. While Vermont is chiefly a farming state, its sawmills have supplied lumber for use in the construction of textile mills and to factories which manufacture furniture, paper, machinery, machine and precision tools, and scales.

On a September day in 1928, President Calvin Coolidge stood on a train platform in Bennington and spoke from the heart of a true Vermonter:

"Vermont is a State I love. I could not look upon the peaks of Ascutney, Killington, Mansfield, and Equinox without being moved in a way that no other scene could move me. . . . I love Vermont because of her hills and valleys, her scenery and invigorating climate, but most of all because of her indomitable people. They are a race of pioneers who have almost beggared themselves to serve others. If the spirit of liberty should vanish in other parts of our Union and support of our institutions should languish, it could all be replenished from the generous store held by the people of this brave little State of Vermont."

The Green Mountain State

NEW HAMPSHIRE
"The Granite State"

THERE IS a story about a farmer whose property was partly in Vermont, partly in New Hampshire. Then a team of surveyors, checking boundary lines, decided that all of the property was in New Hampshire.

"Thank goodness!" the farmer exclaimed. "Now I won't have to live through another danged Vermont winter!"

As residents of the northernmost of the original thirteen colonies, New Hampshiremen have always held this not-too-secret sense of belonging to a rather special world of their own. "Here God Almighty makes men!" proclaimed Daniel Webster, one of the state's most distinguished sons.

The first white man to gaze upon this remarkable land, so closely joined to heaven, was probably Martin Pring in search of bark from the sassafras tree, which Englishmen liked to brew as

they would tea. Pring, sailing along the coast of New England in 1603, entered the Piscataqua River, and eleven years later Captain John Smith landed on the Isles of Shoals. Some believe that Samuel de Champlain paddled across his lake to the New Hampshire shore in 1605.

Thus the existence of the land became known. The men who would build the colony were of as many different types as Pring, Smith and Champlain.

John Mason,
Father of New Hampshire

The founder — and father — of New Hampshire probably never saw the colony. In 1629 two royal grants brought John Mason title to the land between the Merrimack and the Piscataqua. Since he had served for years as governor of Portsmouth Castle in England, he gave the name of Portsmouth to New Hampshire's first city, and the colony itself he named after Hampshire in southern England, where he once had held a most lucrative office. Mason's notion of what made a good colony was to establish baronies and lordships similar to those of England and Scotland. In short, those who settled the land were to be tenants obeying the orders of their masters. Since Mason was also a staunch royalist, completely at odds with the aims of the Calvinistic Puritans, his plan of colony had practically nothing in common with the dreams of poor men seeking to establish a thoroughly self-sufficient way of life in Massachusetts and Connecticut.

Probably the first settlement in New Hampshire was established in 1623 at Little Harbour, now in the town of Rye, and the first town government was organized at Dover in 1633. Five years later Exeter was founded by the Reverend John Wheelwright, who had been banished from Massachusetts for his "radical" religious views. Wheelwright claimed that he had bought the land where he settled from the Indians, and indeed the four original towns of New Hampshire — Dover, Portsmouth, Exeter and Hampton — were virtually forced to operate as independent republics since they developed outside of any established jurisdiction. But Puritan Massachusetts used a technicality to get the better of these rascals — its old enemy Wheelwright and his followers, at Exeter — and a second group of religious rivals, the Anglicans, at Portsmouth (or Strawberry Banke).

Battle for a Colony

Massachusetts, going back to its original charter drawn under the impression that the entire course of the Merrimack flowed eastward, pointed out that its northern boundary was described as three English miles north of the Merrimack River, which extended its jurisdiction over the settlements of both religious opponents. So in 1639 Massachusetts began to rule the colony, and although New Hampshire obtained a royal charter as a separate colony in 1679, Massachusetts continued its domination over the region until the Revolutionary War.

Meanwhile Indian troubles were growing more threatening, so that the New Hampshire settler found himself in the middle of a tug of war with religious bigots on one end and wild savages on the other. Planter and trader, fisherman and lumberman — the real builders of the colony were men who faced reality and drew a line beyond which they refused to be driven by anyone. Both before and during the French and Indian Wars, the colony was ravaged by Indian attacks. By 1770 it became difficult to find a family among the colonists of the tidewater towns who could not tell of at least one ancestor scalped and murdered, and perhaps of another carried off into the wilderness as a captive.

New Hampshire grew steadily nonetheless, and as the Revolution approached, counted its population at about 80,000. By June, 1775 it had its royal governor in flight and the following January it became the first state to

The Granite State

form a government independent of England. New Hampshiremen, fighting beside Vermont's Green Mountain Boys, gave the Continental cause the important victory at Bennington in August of 1777. Eleven years later — on June 21, 1788 — New Hampshire, as the ninth state to adopt the Federal Constitution, supplied the two-thirds majority necessary for adoption and the establishment of the United States!

Industrial Boom Years

About 1800 New Hampshire began an industrial growth that was still going strong a century and a half later. A wool-carding mill at Ipswich in 1801, a textile mill at Manchester in 1809, a shoe factory at Weare in 1823 found the home craftsman leaving his farm to shape a new future in New Hampshire. In 1813 the Abbot and Downing Company began building the famous Concord Coach, a vehicle that carried nine passengers inside "and as many more as could cling to the roof." Wherever people traveled or mail was carried — in Australia and South Africa as well as in frontier America — the Concord Coach, with its clouds of dust, became a symbol of progress.

The Concord Coach has disappeared, but boots and shoes and textiles still remain bulwarks of New Hampshire's industrial economy. Lumber and wood products, paper and machinery are other old manufacturing stand-bys that still are steady income producers for New Hampshire, yet the growth of such industries as electronics, fabricated metals and plastics reflects the impact of more recent times. Not with-

Daniel Webster

New Hampshire

SEAL OF THE STATE OF NEW HAMPSHIRE · 1776

MILES
0 5 10 15 20 25

PENNACOOK
INDIANS

VERMONT

MAINE

CONNECTICUT RIVER

MT. WASHINGTON

PEMIGEWASSET R.

MERRIMACK

PISCATAQUA R.

Concord

Portsmouth

Manchester

Nashua

R.

MASS.

*The
Granite
State*

out reason is New Hampshire called "the Granite State," and other valuable mineral resources that have played their role in the development of New Hampshire are garnet, feldspar and mica.

But man does not live by bread alone, nor does a state — New Hampshire least of all. Historically, the state points with pride to the fact that when, in 1777, John Paul Jones sailed the Portsmouth-built *Ranger* from Badger's Island, the ship was the first ever to fly the Stars and Stripes. The first free public library in New Hampshire was established in Dublin in 1822, and in the little red schoolhouse at Newport, Sarah Josepha Hale wrote "Mary Had a Little Lamb." At Portsmouth, in 1905, the treaty was signed that ended the Russo-Japanese War.

Strictly New Hampshire

To have been the birthplace of "Black Dan" Webster, who, as everyone knows, could talk down the devil, would seem honor enough for any state, but New Hampshire counts among its distinguished sons and daughters many others, including Franklin J. Pierce, fourteenth President of the United States; Salmon P. Chase and Harlan F. Stone, who became Chief Justices of the United States Supreme Court; Mary Baker Eddy, founder of the Christian Science religion; Leonard Wood, hero of the Spanish-American War and World War I; Henry Dearborn, hero of the Revolution; Horace Greeley, famous editor; and poet Robert Frost.

There are really two New Hamp-

shires. One is the skiing paradise to which winter-sports enthusiasts are drawn at North Conway with its Cranmore Skimobile, Mount Sunapee State Park with its popular chair lift, and Laconia, Hanover and Waterville Valley. It can get cold in New Hampshire — there's a low of −46° F. on record. The snow piles deep. Even as spring comes on, there is likely to be good skiing in Tuckerman's Ravine on Mount Washington.

With summer, New Hampshire assumes another characteristic — green-cloaked, except where the rocky peaks of its majestic White Mountains intrude. There are thirteen hundred lakes in New Hampshire, including seventy-two-square-mile Lake Winnipesaukee and the Lake of the Clouds in the lee of stately Mount Washington, which is said to be "a mile in the sky."

Gentle Wilton in the narrow valley of the Souhegan River, the majestic Presidential Range of mountain peaks and the natural stone profile of the Old Man of the Mountain seen from Franconia Notch, a granite quarry at Milford, the Crystal Cascades at Pinkham Notch, the maple-lined mall in the one-street town of Orford, the cog railway on the slope of Mount Washington, the pulpwood stack outside a paper mill on the Upper Ammonoosuc River, the industry of Manchester, Nashua and Keene ... these are a few of the images that flash through the mind of the New Hampshireman when he thinks of the state he loves. And Robert Frost will tell you:

She's one of the two best states in the Union. Vermont's the other.

MAINE

"The Pine Tree State"

MOUNT KATAHDIN, the highest point in Maine, rises 5,268 feet above sea level. Upon its peak each morning the rising sun sheds its first rays upon the territory of the United States.

Once Maine belonged to Massachusetts, and to reach it from the mother state a traveler journeyed north and east. So Maine became known as "Down East" and its natives as "Down Easters."

With each morning's light Down East, a wide variety of activities begins. The chances are that the lobstermen have already sailed off. Soon the ringing axes of the lumberjacks will send echoes through the forests where trapper and hunter follow traplines and tracks. At Bath and South Portland, the shipbuilders continue a tradition of craftsmanship going back to Colonial times.

Year round, Down Easters lead a good life, filled with hard work and salty humor. During the summer, the state puffs out its sides like a blowfish — or so it seems, as vacationists arrive by the tens of thousands.

Discovering "The Maine"

When was the rock-bound coast of Maine first discovered by the white man? A good guess is the year 1000 when Norsemen under Leif Ericsson visited North America. Next to see and explore the coast of Maine was an Italian-born English navigator, John Cabot, who reached the New World only six years after Columbus. England's claim to the continent of North America rested upon Cabot's maps of its coastlines, but in succeeding years the French were more conscientious explorers. In 1604 Samuel de Champlain stepped ashore on Mount Desert Island, and the following year an Englishman, Captain George Weymouth,

New England

MAINE

VERMONT

NEW
HAMPSHIRE

MASSACHUSETTS

CONN.

R.I.

Atlantic

Ocean

The
Pine Tree
State

landed on Monhegan Island, then crossed over to "the Maine" to judge its promise as a site for a colony.

Weymouth liked everything he saw and sent home glowing reports. Near the mouth of the Kennebec River in 1607, the English made their first unsuccessful attempt at a settlement. Someone had misled them. The Maine woods were not — as they had been told — a place where dates and figs would grow. A fort was built before the settlers dug in for a quarrelsome, downhearted winter.

Other efforts at colonizing Maine were tried in 1623 — first on Monhegan Island, which was a failure, and then on the Saco River, which was a success. By royal charter the proprietor of "The Province of Maine" had become Sir Ferdinando Gorges, who gets credit for establishing the first organized government in Maine (1636) and for incorporating the first city (1642) on territory now part of the United States. Not too mysteriously, it was named Gorgeana. But Gorges' influence, like his title to the land, was not destined to endure. Men in search of freedom and profits from beaver pelts were the real colonizers — in Maine as elsewhere in New England.

Indian Troubles

Massachusetts claimed Maine as part of its province, and settled for the rights to the land with the descendants of Gorges. In 1691 a grant from William and Mary formally joined Maine to Massachusetts. Meanwhile, the French insisted that they owned the regions east of the Penobscot, from Pemaquid

to the Saint Croix River, and they fell back on their favorite trick of stirring up the Indians to raid, burn and pillage the English settlements.

Maine became a bloody ground. There would be a wave of trouble, a patched-up peace, another wave of trouble. The English, let it be said, never leaned backward in trying to understand the bruised spirit of the red man. Rather, the British colonist appeared determined to push the red man off the land forever, and in the end he succeeded, for when the Indian wars were over, the Indian was finished in Maine. Meanwhile, for long years, on any night a dog barking could give warning that the marauders had swept back through the forests. Whole settlements burned. Screams, scalping knives added to the night terror. Women and children were marched away through the snow to Quebec. As one observer commented, those who were still alive in Maine when the frightful business was over could survive anything.

Steps Toward Statehood

Off Machias in 1775 the first naval battle of the American Revolution was fought and the British frigate *Margaretta* was captured. That year the town of Falmouth was almost completely destroyed, a grim indication of the price Maine could expect to pay for supporting the American cause. Thereafter, Down Easters might see, suddenly emerging through any sea mist, the forbidding hulk of a British raider — especially after 1779, when the British began using the Castine Peninsula as a jumping-off point for its raids upon

SAINT JOHN RIVER

CANADA

CANADA

LEIF ERICSSON

MILES
0 10 20 30 40 50

MT. KATAHDIN

ST. CROIX RIVER

KENNEBEC R.

PENOBSCOT RIVER

NEW HAMPSHIRE

ANDROSCOGGIN R.

Bangor

Augusta

Lewiston

Portland

PISCATAQUA R.

N

DIRIGO
MAINE

Maine

DARWIN

Maine's ships and shipbuilding centers.

One benefit Maine gained from this conflict came after the war when large tracts of land were sold to veterans of the Revolution for one dollar an acre. Again, though Maine suffered raids and other hardships during the War of 1812, the direct benefit was the growth of her shipbuilding interests. By now, Maine's position as a province of Massachusetts was a source of expanding irritations. Not without cause, Down Easters grumbled over poor roads that made it next to impossible to reach the seat of government, and, as a consequence, they were virtual victims of taxation without representation. Also, the War of 1812 certainly had demonstrated that Maine would be sadly beleaguered if she depended on Massachusetts for her defense in times of stress!

The break between Maine and Massachusetts came in 1819. At the next session of Congress — in keeping with the spirit of the Compromise of 1820 — Maine was admitted to the Union as a free state and Missouri as a slave state so that the delicate political balance between North and South would be maintained.

Down Easters — at War and Peace

In 1839, as our twenty-third state, Maine became involved in a bitter boundary dispute with Canada that was dignified with the somewhat formidable title of the Aroostook War. Maine called out its militia and marched into New Brunswick, Canada. At the root of the trouble was the arrest of a Maine census-taker by New Brunswick authorities and the invasion of the Aroostook region by Canadian lumbermen. The rival militias came face to face across a shallow stream, but then wiser heads prevailed, and, happily, no lives were lost.

Still, the Down Easter had demonstrated his spunkiness of mind and disposition, and in passing years this trait became more and more a dominant part of his history. Thus, in 1846, strong-minded Maine passed the nation's first prohibition law. The Down Easter, as should have been expected, was a militant opponent of slavery, and he was proud to see a son of Maine, Hannibal Hamlin, stand as Abraham Lincoln's running mate in the election of 1860. Another son of that period in whom Maine took pride was the poet, Henry Wadsworth Longfellow, just as later the state would take pride in a native daughter — Edna St. Vincent Millay, the first woman poet to win the Pulitzer Prize.

Modern Maine

Modern Maine points to many achievements. One out of every seven potatoes raised in the United States and about ninety-five per cent of the nation's blueberries grow in Maine. Maine granite can be found in Grant's Tomb in New York City, in the extension of the House of Representatives building in Washington, D.C., in the Philadelphia Mint and in the St. Louis Post Office. For more than a century and a quarter, Maine's limestone beds have been productive, and twenty-five per cent of the nation's feldspar comes from Maine.

It is the boast of Down Easters that their factories and shipyards can produce everything from toothpicks to destroyers, or from wooden checkers to jet plane engines. The 16,000,000 acres of forest land in Maine supply more than a thousand wood-using plants, and its spruce and fir stands keep numerous paper mills busy. Maine's fleets, operating in some 200,000 square miles of the world's finest fishing grounds, employ 11,000 fishermen. Five large rivers, over 5,000 streams and small rivers, and some 2,500 lakes and ponds are part of the reason why Maine is just about the fishin'est state in the Union!

You get a Down Easter boasting, and what are you likely to hear? Well, maybe the fact that when Admiral Perry went to the North Pole he traveled on a pair of Maine-made snowshoes! Or that the first Liberty Pole in America was erected in Machias in 1775. Or that the oldest public building in New England is the York gaol, erected in 1653. Or that the first ship built on the American continent, the *Virginia*, was constructed in 1607 in the Kennebec River. Or that the first Federal Fish Hatchery, for propagating Atlantic salmon, was established in Bucksport. Or that Maine — "Land of Remembered Vacations" — is practically as big as the five other New England states combined, and that truer words were never written than in the concluding lines of the official state song:

And tho' we seek far and wide
Our search will be in vain,
To find a fairer spot on earth
Than Maine! Maine! Maine!

The Pine Tree State

Gateway to the Atlantic

Henry Hudson

NEW YORK

"The Empire State"

BEFORE 1825 one guess was as good as another whether Philadelphia or Boston would outdistance New York City as the commercial capital of America. But that year the Erie Canal was opened and all doubt quickly ended. Within two decades an average of one boat every seventeen minutes, day and night, passed through the important locks of the canal, and 25,000 men, women and boys worked along the towpaths. The "canawler" — half sailor, half landlubber — was a hard-working, hard-drinking, hard-fighting specimen. To the accompaniment of a "squawk fiddle," he liked to sing about his life carting freight and people on the old Erie:

So haul in your bowlines,
Stand by the saddle mule,
Low bridge, boys, dodge your head,
Don't stand up like a fool.
For the Erie is a-risin'
An' the whiskey's gettin' low.
I hardly think we'll get a drink
Till we get to Buffalo.

"Canawlers" used to tell the story of the captain who sent his son into town to buy their lunch. When the lad returned with two loaves of bread and a jug of rum, the captain whipped the boy within an inch of his life for wasting so much money on bread.

A brawling business though life on the old Erie was, it changed forever the destiny of New York — and of

America. By 1845 canal packets were carrying 40,000 settlers a year to new homes in the West.

Early Dutch Settlers

In the same year — 1609 — that Henry Hudson sailed the *Half Moon* up the river bearing his name, the French explorer, Samuel de Champlain, entered the northern districts of New York in an effort to aid the Algonquins, who were fighting the Five Nations of the Iroquois for the land. Later, with the arrival of the British, the cast of contestants in the struggle for the state was completed.

Not long after Hudson's visit the Dutch, with characteristic industry, began stringing trading posts along the Hudson Valley. In 1621 they built Fort Manhattan — at the present site of 41 Broadway — on the island that the Indians called "Ma-na-hat-ta," meaning "Heavenly Land." Their eventual settlement here they named New Amsterdam, and north of the village the boundary was marked by a wall — roughly parallel to today's financial center, Wall Street. In 1624 some thirty families carried Dutch rule to a settlement at Fort Orange (Beverwyck or Albany). Subsequently, other Dutch villages appeared at Wiltwyck (New Kingston), Rensselaer and Schenectady.

In many respects the Dutch were good colonizers, but self-government was not one of the products they brought to the New World. To know the Dutch, one needed to know their governors, of whom Wouter Van Twiller was a good specimen. Washington Irving has described this early Father Knickerbocker as a man "shut up within himself like an oyster," who never laughed, and who cared not whether the sun revolved around the earth or vice versa since he had lived in the world long enough to understand all its essential perplexities. Faithful to chores and duty — such, in a phrase, was the trim, efficient Dutch formula for planting a prosperous colony in the New World.

The Empire State

Beginnings of "New York"

Neither Indian raids nor the encroachments of English settlers from north and south, but a war in Europe between England and the Netherlands brought the Dutch rule to an end. In 1664 a British fleet under Colonel Richard Nicolls appeared in the bay, and the authorities of New Amsterdam, having no other practical choice, capitulated. The British now had a wonderful time changing names as New Amsterdam became New York and Beverwyck became Albany. In 1673 the Dutch recaptured the colony, but a treaty the following year restored control to the English.

To the north, the French were not idle. La Salle pushed down from Canada and in 1678 built a storehouse at Niagara. Soon Europe erupted in a war between the British and the French that produced a succession of bitter, savage conflicts in the New World — the French and Indian Wars — which continued until 1760. The battles and scars of those bloody years are preserved in the memories of Crown Point, Fort Niagara, Fort Stanwix (Rome) and Ticonderoga.

*The
Empire
State*

By 1763, when the French and British finally patched up their grievances around a peace table in Paris, New York ranked seventh in population among the thirteen colonies. The Dutch had moved up the Hudson and into the Mohawk Valley. From New England had come English settlers along the east bank of the Hudson. Scots and Scotch-Irish lived along the west Hudson, in Cherry Valley and the vicinity of Johnstown. Huguenots held New Paltz and New Rochelle. Negro slaves made up about ten per cent of the population.

"I Swear — So Help Me God!"

Among New York's mixed population was a strong group of Loyalists — perhaps as many as two-fifths of the total population — who were eager to help the mother country when the Revolution came. Both on land and sea, a good part of the war directly affected New York. The British occupied New York City in September, 1776, and the Battle of White Plains was fought that October. The following year brought the climactic battles at Oriskany and Saratoga and the surrender of the British general, Burgoyne. The Tories enlisted the Iroquois as allies, resulting, in 1780, in the frightful massacres in the Mohawk and Schoharie valleys. The last battle of the Revolution in New York was fought at Johnstown on October 25, 1781, and two years later, at Newburgh, George Washington refused the crown offered him by a military faction. New York ratified the United States Constitution in 1788.

The state's greatest day in history came on April 30, 1789. At sunup that day New York City's streets and taverns already were jammed. In the harbor, boats and sloops of many nations were decked with colorful flags. Every window held a dozen heads, all turned toward the balcony of the Federal Building. There stood the tall, noble man, hand outstretched on the Bible. A sober voice stated the oath:

"I do solemnly swear that I will faithfully execute the Office of President of the United States, and will, to the best of my ability, preserve, protect and defend the Constitution of the United States."

George Washington responded: "I swear — so help me God!"

On Its Way!

The closing phases of the War of 1812 were largely fought near the New York-Canadian border and along Lake Champlain, but with the coming of peace New York began moving steadily forward. Slavery was prohibited (effective within ten years) in 1817, and in 1819 New York was called for the first time the "Empire State." As early as 1811 the legislature authorized the digging of the Erie Canal, and the first shovels of dirt were turned over at Rome on July 4, 1817. Then, on October 2, eight years later, came the day of rejoicing. Salvos of cannon, set within earshot of each other, announced the opening of the canal from New York City to Buffalo.

Now, truly, the "Empire State" was on its way — sometimes in so many directions that no one could keep them all straight. In Palmyra in 1823, for example, Joseph Smith had the vision

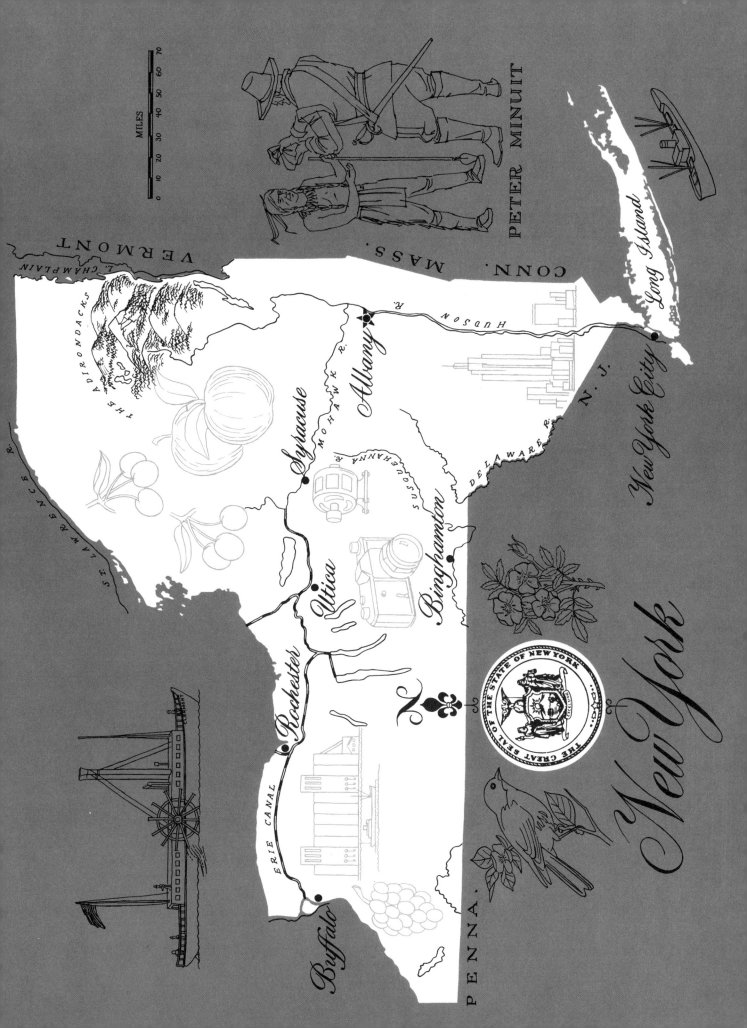

MILES

PETER MINUIT

VERMONT

L. CHAMPLAIN

THE ADIRONDACKS

ST. LAWRENCE R.

CONN.   MASS.

Long Island

HUDSON R.

N. J.

New York City

MOHAWK R.

Albany

Syracuse

SUSQUEHANNA R.

DELAWARE R.

Utica

Binghamton

Rochester

THE GREAT SEAL OF THE STATE OF NEW YORK
EXCELSIOR

ERIE CANAL

New York

Buffalo

PENNA.

*The
Empire
State*

upon which the Mormon religion is based. In 1848 the first convention for women's rights were held in Seneca Falls and as Mrs. Amelia Jenks Bloomer strode down the street in her individual pantaloons, children, tagging along, sing-songed:

*Hi Ho,
In sleet and snow,
Mrs. Bloomer's all the go.
Twenty tailors to take the stitches,
Plenty of women to wear the britches.*

Sources of Greatness

Always, New York's principal resource has been its people, who, coming in through its seaport and journeying over its canal to the Great Lakes, have made it, truly, a melting pot. All nationalities, all shades of temperament, all varieties of political background have merged to make the New Yorker, including the mayor with pro-Southern sympathies who tried to have New York City secede from the Union during the Civil War. And Jemima Wilkinson, of Yates County, who insisted that she had been raised from the dead. And Abner Doubleday, who is credited with inventing the modern form of baseball. Six New Yorkers, native sons or elected officials, have become President of the United States — Martin Van Buren, Millard Fillmore, Chester A. Arthur (born in Vermont), Grover Cleveland (born in New Jersey), Theodore Roosevelt and Franklin D. Roosevelt — and nine have been Vice President. In every field of endeavor, New Yorkers, representing all the races and religions on earth, have excelled.

Geography has favored New York, the only state that touches both the Atlantic Ocean and the Great Lakes. Her mountain ranges are the Adirondack, Catskill, Shawangunk and Taconic. In addition to the Hudson and its chief tributary, the Mohawk, the rivers of New York include the Allegheny, Black, Delaware, East, Genesee, Oswego, Seneca and the Susquehanna and its three chief tributaries — Chemung, Chenango and Unadilla. The spectacular Niagara is one of many waterfalls, Lake George and Lake Placid two of the many fine lakes. Rich in manufactured products, mineral resources and farming, the state's chief cities are Albany, Auburn, Binghamton, Buffalo, Elmira, Ithaca, New Rochelle, Niagara Falls, Poughkeepsie, Rochester, Saratoga Springs, Schenectady, Syracuse, Troy and Utica. The United States Military Academy is located at West Point.

"The Golden Door"

New York City is often called the world's greatest city. Washington Irving named the city Gotham, after an English village celebrated for the foolish antics of its citizens, and sometimes it is known as Manhattan, after the island that Peter Minuit reputedly bought from the Indians for beads, cloth and trinkets worth about twenty-four dollars. In many respects, New York is a city of many villages — *Wall Street* and the financial district where split-second money quotations come in from around the world; *Chinatown* with its restaurants, curio shops, groceries, and Oriental boys and girls

fighting over their games in American slang; the *Lower East Side,* close to Chinatown, with its grimy warehouses and factories and its pushcart merchants around whom customers haggle in Turkish, Persian, Italian, Yiddish, Greek, Russian, Spanish, German and a dozen other languages; *Greenwich Village* and *Washington Square;* the *Garment District, Rockefeller Center, Times Square* and the *Great White Way; Fifth Avenue* and *Park Avenue* with their elegant shops, hotels and restaurants; and *Harlem,* with its concentrations of Negro, Spanish and Italian inhabitants.

People in all these places—working, living, playing — give New York City its spirit, its vitality. And the noise of its taxis, the rumble of its subways, the surge of crowds crossing a street with a changing traffic light — these, too, are New York City. And perhaps the Empire State Building, towering 1,250 feet, the tallest building in the world. And out in the world's busiest harbor, the Statue of Liberty, with these lines by Emma Lazarus carved on its base:

Give me your tired, your poor,
Your huddled masses yearning to
  breathe free,
The wretched refuse of your teeming
  shore.
Send these, the homeless, tempest-tost,
  to me,
I lift my lamp beside the golden door!

And New York City is one other image, at dusk, with the sky golden and pink and orange and yellow—with beauty overhead and joy in the heart and hope for a bright tomorrow reflected in the simple, majestic dignity of the United Nations Building.

The Empire State

NEW JERSEY

"The Garden State"

THE TRAVELER by train or automobile between New York City and Philadelphia acquires a distorted impression of New Jersey. Swampy meadows, sprawling industrial plants, grimy towns and cities huddled along the railroad, oil refineries, wisps of farmland, the unattractive sign reading "Trenton Makes, the World Takes" on the bridge over the Delaware joining New Jersey and Pennsylvania—these become the "Garden State" to the majority of transient observers.

To the native New Jerseyite the state possesses an altogether different character. He visualizes New Jersey as beaches and pounding ocean surf along a coastline reaching from Atlantic Highlands, just south of the entrance to Lower New York Bay, to the tip of Cape May, some forty miles below the Mason-Dixon line. The rolling farms of Monmouth, Ocean, Burlington and Gloucester counties are another image that he treasures. And western New

Jersey, with its fine dairying country and gentle mountains, approaches in the view of the proud New Jerseyite the best that Vermont has to offer.

At the same time the New Jerseyite cannot deny that, historically, the story of his state has been strongly influenced by its position as the link between New York and Pennsylvania. From across the Hudson came the Dutch and English, and from across the Delaware came the Swedes and Quakers. They were the pioneers, the settlers.

The Two New Jerseys

Not to be outdone by any state, New Jersey begins its history in 1524 when Giovanni da Verrazano, sailing for France, coasted along the New Jersey shore and anchored off Sandy Hook. Next on the scene was Henry Hudson who, in 1609, sent a party from the *Half Moon* to explore Newark Bay. A Dutch navigator, Cornelius Mey, sailed his *Glad Tidings* in 1620 around the southern cape of New Jersey into

Delaware Bay, giving his name to this strip of land which, to the captain's great delight, possessed a climate much like that of Holland.

About this time the Dutch crossed the river from New Amsterdam to found a settlement near present-day Jersey City. As industrious farmers who got along amicably with the Lenni-Lenape Indians, these Dutchmen began in New Jersey a tradition of peaceful co-existence between the red man and white. The Swedes, who were among the first to cross the Delaware into New Jersey, and the Quakers who followed, established the same cordial feeling. When, in 1664, New Amsterdam was surrendered to the English, New Jersey was divided into two provinces. East New Jersey, under Sir George Carteret, had its capital at Perth Amboy, and West New Jersey, under Lord Berkeley, had its capital at Burlington. A diagonal line from Little Egg Harbor to Pensauken Creek above Camden roughly separated the two New Jerseys. Neither small province fared very well on its own, however, and in 1702 both were united into a single crown colony.

In other directions, New Jersey began to move ahead. In 1682 Mark Newbie, arriving in Camden County with sea chests full of halfpence that had been struck in Dublin, opened the first bank in the colonies. Whaling in Delaware Bay attracted hardy fishermen from New England to Cape May. As early as 1688 there was a pottery at Burlington. Caspar Wistar began a glass factory — New Jersey's first — near Salem in 1740 and three years

later the state's important iron industry made its start.

Highway of the Revolution

As the highway between the northern and southern colonies, the soil of New Jersey became bloody ground during the American Revolution. Although the state had an active Tory element — including that notorious band of Tory raiders called the "Pine Robbers" — the large majority of New Jerseyites stood firmly for the Continental cause and on July 2, 1776 New Jersey issued a declaration of independence from the mother country. Food from South New Jersey, iron from North New Jersey, salt from the marshes along Toms River played as important a role as New Jersey Minutemen during the war years. In moving across the state to confuse the British in New York, George Washington three times took to the Jersey hills — twice in Morristown and once in Middlebrook — and perhaps as many as one hundred battles and skirmishes were fought in New Jersey.

On Christmas night, 1776, General Washington inspired American patriots by crossing the icy Delaware and launching a surprise attack upon the Hessians at Trenton. "Our men entered the town in a trot, and pursued so close that in less than one hour we made ourselves master of all their field pieces (six in number), baggage, etc., and 919 prisoners, amongst them 30 officers," wrote a colonel of the First Virginia Regiment. "The whole loss on our side . . . was not more than three privates killed and two brave officers wounded." Battles at Princeton and Monmouth and

The Garden State

The Garden State

savage fighting around Elizabeth and Newark preceded the swift march across "the Jerseys" in 1781 that enabled Washington to outmaneuver the British in New York and set the trap for the crushing defeat of Cornwallis at Yorktown.

Mecca of Inventors

From late June to mid-November, 1783, Princeton served as the Federal capital, and here news was received of the signing of the peace treaty. Four years later New Jersey ratified the Constitution. During the period from 1790 to 1800, when the national capital was at Philadelphia, epidemics of yellow fever three times forced governmental departments to move to Trenton.

In large part, New Jersey owed its enormous industrial growth during the nineteenth century to its inventors and engineers. At Hoboken, in 1824, John Stevens built the first locomotive to pull a train on a track. At Morristown, in 1819, the Speedwell Iron Works made the driving shaft of the *S. S. Savannah,* the first steam-driven vessel to cross the Atlantic, and here on January 6, 1838 Samuel F. B. Morse and Alfred Vail ticked out the first message sent by telegraph: "A patient waiter is no loser." At Trenton, twenty years later, the first transatlantic telegraph message was received.

At Menlo Park, in 1876, Thomas Alva Edison listened to his own voice reciting four lines of "Mary Had a Little Lamb" on the "talking machine" he had invented, and here on New Year's Eve, three years later, three thousand visitors came to witness a demonstration of his incandescent electric light. John P. Holland, who launched the first successful submarine

Thomas Alva Edison

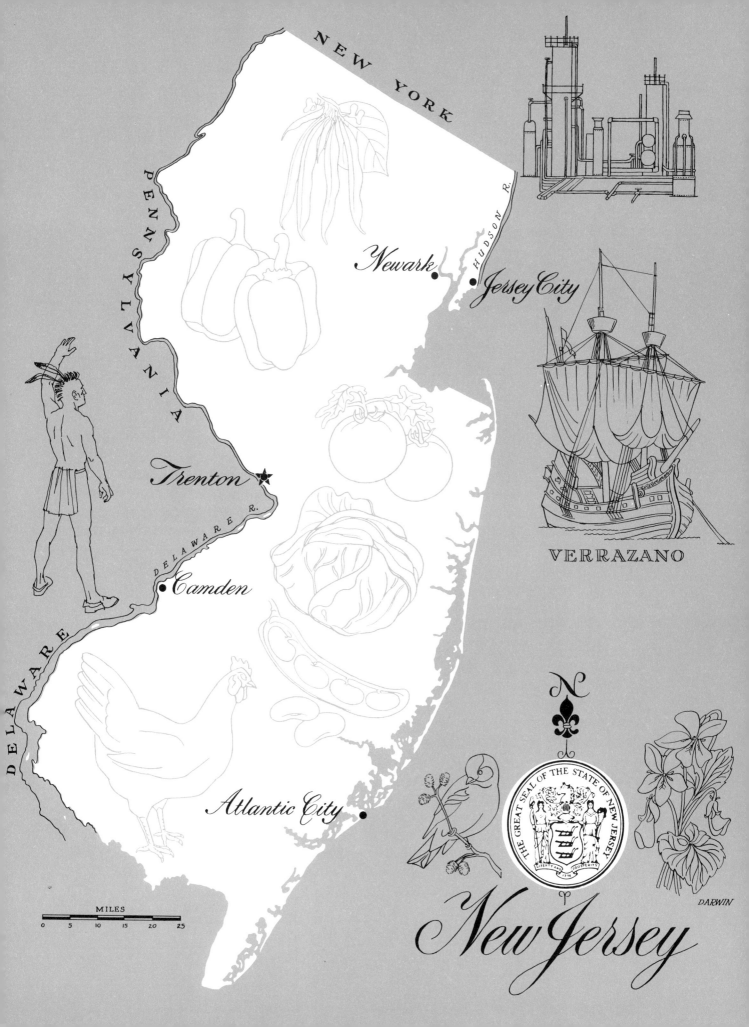

NEW YORK

PENNSYLVANIA

HUDSON R.

Newark

Jersey City

Trenton

DELAWARE R.

DELAWARE

Camden

Atlantic City

VERRAZANO

THE GREAT SEAL OF THE STATE OF NEW JERSEY

LIBERTY AND 1776 PROSPERITY

DARWIN

New Jersey

MILES
0   5   10   15   20   25

The
Garden
State

in the Passaic River (1881), Joseph Henry, who transmitted the first radio impulse at Princeton (1840) and John A. and George Washington Roebling, father and son, who built the Brooklyn Bridge, were other New Jerseyites who changed the industrial future of the state and nation.

In other fields prominent New Jerseyites have included President Grover Cleveland, who was born in Caldwell, and President Woodrow Wilson, who served as governor of the state; authors like Van Wyck Brooks, Stephen Crane, Joyce Kilmer and Edward L. Stratemeyer, creator of the Rover Boys; and General Stephen W. Kearney, Admiral James Lawrence, immortalized for his cry of "Don't give up the ship!" and Admiral William F. Halsey, who commanded the U. S. Third Fleet in the Pacific during World War II.

Modern New Jersey

The nickname of the "Garden State" is not the misnomer it may sometimes seem to the traveler hurrying through New Jersey en route from New York City to Philadelphia. The state supports a vigorous agriculture in dairy products, eggs and poultry, fruits and berries, potatoes, corn, flowers and nursery products, hogs, bees and honey. At the same time the state's enormous industrial strength is indicated in the number and variety of its ports—Edgewater, Hoboken and Weehawken on the Hudson River, Elizabethport and Newark on Newark Bay, Bayonne and Jersey City on New York Bay, Perth Amboy on Raritan Bay, and Camden and Trenton on the Delaware River.

New Jersey's chief manufactures include chemicals, petroleum-refining products, ships, drugs and medicines, paints and varnishes, machinery, clay products, processed foods and communication equipment. The state's mineral resources include zinc, gravel and sand, stone, clay, iron ore, greensand marl and talc.

Yet New Jersey's best "product," perhaps, is the New Jersey Shore. From Sandy Hook to Cape May stretch 127 miles of sandy beaches — a mecca for bathers on steaming summer days, for pre-dawn fishermen, for strollers by the tens of thousands along the boardwalks at such world-famous resorts as Asbury Park and Atlantic City. People of all sizes and ages sitting on bridges and piers holding a crab line — that, surely, is a Jersey image as typical as the mosquitoes that still breed, although not so plentifully as in times of yore, in its salt marshes. Oysters, clams, sturgeon, bluefish, weakfish, shad, cod, mackerel thrive in Jersey waters.

To love the New Jersey Shore is a New Jerseyite's birthright — and to love it passionately as New Jersey's Revolutionary poet, Philip Freneau, loved it, writing of the highlands off Sandy Hook:

These hills, the pride of all the coast,
To mighty distance seen,
With aspect bold and rugged brow
That shade the neighboring main;
These heights for solitude designed,
This rude resounding shore,
These vales impervious to the wind,
Tall oaks that to the tempest bend,
Half Druid I adore.

PENNSYLVANIA

"The Keystone State"

LATE in the fall of 1681 William Penn reached the "greene countrie towne" that became Philadelphia. Penn's agents already were laying out streets and naming them after famous people. But Penn objected to this "man-worship." To streets running north and south he gave numbers, and to intersecting streets the names of trees and flowers. Today's children in Philadelphia have Penn to thank as they prance along the sidewalk, sing-songing a favorite jingle:

High, Mulberry, Sassafras, Vine;
Chestnut, Walnut, Spruce and Pine.

Penn's aversion to any variety of "man-worship" dominated Pennsylvania as it grew as a colony. Penn's spirit of religious tolerance and his respect for the dignity of all men not only produced friendly relations with the Indians, but also with the Dutch, Swedes and Finns who were settled on the land when he arrived to take over the colony. Germans fleeing from religious persecution were warmly welcomed, and from their first settlement at Germantown they pushed out to found a number of flourishing towns and cities. The Welsh and Scotch-Irish were other early home-builders. Later into the coal regions came Poles, Slovaks, Croatians and Slovenians, Ruthenians, Moravians and Czechs, Bulgarians, Serbians, Montenegrins, Russians, Dalmatians, Bosnians and Herzegovinians — and the steel mills were largely responsible for adding Italians and Jews from eastern Europe.

Since there were six colonies to the north and six colonies to the south, Pennsylvania became known as the "Keystone State." But it was in the graceful mixture of many nationalities into the Pennsylvania character, rather

The
Keystone
State

than in the accident of geographical location, that gave the state its right to this proud designation.

"... But to Do Good"

Like the other Middle Atlantic states, Pennsylvania's early history was shaped by alternate waves of Dutch, Swedish and English colonists who vied for possession of the land. Ultimately war in Europe between England and the Netherlands settled the issue and gave England control over Pennsylvania and the Lower Counties (Delaware). In 1681 Charles II conveyed a grant for almost all of present-day Pennsylvania to William Penn in settlement of a debt of £16,000 that the king owed to Penn's father.

Penn's own name for the colony would have been New Wales, but a Welshman on the Privy Council objected, so Penn selected the name of "Sylvania" because of the fine forests in the territory, and Charles II added "Penn." From the outset Penn's good character and fairness of mind made him an unusual leader in Colonial America. Toward the close of 1682, under an elm at Shackamaxon (now part of Philadelphia), he met with the chiefs of the Lenni-Lenapes, Susquehannocks and Shawnees to effect a "treaty of purchase and amity." As a Quaker, Penn told the Indians, his religion "forbade the use of hostile weapons." He came, Penn declared, "not to injure others but to do good."

For the colony itself, Penn presented in April, 1682 his Frame of Government — Pennsylvania's first written constitution — that stated: "I know what is said by the several admirers of monarchy, aristocracy, and democracy, which are the rule of one, a few, and many, and are the three common ideas of government, when men discourse on that subject. But I choose to solve the controversy with this small distinction, and it belongs to all three; any government is free to the people under it (whatever the frame) where the laws rule, and the people are a party to those laws, and more than this is tyranny, oligarchy, and confusion." A Charter of Liberties, granted the following year, strengthened Penn's policy of representative government.

The Walking Purchase

Penn's colony prospered. By 1685 there were 7,000 inhabitants and Germantown was already two years old. A portent of the future in 1690 saw William Rittenhouse building America's first paper mill on a branch of Wissahicon Creek. But growth and industrial awakening brought problems, especially with the Indians as they watched the settlers pushing deeper into their domain. Penn's original agreement had been to purchase as much land as a man could walk in three days. After a day and a half of pleasant, unhurried travel, Penn decided that he had covered all the land he needed "at present." Almost twenty years after Penn's death, in order to fulfill his Walking Purchase, another day and a half of walking was arranged in 1737.

There was none of Penn's sense of fair play in the way the Proprietaries of the colony planned for this event. At most, the Indians expected to sur-

Pennsylvania

INDEPENDENCE HALL

DARWIN

N. Y.

NEW YORK

OHIO

W. VA.

M D.

N. J.

Erie

Scranton

Reading

Philadelphia

Harrisburg

Pittsburgh

DELAWARE R.

SUSQUEHANNA R.

ALLEGHENY RIVER

OHIO R.

MONONGAHELA R.

SEAL OF THE STATE OF PENNSYLVANIA

MILES

0   10   20   30   40   50

Ben Franklin

render another forty miles of land, but for "walkers" the Proprietaries selected a noted hunter named Edward Marshall, James Yeates, who was known for his speed, and Solomon Jennings, who was known for his strength. To the one who traveled the farthest, £5 and 500 acres were promised.

The Indians cried fraud when, on the appointed day, they discovered how the affair was being run. Settlers, placing bets on the race, favored Yeates, who, according to a contemporary account, started off "stepping as light as a feather." Jennings followed with "a strong, steady step," but didn't last out the first day. Marshall, carrying a hatchet to balance his body movement, came on doggedly and at sunset reached the north side of Blue Mountain. Next morning at sunrise he pressed on. At the foot of the mountain he found that Yeates had collapsed in a creek and he dragged him out. Then Marshall strode on to victory, covering eighty-six miles in the day and a half. Yeates, blinded, died within three days. Jennings never recovered in health. Marshall lived to the age of ninety — long enough, certainly, to know that war and massacre were the final price the white men paid for breaking Penn's faith with the Indians.

Ben Franklin's Philadelphia

A notable day in Pennsylvania's history was a cold Sunday in 1723 when a bedraggled lad arrived in Philadelphia with only a Dutch dollar in his pocket. Within three decades Benjamin Franklin became Philadelphia's — and America's — first citizen. His *Poor*

Richard's Almanack was read second only to the Bible. He was founder of the town's library, hospital, fire department and university, inventor of a stove and a pair of spectacles, and discoverer of the fact that lightning is a discharge of electricity. Those who read his *Pennsylvania Gazette* would find in its pages, as early as the middle of the 1750's, a militant warning to the American colonies: "Unite or die."

Franklin's spirit dominated pre-Revolutionary Pennsylvania just as Penn's spirit had once dominated the colony. In Ben Franklin's Philadelphia convened the first two Continental Congresses. Here in Independence Hall the Declaration of Independence was adopted, and here on June 14, 1777 was unfurled the United States flag of thirteen red and white stripes and thirteen white stars on a field of blue, made by a Philadelphia seamstress, Betsy Ross. A month later the British, seizing Philadelphia, forced Congress to seek refuge in Lancaster and York.

Much of the war was fought in Pennsylvania. The cruel, cold winter of 1777-78 at Valley Forge became an American epic — a symbol, truly, of the devotion and sacrifice with which independence was purchased. The stories of the battles at Brandywine, Paoli, Fort Mifflin and Germantown each had heroic passages. Yet the struggle was worthwhile, for in Ben Franklin's Philadelphia from May 24 to September 17, 1787 — and largely under the wise and patient leadership of Franklin — met the convention that drafted the Constitution. Pennsylvania became the second state to ratify that document.

Lincoln at Gettysburg

Turnpikes and railroads began to spread across Pennsylvania, and Pittsburgh became known as the "Gateway to the West," whence hardy pioneers struck out to conquer a continent — carrying their trusty Pennsylvania rifles and carting family and household goods overland in a Pennsylvania-made Conestoga wagon! The first steamboat to operate on the Ohio and Mississippi was launched at Pittsburgh in 1811; and in 1836, in Philadelphia, gas was used for the first time by industrial and private subscribers. The following year at Mauch Chunk (now Jim Thorpe) anthracite was used in smelting ores, and in 1859 E. L. Drake drove the first spouting petroleum well in history near Titusville. Clearly, Pennsylvania was an industrial marvel, due to its enormous mineral resources and to great rivers like the Delaware, Susquehanna, Allegheny and Monongahela that supplied cheap power and transportation.

Meanwhile, the clouds of civil war darkened the national horizon despite all that a Pennsylvania-born President, James Buchanan, tried to achieve in the way of compromise that would avoid the conflict. As early as 1780, Pennsylvania had passed an act providing that no child born in the state thereafter should be a slave, and Pennsylvania Quakers were prime organizers of the Underground Railroad that led slaves to freedom in Canada.

Pennsylvania stood solidly behind the Union and three times rebel troops invaded her soil. In 1862 Confederate cavalry raided the state, principally to

The Keystone State

*The
Keystone
State*

obtain horses and fodder. On July 1, 2 and 3, 1863, Union forces under Pennsylvania-born General George G. Meade fought General Robert E. Lee in one of the greatest battles of the war at Gettysburg. In the summer of 1864, rebel raiders returned and burned Chambersburg.

Yet for Pennsylvania its finest moment of the war came unexpectedly in November of 1863 when, dedicating a national cemetery at Gettysburg, Abraham Lincoln spoke for only two minutes. "This nation, under God, shall have a new birth of freedom," the President said. "Government of the people, by the people, for the people, shall not perish from the earth."

"Kissin' Wears Out. Cookin' Don't."

Nor has it. No one realizes this fact more forcefully than a visitor to the Pennsylvania Dutch country. Here one meets the bearded Amishman, whose grave eyes look out from beneath the brim of his flat black hat and whose clothes are fastened with hooks and eyes instead of buttons. He travels now, as he did a century ago, in a horse-drawn, covered family wagon. Beside him sit wife and daughter in bonnet and shawls, the same style of clothes both would have worn a century ago. Nowhere in the world is there a more rugged individualist than this Amishman. He lives, thinks, works, dresses and worships exactly as he pleases. It was for this dream that, almost three centuries ago, his ancestors first came to America.

Not all Pennsylvania Dutch are as strict or as stand-offish in customs and habits as the Amish. In homely sayings the Pennsylvania Dutch preserve the philosophy by which they live and play: "Kissin' wears out. Cookin' don't." . . . "Them that works hard eats hearty." . . . "A plump wife and a big barn never did any man harm." Sometimes even the names a Pennsylvania Dutchman gives his towns suggest his nature — Paradise, Bird-in-Hand. A few still cling to old country superstitions — the *hexerei* — but these are mostly the *Busch Deutsch* or "hill-men." Most who decorate their barns do so, as they say, just to show what fancy is! And a document adopted in Philadelphia in 1776 makes it reasonable that here in Pennsylvania, of all places, every man has a right to "the pursuit of happiness!"

DELAWARE

"The First State"

IF YOU pronounce the name "Del-a-ware," the harsh sound will grate on the native of this state, who always says "Del-a-wur."

Down in Sussex County, where "corn" is pronounced "carn" and "houses" become "housen," a Delawarean says "our folks" in place of "you-all" or "friends." When he asks, "Our folks going to church?" he means, "Are you going to church, friends?" Many uses are given to "mung-ye" instead of "among you." In southern Delaware, "Are you and your family coming to church?" is shortened to "Mung-ye comin' to church?"

Thus the human ear records history, proving that though the Dutch and the Swedes once contested bitterly for control of Delaware, the English left the enduring mark upon the people.

Coming of the Dutch

The Dutch claim to Delaware dates from August 28, 1609 when Henry Hudson, seeking the northwest passage to China, sailed the *Half Moon* into Delaware Bay and discovered the Delaware River. Hudson found the bay too shallow for his boat, so he sailed on and discovered still another river — the majestic Hudson. A year later (lacking one day) an Englishman, Captain Samuel Argall, was blown into the bay during a storm. Argall named the place for his patron, Baron De La Warr, also known as Lord Delaware.

In 1631 a group of Dutchmen founded the first white settlement near present-day Lewes, calling their town Zwannendael, or "valley of swans." These thirty hardy individuals saw dense forests growing to the edge of the water. Sometimes huge flocks of birds seemed to blot out the sun, and the runs of herring choked the small streams. Hard-headed traders above all else, the Dutch dreamed of a bright future when beaver and deer skins could be taken by the thousands.

DARWIN

NEW   YORK

SYLVANIA

NEW

JERSEY

MARYLAND

DEL.

The Atlantic Gateway

*The
First
State*

Tragedy came unexpectedly. A tin coat-of-arms of Holland, nailed to a post, started the trouble when a young Indian chief appropriated the tin to shape into a pipe. Harsh words produced dark thoughts of revenge. When the next shipload of Dutchmen arrived at Zwannendael all they found were burned houses and bleached bones.

New Sweden

Yet the Indians of the region — the Lenni-Lenapes—were by nature peaceful fishermen and hunters. The name, in Algonquin, meant "original people," and other Indians called them, respectfully, "Grandfathers." The Lenni-Lenapes never quite lost their sullen attitude toward the Dutch, whereas they exhibited a warmth of feeling amounting to affection for the Swedes, the next settlers in Delaware. Actually, a Dutch group under Peter Minuit organized this Swedish venture to plant a colony in the New World. Two boats brought the first Swedish settlers in 1638 to present Wilmington, where they built a fort, naming it "Fort Christina" in honor of the young queen of Sweden.

In succeeding years twelve more expeditions were sent from Sweden, and soon the Delaware wilderness became dotted with the characteristic structure of the Swedish settler — the log cabin. In 1640 Reorus Torkillus, the first Lutheran clergyman to serve in America, arrived. For the New Sweden Colony the happiest years were from 1643 to 1653 under the governorship of corpulent Johan Printz, whom the Indians called "the big tub." Printz built mills, houses, boats and wharves, and encour-

aged such industries as cooperage, brewing, baking and weaving. Johan Rising, who followed Printz as governor, seized the Dutch post at New Castle, sowing the seed for a bitter harvest in 1655 when Peter Stuyvesant sent a fleet from New Amsterdam to subjugate the Swedish forts and take over the colony.

Under Dutch rule the region prospered. The Dutch purchased land from the Indians to protect their title, traded in furs, encouraged farming and built canals and dikes to control the marshes. New Amstel (New Castle) grew from a fort into a full-fledged town. Despite the habitual dictatorial military governorship of the Dutch, they instituted town and village government and were highly tolerant of Swedish religious customs. Then war in Europe between England and the Netherlands produced repercussions in the New World, and in 1664 a British expedition under Sir Robert Carr subdued the Dutch authorities after a short skirmish. New Amstel now became New Castle and the South River became the Delaware.

The Three Lower Counties

Colonists in Delaware who had settled under the Swedish and Dutch were permitted to retain their lands by pledging allegiance to the King of England. In 1681 Charles II granted the Province of Pennsylvania to William Penn, whose agents appeared on the Delaware River and fell into an immediate fret, for should the colonies on either side of Delaware River or Bay become hostile, Penn's followers would be trapped in a land-locked province. But, in a

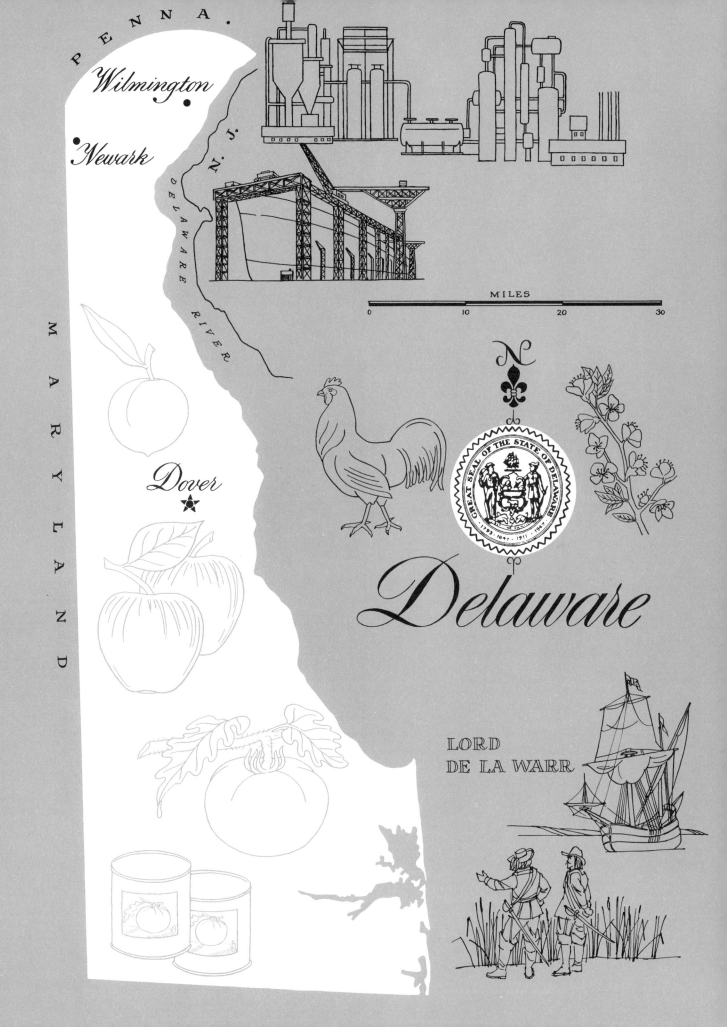

PENNA.

Wilmington

Newark

N. J.

DELAWARE RIVER

MARYLAND

MILES

0   10   20   30

N

Dover

Delaware

GREAT SEAL OF THE STATE OF DELAWARE
1793 · 1847 · 1911 · 1947

LORD
DE LA WARR

cheery mood, the Duke of York conveyed to Penn the land on the west side of the bay and river — the counties of New Castle, St. Jones (Kent) and Deale (Sussex) — and that October Penn landed at New Castle to take possession of the land and receive the oath of allegiance from the settlers. The following year the Three Lower Counties were annexed to the Province of Pennsylvania with all the privileges guaranteed in Penn's "Frame of Government" [see Pennsylvania, pp. 53-58].

Trouble followed in many quarters. Whenever there was no other cause of friction, Lord Baltimore of Maryland could always be counted upon to dispute boundaries with Penn. The heirs of both gentlemen kept up the old arguments even after two noted English mathematicians and astronomers, Charles Mason and Jeremiah Dixon, surveyed 244 miles of disputed boundary in 1763-68. Of greater moment to the colonists were the occasional forays of French and Spanish pirates. Pleas for military and financial assistance were ignored at Philadelphia. The rising dissatisfaction of the Three Lower Counties could not be forever brushed aside. In 1704 a separate assembly was established at New Castle.

Brighter days resulted. Soon the southern colonies and the West Indies provided a steady market for flour milled in Delaware and for food raised on its farms. Towns like Wilmington, New Castle, Duck Creek, Dover and Lewes began to flourish. But now came a succession of colonial wars to drain off this prosperity and to stunt the colony's growth — Queen Anne's War, War of Jenkins' Ear, King George's War, the French and Indian War — so that between 1702 and 1763 peace was at best a patched-up, temporary affair.

Caesar Rodney's Ride

The life and fortune expended in these wars by the colonists made them believe when the Stamp Act came along that their devotion and loyalty to the British crown was being ill-repaid. In the end, colonial patience and temper snapped — in Delaware as soon as anywhere. On July 2, 1776, Caesar Rodney, one of the delegates from the Three Lower Counties to the Continental Congress, was in Dover suppressing a Tory rebellion when he received an urgent summons to Philadelphia. The resolution for the adoption of the Declaration of Independence was before the Congress and Rodney's vote was needed. On horseback Rodney rode the eighty-six miles to Philadelphia; then, striding into Congress, he cast the deciding vote that welded the colonies into a new nation.

The Three Lower Counties formed the independent government of Delaware that year, and on December 7, 1787 it became the first state to ratify the United States Constitution. In the War Between the States, although a slaveholding state, Delaware did not secede from the Union, and, in fact, sent four small regiments to fight for Mr. Lincoln.

Thomas Jefferson's Jewel

Modern Delaware supports a vigorous industry. First among Delaware's manufactures are chemical products; and the dyes, cloth and cloth finishes, cellophane, paints and varnishes that come from the Wilmington area are used around the world. Ever since Jacob Broon built a cotton mill on the Brandywine in 1795 — and since, six years later, Eleuthère Irénée du Pont imported a merino ram from Spain to start a wool industry — textile mills have been important to Delaware's economy. Leather-making as a Delaware enterprise goes back more than 250 years to when the Quakers prepared buckskin and chamois leather. Other industries include clothing, dental supplies and canned food. Shipbuilding has been a Wilmington stand-by since Colonial days and paper-making has continued in Delaware since Joshua and Thomas Gilpin opened their mill on the Brandywine in 1787.

Agriculture remains a basis of Delaware's economic security, and not without reason is Delaware sometimes called the "Blue Hen State," since each year it supplies about 90,000,000 broilers for the nation's tables along with some 113,000,000 eggs and 650,000 turkeys. Clams canned in Lewes and oysters canned at Rehoboth Beach are products of its fisheries. Kaolin, a pottery clay, is its only significant mineral resource.

Delaware's distinguished sons and daughters include authors Henry Seidel Canby, John P. Marquand and Howard Pyle; Annie Jump Cannon, the world's greatest woman astronomer, known as "the census taker of the sky"; Thomas Holcomb, who commanded the United States Marine Corps in World War II; and Emily Bissell, who, in 1907, originated the sale of Christmas seals in the United States to raise funds to fight tuberculosis.

Delaware's motto is "Liberty and Independence," and she cherishes both as she cherishes the memory that Thomas Jefferson once called Delaware "a *jewel* among the States."

The First State

MARYLAND
"The Old Line State"

"IT'S BAD luck to swear while fishing." So insist the hardy, two-fisted men who earn their living from the waters of Maryland's Chesapeake Bay, and the world doesn't possess better fishermen! "If you would catch oysters, sing; if fish, be still" — this also is Chesapeake Bay lore that father hands down to son. Superstition? Not a bit of it! Wisdom comes in many disguises, and along the shores of Maryland it takes the form of a chanty:

When the wind is from the north,
Sailors don't go forth;
When the wind is from the east,
'Tis neither fair for man nor beast;
When the wind is from the south,
It blows the bait in the fish's mouth;
When the wind is from the west,
Then it's at its very best.

Into the sparkling waters of Chesapeake Bay on a bright spring day in 1634 — when, perhaps, the wind was at its very best — came two boats, the *Ark* and the *Dove,* with Maryland's first settlers.

Stronghold of Religious Tolerance

Leader of these first Marylanders was Cecil Calvert, second Lord Baltimore, who was carrying out his father's dream of founding a colony in America. Calvert's party touched the soil of the New World on an island in the Potomac, which, as good Catholics, they named St. Clements. Then they bought a village from the Indians, including the wigwams, and renamed this ready-made settlement St. Mary's. A conflict with the inhabitants of trading posts on Kent Island, established in 1631 by William Claiborne of Virginia, threatened a minor war until the Governor of Virginia intervened and arranged a peace with the islanders.

Lord Baltimore was absolute owner

of the colony, empowered to make almost any law that pleased him. But his lordship was both a wise and tactful man who, though he wished to call his colony Crescentia (Land of Increase), permitted the king to name it in honor of the queen. With like prudence, Lord Baltimore encouraged his colonists to suggest laws. Although the colony had been founded as a refuge for persecuted Catholics, when, in 1642, Thomas Gerard, a Catholic and member of the council, seized the key and Book from a Protestant chapel, he was fined five hundred pounds of tobacco toward the support of the first Protestant minister arriving in that section.

The Toleration Act followed in 1649, setting severe penalties for molesting the religion of any "believer in Christ," and making it a misdemeanor to deride anyone as a "Heretick, Schismatick, Idolator, Puritan, Presbyterean, Independent, Popish Priest, Jesuit, Jesuited Papist, Lutheran, Calvinist, Anabaptist, Brownist, Antinomian, Barrowist, Roundhead, Separatist," which pretty well covered religious persecution midway through the seventeenth century.

"Troops of the Line"

After 1654 a group of Puritans from Virginia seized power in Maryland, and freedom of conscience was denied to the "Popery or prelacy," but this tyranny was short-lived. The Protestant Revolution in England that placed William and Mary on the throne had its repercussions in Catholic Maryland, and for twenty-five years the colony was run under the direct authority of the crown, while the capital was

changed from St. Mary's to Annapolis. In 1715 power was restored to the original proprietors when the fifth Lord Baltimore renounced publicly "the Romish errors."

Aside from these religious tensions, the story of Maryland in the years leading up to the Revolution was similar to that of other Middle Atlantic states. None, for example, disputed more vigorously with Penn over boundary lines. No district in Colonial America suffered more than western Maryland from the raids, scalpings and burned houses that became a sadly familiar part of the French and Indian War. No colony resented more belligerently the Stamp Act and the other Parliamentary excesses that kept America in ferment for a decade, and Marylanders staged their own "tea party" when they forced the owner of the tea-laden *Peggy Stewart* to burn and sink his vessel at Annapolis in 1774.

It was the rugged character of Maryland soldiers during the War of Independence — these "troops of the line" — that gave Maryland its nickname as "The Old Line State." The Treaty of Paris, ending that conflict, was ratified by the Congress of the Federation, sitting in Annapolis on January 14, 1784.

"The Rockets' Red Glare"

A dispute with Virginia, principally over navigation, produced a meeting in Annapolis that was a forerunner of the Philadelphia Convention of 1787. Maryland stood firm on its belief that the Northwest Territory should be held in trust by Congress for the formation of new states, and its action resulted in

The Old Line State

*The
Old Line
State*

the famous Ordinance of 1787. The following year Maryland — the seventh state to do so — ratified the United States Constitution.

The War of 1812 brought British men-of-war into Maryland's coastal waters. On September 13, 1814, anchoring off Fort McHenry, these warships hoped with nightfall to gain the entrance of the Patapsco River and to capture Baltimore. An imprisoned Washington lawyer, Francis Scott Key, watched the great unfolding battle from aboard a British vessel as the warships tried to sneak by the fort. The guns of Fort McHenry blazed with defiance. Key thought prayerfully, "If at daybreak the American flag still waves over the fort, Baltimore will be saved!" The tune of an old English song, "Anacreon in Heaven," throbbed in Key's mind. Watching the duel between warships and fort, he put new words to an old melody:

*And the rockets' red glare, the bombs
     bursting in air,
Gave proof through the night that our
     flag was still there.*

And there the flag remained in the morning, proudly spanking in the breeze above Fort McHenry! The British had lost their conquest of Baltimore and in "The Star-Spangled Banner" we had gained a National Anthem.

Divided Loyalties

As a slaveholding state, Maryland suffered the agonies of divided loyalties during the Civil War, even though it did not secede from the Union. The first blood of the war shed on Mary-

land's soil occurred in April, 1861 when a Baltimore mob attacked troops of the Sixth Massachusetts as they were passing through the city en route to Washington. Four soldiers, as well as a number of citizens, were killed. In New Orleans a young Baltimorean, James Ryder Randall, deeply affected by the incident, wrote "Maryland, My Maryland," a song that rallied the entire South to a more determined war effort. Still the state song, the opening verse begins:

*The despot's heel is on thy shore,
     Maryland!
His torch is at thy temple door,
     Maryland!
Avenge the patriotic gore
That flecked the streets of Baltimore,
And be the battle-queen of yore,
     Maryland, my Maryland!*

One of the great battles of this tragic conflict, fought in 1862 along the slopes of Antietam Creek at Sharpsburg, has been called "the bloodiest day of the war." General Robert E. Lee had invaded Maryland, expecting its pro-Southern population to rally to the Rebel banner. Nothing of the sort occurred. Then a Union soldier found a copy of Lee's secret orders wrapped around some cigars. The Yankees surprised Lee at South Mountain and he retreated to Sharpsburg, where his superb generalship stood off the Union's superior forces and made possible his escape into Virginia.

Modern Maryland

In time the wounds of war healed, and by 1900 shipping and manufactur-

PENNSYLVANIA

DEL.

LORD CALVERT

DARWIN

CHESAPEAKE BAY

Baltimore

Annapolis

PATUNXET RIVER

RIVER

POTOMAC R.

Washington, D.C.

Hagerstown

VIRGINIA

MONOCACY R.

Cumberland

POTOMAC RIVER

W. VA.

MILES

50
40
30
20
10
0

Maryland

TVÆ · CORONASTI · NOS · VOLVNTATIS · BONE · SCVTO · 1632

*The
Old Line
State*

ing had begun to build Maryland's industrial strength. An iron furnace and forge, built in 1715 on Principio Creek in Cecil County, has been called Maryland's first manufacturing plant. More prophetic for the future was the first iron ship built in Baltimore in 1839, for in this seaport, steel and shipbuilding would be S's turned into dollar signs in Maryland's economy. Chemicals, aircraft, clothing, stone, clay and glass products, tin cans, canned food, malt liquor, fertilizer, printing, oil, sugar and refined copper are other manufactured products that enrich Maryland. Since 1829, when the Baltimore and Ohio Railroad started west from Baltimore, Maryland has pioneered in transportation. Citizens of Baltimore watched the first electric streetcars running through their streets in 1885.

The diversity of soils in Maryland has, since colonial times, made the state rich in agriculture, and today farmers in the "Old Line State" do well with dairy products and poultry, fruits and vegetables, and tobacco. Maryland's mineral resources include coal, sand, gravel and crushed stone. And, of course, for oysters, crabs, shad, mackerel and terrapin, no one can excel the fisheries in Maryland where "fish begin to bite when the dogwood is in blossom."

Maryland's sons and daughters include, among others, Stephen Decatur, naval officer who won a sharp little war against the pirates of Tripoli, and Frederick Douglass, leader in the movement to free Negro slaves; Johns Hopkins, financier and founder of the great university that bears his name, and John Paul Jones, Revolutionary naval hero; Henry L. Mencken, editor and author, and Glenn L. Martin, pioneer of aviation and aircraft manufacturing; Babe Ruth, baseball's all-time immortal, and Mason Locke Weems, whose fictionalized biography of George Washington created the legend of Honest George, his Papa, his hatchet and the cherry tree.

The visitor to Annapolis, with its fine old houses and the campus of the United States Naval Academy, looks across Chesapeake Bay on a sparkling day in spring and thinks how true were the words in Randall's song: *"Thy shield is bright and strong, Maryland!"*

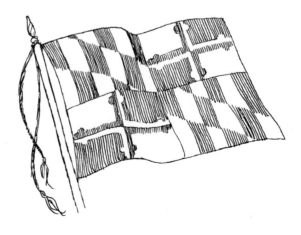

The South

VIRGINIA

"The Old Dominion State"

"I TELL THEE, gold is more plentiful in Virginia than copper is with us, and for as much red copper as I can bring, I will have thrice the weight in gold!" Thus spoke the hero of a play called *Eastward Ho!* that fascinated London playgoers in 1605.

The belief that Virginia abounded in precious metals was the chief attraction two years later that lured the first settlers to a safe mooring at Jamestown. Among the colonists were two goldsmiths, two refiners and a jeweler. Hardly had the newcomers offered up a prayer for their safe voyage than a ship started up the James River in quest of a fortune in gold. When the vessel returned, it was loaded with dirt shining with yellow flecks.

Captain Newport carted this cargo back to London before anyone could tell him that his gold was simply pieces of mica.

Lean Years and Triumph

Had these first settlers in Virginia decided deliberately to select the worst site imaginable for a village, they could not have surpassed the low, marshy, malarial peninsula on which Jamestown was located. Without the leadership of Captain John Smith, who drove these transplanted "gentlemen" to building houses and even a glassworks, the colony could not have endured. Even so, the winter of 1609-10 brought "the starving time" when nine out of every ten settlers perished and those who survived lived on horses, dogs, cats, rats and mice, and men

*The Old
Dominion
State*

searched the woods eager "to feed upon serpents and snakes." John Smith declared that one man killed his wife, then salted and "powdered" her, and added: "Of such a dish as powdered wife I never heard of." With spring the ghosts of people who endured at Jamestown resolved to quit Virginia forever, and were sailing down the James River when a fleet under Lord Delaware, bringing fresh supplies, persuaded them to turn back.

James I, who then occupied the throne, was such a hater of tobacco that he had even written a pamphlet attacking the use of tobacco as "harmful to the brain" and "dangerous to the lungs." Yet the weed that the king despised was destined to save his colony. In 1612 John Rolfe experimented with growing the sweet varieties of tobacco from the Caribbean and South America in place of the native Virginia tobacco that had a strong, bitter taste. So successful was Rolfe's "experiment" that soon even the streets between the houses were plowed by residents for growing the weed.

A remarkable man, John Rolfe! There is a tale — perhaps true, perhaps legend — that the life of John Smith once was saved by Pocahontas, an Indian princess, who threw herself across his body as he was about to be slain. Later Pocahontas was baptized, taking the Christian name of Rebecca, and married to Rolfe. She made a beautiful bride, according to an account of the time. A glittering band decked her forehead and feathers were fastened in her hair. Over a tunic of white muslin hung a robe she had embroidered.

A Fateful Year

Three events made the year 1619 fateful in the history of Virginia. One was the arrival of a ship filled with "maids young and uncorrupt" who were to become wives to the settlers and thus give Jamestown a more stable future. Another was the arrival at Point Comfort of a Dutch man-of-war in need of provisions with nothing to trade "but 20 and odd Negroes," thus bringing the first slaves into the colonies. But an event of greater moment occurred that summer in a church at Jamestown when Sir George Yeardley, the new governor, summoned into session the first representative assembly in America!

Delegates from eleven Virginia settlements met, passed laws against "idleness," gaming at dice, drunkenness and "excess in apparel," established a code of proper behavior with the Indians, devised laws for the systematic cultivation of corn, mulberry trees, silk-flax, aniseed and vineyards, and prescribed such punishments as excommunication from church and seizure of property for "enormous sins."

To America that summer of 1619 came a new concept of government, and, in the view of history, one sees planted here the seed that eventually produced the tree of liberty. Virginia's House of Burgesses, begun that summer, endured for the next 157 years, and when on May 6, 1776, as the oldest representative body of government in British America, the Burgesses declared their work ended, the Grand Union Flag of America waved from the staff of the Capitol!

MD

MARYLAND

Norfolk

Williamsburg

Richmond

Charlottesville

MARYLAND

VIRGINIA

SHENANDOAH

JAMES R.

WEST VIRGINIA

VIRGINIA

Virginia

SIC SEMPER TYRANNIS

VIRGINIA

Roanoke

KENTUCKY

TENN.

NORTH CAROLINA

MILES
0 10 20 30 40 50

WILLIAMSBURG

DARWIN

*The Old
Dominion
State*

Cradle of Revolution

Fire in 1698 destroyed the State House at Jamestown and the capital of Virginia was moved to Middle Plantation or Williamsburg — "a healthier and more convenient place." For more than seventy years thereafter the relationship between Virginia and the mother country was of the same loyal, cordial character that had led Charles II to call the colony, affectionately, "the Old Dominion." Since Virginia considered the Ohio River as part of its domain, the persistence of the French in stringing forts along its banks promised nothing but trouble. Governor Robert Dinwiddie sent young George Washington on a hazardous mission to warn the French, but he might as well have saved his breath. The bitter French and Indian War followed, and it was the Virginia regiments rather than the Redcoats who did the effective fighting.

Then in 1765 the change came, beginning with the Stamp Act and running through a series of events that, during the next decade, once caused John Adams to remark: "The Revolution was effected before the war commenced. The Revolution was in the minds and hearts of the people." Nowhere more than in Williamsburg was this true! Here on a March day in 1765 came Patrick Henry, on his lean horse, to blast the Stamp Act and cry, "If this be treason, make the most of it!"

Among those who listened to the thin-boned Henry that day was young Tom Jefferson, who would write the Declaration of Independence. Here along Duke of Gloucester Street often was seen George Washington, who called Williamsburg his "metropolis." When the squire of Mount Vernon dined at Raleigh Tavern, his companions might well have included any of the other great Colonial leaders who made Williamsburg a "rebel's roost" — George Wythe, Richard Henry Lee, Richard Bland, Peyton Randolph, George Mason. Together these Virginians forged a spirit of unity and accepted the risk of war for the reasons that Jefferson wrote in the Declaration of Independence:

"We hold these truths to be self-evident, that all men are created equal, that they are endowed by their Creator with certain unalienable Rights. . . . Governments are instituted among Men, deriving their just powers from the consent of the governed. . . . But when a long train of abuses and usurpations, pursuing invariably the same Object evinces a design to reduce them under absolute Despotism, it is their right, it is their duty, to throw off such Government, and to provide new Guards for their future security."

Triumph of Faith

So the Revolution, won by 1776 in the minds and hearts of the people, still had to be won on the fields of battle. The climax of that valiant struggle approached on a summer day in 1781 when George Washington, beloved commander-in-chief of the Continental armies, returned to Williamsburg with the peninsula between the York and James River sealed off and the British under Cornwallis trapped in Yorktown.

By October 19 of that year, the forces of Cornwallis had been defeated and, mounted on a white charger, General Washington rode to the field to receive their formal surrender.

The sun shone warmly that day. In sparkling uniforms the French legions formed behind their two strong leaders — Rochambeau and Lafayette. Soldiers from Massachusetts and Virginia, New Jersey and the Carolinas, Pennsylvania and Maryland, New York and Connecticut stood shoulder to shoulder, seasoned comrades now. Down the road sounded the doleful fifes and drums of the surrendering army — "much in liquor," one observer said. Another thought that "the British officers in general behaved like boys who had been whipped in school." But the end had come and one Hessian remembered: "After we had marched through both armies . . . we and all the regiments of Lord Cornwallis' army — Alas! — laid down our weapons and armor."

News of the surrender of Yorktown swept through a joyous nation. In Philadelphia an old German watchman awakened the city by crying, "Basht dree o'glock, und Cornval-lis isht daken!" When the news reached London, the prime minister moaned, "Oh God! It is all over!"

He was right.

"Mother of Presidents"

In 1788 Virginia ratified the Federal Constitution and the following year George Washington was inaugurated as our first President. Since then, Virginia, as the "Mother of Presidents," has sent seven other sons to the highest office in the land — Thomas Jefferson, James Madison, James Monroe, William Henry Harrison, John Tyler, Zachary Taylor, Woodrow Wilson.

America has been indebted to Virginians in nearly every crisis in its history. Virginia-born George Rogers Clark won the Northwest Territory and Virginia-born Sam Houston freed Texas. Two great generals of the Old Dominion, Zachary Taylor and Winfield Scott, carried the United States to victory in the Mexican War. The territory secured through Jefferson's Louisiana Purchase was explored by two fellow Virginians, Meriwether Lewis and William Clark. It is difficult to measure the influence of Virginians by modern boundaries, for as the "Mother of States," the original territory, chartered in 1609, now embraces also in part or full the states of West Virginia, Kentucky, Ohio, Illinois, Indiana, Wisconsin and Minnesota.

With the firing on Fort Sumter, civil war divided North from South and Virginia faced the decision which she long had been reluctant to make. On April 17, 1861 a state convention passed an ordinance of secession, and shortly thereafter the capital of the Confederacy was moved to Richmond. Thousands of Virginians risked their lives and fortunes for the South, and the battlefields of the war pock-marked the soil of Virginia — twice at Manassas (Bull Run), on the Peninsula from Yorktown to the outskirts of Richmond, at Winchester, Port Republic, Fredericksburg, Chancellorsville and the Wilderness, Spotsylvania, Cold Harbor, Cedar Creek, Petersburg.

The Old Dominion State

The Old Dominion State

Greatness at Appomattox

Private John Dooley of the First Virginia Volunteers described what, by late 1862, the war had meant to his beloved Old Dominion: "The fences are burned, the meadows trampled down, the cattle all gone and the harvests unharvested; proud homesteads in ruins, the master on the war trail and the old couple and daughters sit mournful and comfortless around expiring embers."

A grim picture — yet Virginians fought on, bravely, magnificently. Why? A good deal of the answer was in the quality of the generals Virginia produced — Stonewall Jackson, Joe Johnston, Jeb Stuart, A. P. Hill, R. S. Ewell, Jubal A. Early. And, of course, Robert E. Lee — the Gallant Lee whom soldiers called "Uncle Robert" and the poet Sidney Lanier compared to a god of legend. "Human virtue should be equal to human calamity," Lee taught his soldiers, and in that spirit on Palm Sunday, 1865, he met General Grant at Appomattox Court House and ended the war in Virginia.

Modern Virginia

Virginia suffered less than other Southern states during Reconstruction, and, readmitted to the Union in 1870, began to go ahead. After the turn of the century, her strides forward became especially rapid. Today, tobacco products, textiles, ships, chemicals, paper and pulp, lumber and wood products, canned foods, leather products, metals and machinery are Virginia's principal manufactures. Her chief seaports are Hampton, Newport News, Norfolk and Portsmouth.

Agriculture still plays an important part in Virginia's economy, and among the greatest tobacco markets in the United States are Danville, Petersburg, Lynchburg, South Hill and South Boston. Dairy products, corn, wheat, oats, potatoes, sweet potatoes, fruits, peanuts, hogs and pork, poultry and eggs, cattle, horses and mules, sheep and wool, all give Virginia farmers a good income. Clay, stone, sand and gravel, lime, commercial clays, lead, zinc, manganese, titanium ores and mineral waters constitute Virginia's mineral resources. Her fisheries catch oysters, clams, crabs, shrimps and the usual runs of Chesapeake Bay fish.

Sic Semper Tyrannis reads the motto of Virginia, adopted in 1776. It means: "Thus Always to Tyrants." The deep feeling of a Virginian for the Old Dominion may make history the state's best product, her most profitable "natural" resource. The state song — not surprisingly — goes as follows:

Carry me back to Old Virginia,
There's where the cotton and the
corn and 'tatoes grow,
There's where the birds warble sweet
in the springtime,
There's where the old darkey's
heart am long'd to go.
There's where I labor'd so hard for
old Massa,
Day after day in the field of yellow
corn;
No place on earth do I love more
sincerely,
Than old Virginia, the State where
I was born.

Sir Walter Raleigh

NORTH CAROLINA

"The Tarheel State"

THERE are two stories about how North Carolina got its nickname, and both could be correct. Some say that when Cornwallis was marching his Redcoats from Wilmington, North Carolina, toward Yorktown his troops were forced to wade across rivers into which tar had been dumped.

The other story is set in Civil War times. Among North Carolina's chief products in those days were "tar, pitch and turpentine," giving cause for a regiment from another state to tease the North Carolinians: "Any more tar down in your state, boys?"

"Not one bit," shot back the North Carolinians. "Jeff Davis has bought it all up."

"That so? What's he goin' to do with it?"

"Put it on your heels to make you stick better in the next fight!"

Hearing of the incident, General Robert E. Lee reputedly exclaimed:

"God bless the Tar Heel boys!" Then and there the "Old North State" had been rechristened.

The Lost Colony

That Florentine navigator employed by France, Giovanni da Verrazano, who first snooped out so much of our Atlantic coastline in 1542, did not ignore North Carolina. Spaniards may have visited the region twenty years earlier, but it remained for the English to plant the settlement on Roanoke Island that made this part of North Carolina "the birthplace of English America."

As the "Father of English America," Sir Walter Raleigh certainly was ill-repaid for the faith and perseverance he poured into trying to found an enduring colony in North Carolina. His three attempts at colonizing probably cost him a fortune of $200,000 as well as his political reputation.

*The
Tarheel
State*

Raleigh's first expedition landed 108 men on Roanoke Island on August 17, 1585. Too much time spent in searching for gold and unfriendly relations with the Indians caused the settlers to sail back to England with three gifts from the New World — tobacco, the white potato and Indian corn.

A second expedition, really intended to supply and reinforce the first, left fifteen men behind to hold England's claim to the land. Another colony, headed by John White, set out in April, 1587. White's first intention was to pick up the fifteen men who had been left on Roanoke Island, but the only trace of them he could find was a single skeleton. White rebuilt the fort, erected a few houses and named the new settlement "the Citie of Raleigh in Virginia." That August — the month when his granddaughter, Virginia Dare, became the first child of English parents born in America — White returned to England for supplies.

War with Spain delayed his return and not until 1591 did he look again upon Roanoke. His colony had vanished! The word "CROATOAN" carved on one tree, the letters "CRO" on another, a few broken pieces of armor — these were all that White found. Had the settlers been murdered by Spaniards? By Indians? The Lost Colony of Roanoke to this day remains an unsolved mystery.

"Rogue's Harbor"

The present states of North Carolina and South Carolina were included in Carolana — "The Land of Charles" — which Charles I granted to Sir Robert Heath. In 1663, dividing the territory among eight favorites, Charles II extended its boundaries to the Pacific Ocean. The colony grew slowly and Virginians looked with contempt upon North Carolina, calling it "Rogue's Harbor." With few schools, churches or other internal improvements, the colony under its proprietary governors was distinguished principally for the hardships reaped by dishonesty and inefficiency. The Tuscarora War, breaking out in 1711, managed to kill off hundreds of whites who had escaped other bedevilments.

In 1729 the king bought out the proprietors and as a royal colony, independent of South Carolina and well run by five successive governors, North Carolina grew from a population of 30,000 in 1730 to 265,000 in 1775. A planter aristocracy, mostly English and Scotch Highlanders, dominated the Cape Fear, Neuse and Albemarle regions. Smaller farmers, largely Germans and Scotch-Irish, transformed the Piedmont into a "prolongation of Pennsylvania." The split that came during the Revolution had been clearly foreshadowed. The Whigs came forward with a declaration of independence in 1775. The large planters and the Scotch Highlander gave the colony an equally devoted Tory legion, who organized an army. At Moores Creek Bridge on February 27, 1776 Whigs and Tories clashed in a battle that crushed the Tories.

"First at Bethel,
Last at Appomattox"

North Carolina troops fought for

VIRGINIA

TENNESSEE

SOUTH CAROLINA

ROANOKE R.

NEUSE R.

CAPE FEAR R.

Durham
Raleigh
Winston-Salem
Greensboro
Charlotte
Asheville
Wilmington

CROATOAN

THE "LOST COLONY"

North Carolina

THE GREAT SEAL OF THE STATE OF NORTH CAROLINA
ESSE QUAM VIDERI
MAY 20, 1775

MILES
0   20   40   60   80   100

The
Tarheel
State

Washington in every major theater of operations during the Revolution. Cornwallis, invading the Carolinas, tested the mettle of the Tarheels in the battles of Kings Mountain (1780) and Guilford Court House (1781) and went yipping back into Virginia, tail between his legs. After the war, North Carolina fussed over ratifying the Federal Constitution, suggesting various amendments guaranteeing states' rights, until she and Rhode Island stood alone among the holdouts. By a whisker, North Carolina escaped being the last to sign.

Again, the Tarheels seemed to progress slowly, as though stuck in their own tar, and at times North Carolina was mocked as "Old Rip Van Winkle." A strong movement for the emancipation of slaves made North Carolina the southern leader in the Underground Railroad until agitation from the North stiffened the states' rights instinct and quite reversed the emancipationist feeling. By the time the Civil War broke out, no one could doubt where North Carolina stood.

About one-fifth of all southern soldiers were Tarheels, and it was a proud boast in North Carolina that her boys in gray were "First at Bethel, farthest at Gettysburg, and last at Appomattox." Wilmington was the last port to fall to the North, holding out until January, 1865. By then, General Sherman had already started north on that part of his famous march which ended in North Carolina. Carpetbaggers (northern adventurers who traveled with "little luggage and less character") made Reconstruction a bitter time in North

Carolina, even for long months after the state was readmitted to the Union in 1868. Not until 1901 did North Carolina really make the turn that led her out of that prostrating period.

Tarheel Pride and Fancy

Yet adversity toughened Tarheel fiber and developed Tarheel individuality. In Illinois a man hoes corn, but in North Carolina he "chops" cotton. "'Tain't so" and "'tain't nothin'" persist in North Carolina because time and custom make them good enough — as, indeed, experience also cultivates a Tarheel's taste for turnip salad cooked with pork, or for fried ham and sweet yams. From tidewater to mountains, ways of thinking, speaking and acting change, but that's the kind of state North Carolina is — cussedly itself. A Tarheel fisherman may very well say "oi" for "i" so that he waits for "hoigh toide." A Tarheel farmer will often tell you there's no sense planting on a "bug day." North Carolinians like "chitlin's" fried and seasoned with pepper sauce. Black walnuts, hickory nuts, chinquapins and scuppernong grapes are native Tarheel delicacies.

North Carolina takes pride in many accomplishments. It was as long ago as 1795 that Hinton James walked 170 miles from Wilmington to Chapel Hill to become the first student in America's first state university. In Durham there is the pungent scent of tobacco from the stemmeries and the sweetish odor of tonka bean used in cigarette manufacture. It reminds Tarheels that about the time General Sherman was receiving General Johnston's surrender at the old Bennett House, Washington Duke was walking home from the war to write history by grinding his Pro Bono Publico tobacco, while his son Jim would do with tobacco "what Rockefeller did with oil and Carnegie with steel." At Kitty Hawk, hidden beyond the dunes of the coast, is the monument to Wilbur and Orville Wright, who proved that man could fly. With Orville at the controls on that historic December 17, 1903, the crude power-driven plane stayed aloft twelve seconds and covered 120 feet. Wilbur was at the controls on the fourth flight. He stayed aloft fifty-nine seconds and covered 852 feet.

Modern North Carolina

The "hornet's nest" that Cornwallis couldn't quit quickly enough after the Battle of Guilford Court House has become, in certain fields of industrial endeavor, a series of beehives. The world's largest cigarette factories are at Winston-Salem, Reidsville and Durham. The South's largest furniture factories are at High Point. Cotton manufacturing supports many towns and cities, while other North Carolina manufactures include lumber products, fertilizers, flour and grist, peanut products, pottery, fish oils, turpentine, chemicals and paper.

Still largely a farming state, North Carolina's Coastal Plain sometimes is called "Tobacco-land," though the state's famous bright-leaf tobacco is grown in all regions. The largest tobacco markets in the world are at Wilson. Other agricultural products include corn, cotton, hogs and pork, horses and mules, peanuts, grains, potatoes, soybeans, cowpeas, flower bulbs and hayseed. With ports like Elizabeth City, Morehead City, Beaufort and Wilmington, shipping and fishing add their share to the state's steady economic growth. Granite, marble, basalt, pottery clays, feldspar, mica, talc, bromine and gold are the chief mineral resources.

The highest point in Eastern America is at Mount Mitchell (6,684 feet above sea level as against 6,292 feet for Mount Washington in New Hampshire), and more than 200 of North Carolina's mountains are 5,000 feet or more above sea level. Black bears can be found walking the paved roads in the Great Smokies, and if you're wise, you'll remember that they are wild animals neither to be fed nor teased.

Famous Tarheels in American history range from statesmen like President Andrew Johnson to literary figures like novelist Thomas Wolfe, and the great writer of short stories, William Sydney Porter, known more familiarly by his pseudonym, O. Henry; from jurists like James Iredell, appointed a Justice of the United States Supreme Court by George Washington, to inventors like Richard Gordon Gatling, whose multiple-firing gun was the precursor of the modern machine gun. *Esse Quam Videri,* reads the state motto, meaning "To be, rather than to seem." Sometimes Tarheels, thinking of their state wedged between Virginia and South Carolina, express this idea a mite differently, describing North Carolina as "a vale of humility between two mountains of conceit."

The Tarheel State

SOUTH CAROLINA

"The Palmetto State"

SOUTH CAROLINA claims these "firsts" in American history:

The first settlement by white men (1526), the first ship built in America to cross the Atlantic (1562-63), the first province to plant rice and indigo (1686), the first free library (1698), the first theater in America devoted entirely to drama (1736), the first cotton mill (1789), the first American steam locomotive used for public service (1830), the first railroad to carry the U. S. mail (1833).

South Carolina claims also the first act in starting two wars — the seizure of Fort Charlotte on the South Carolina bank of the Savannah River on July 12, 1775 and the firing on Fort Sumter in Charleston Harbor on April 12, 1861. And there's more: the first municipal college, the first state to secede from the Union, the first olives grown in the United States, the first

tea farm in America. Two flowers are named for South Carolinians who introduced them into America — the poinsettia for Joel R. Poinsett and the gardenia for Alexander Garden.

It has some "onlys," too. Of the signers of the Declaration of Independence, only those from South Carolina were all natives of the state. The only laboratory in the nation which extracts perfume from native flowers is located in Columbia, South Carolina. And alone on Hilton Head Island can be found "marsh tackys," tiny horses believed to be descended from animals left by early Spanish explorers.

In brief, South Carolina is a state with a lot of individuality.

Discovery and Exploration

As early as 1521, Spaniards from Santo Domingo visited South Carolina, and five years later a settlement was attempted under the leadership of Lucas Vásquez de Ayllón. About 500 people, including Negro slaves, reached Winyah Bay with Ayllón, but after a few months they grew discouraged and abandoned the settlement. A second Spanish attempt at colonizing was made in 1566, and for about twenty years a fort was maintained on Parris Island. Meanwhile, in 1562, other Europeans appeared on an island off the Atlantic coast at the head of Port Royal Sound — 150 French Huguenots under Jean Ribaut, seeking freedom from Catholic persecution at home.

Ribaut built a stone pillar, claiming the land for France, and a fort that he named Charlesfort, in honor of Charles IX, king of France. Then Ribaut returned home for fresh supplies, and soon the colonists who remained behind fell into disputes that developed into a mutiny and the murder of their commander, Captain de la Pierria. They set out for Europe in a flimsy vessel they built, but a British ship came to their rescue and carried the unhappy Huguenots to England.

In 1629 Charles I of England cast covetous eyes on this part of North America already claimed by Spain and France. He issued a grant to his attorney general, Sir Robert Heath, to all the territory from sea to sea between the thirty-first and thirty-sixth parallels, naming the region "Carolana," after the Latin word *Carlus,* from which the king's own name was derived. Nothing much happened, however, until 1663, when Charles II regranted the land to eight friends, extending it to include present North Carolina and Georgia.

Under British Influence

From the beginning, the fundamental laws of the "Lords Proprietors" encouraged the growth of large plantations. Colonists sent by the proprietors settled in April of 1670 at Albermarle Point on the west bank of the river they named after Lord Ashley, calling their little village Charles Town in honor of the king. Ten years later they moved about two miles to the point where the Ashley and the Cooper rivers join to form Charleston Harbor. By 1700 the English from Barbados and the French Protestants who made up the bulk of Charleston's inhabitants had gained a large degree of control over their political affairs. In 1719 they rebelled against the existing government and placed their own candidate, James Moore, in the office of governor.

A half century of progress and prosperity followed. Rice and indigo developed into profitable crops. Deerskins became the bulwark of a flourishing business in pelts that found Charleston the capital of the Indian trade throughout the southern colonies. A tradition of refined social life emerged with the establishment of a free library, a theater, a musical society. But there were also bedevilments as pirates, flying the Jolly Roger, made the bays and islands of the Palmetto coast a favorite haunt. Stede Bonnet, the "gentleman pirate" who, it was said, was driven to his seamy profession to escape a nagging wife, ended his career dangling from a rope on Charleston's Battery. Blackbeard, Richard Wormley and Anne Bonney were other followers of

The Palmetto State

The
Palmetto
State

the skull and crossbones whose names had an all-too-familiar ring among the coves and inlets of Carolina.

War and Rebellion

Little wars kept nibbling at Carolina — with the Spanish in 1686, 1702-1704 and 1740, with the Spanish and French in 1706, with the Yemassee Indians in 1715 and the Cherokees in 1760-61 — and a spirit of self-sufficiency and independence, developing in Carolinians, made them leaders in the rebellion that ended in the American Revolution. The scars of that conflict crisscrossed the colony in bitter battles at Fort Moultrie, Charleston, Camden, King's Mountain, Cowpens, Hobrick's Hill and Eutaw Springs. Meanwhile, South Carolina's distinguished statesman, Charles Pinckney, played an influential role in developing the Constitution with determination to protect both states' rights and slavery, and it was Pinckney's leadership that stilled the fears of the people when they protested against the broad authority granted to the central government. Finally, on May 23, 1788, South Carolina approved the Constitution.

Free trade and slavery were essential to the plantation life and economy that grew in South Carolina in succeeding generations, and the great crisis over the Clay Tariff Act in 1832 (the Nullification Crisis) brought the state to the brink of secession. Under the compelling statesmanship of John C. Calhoun, South Carolina kept its position firm in the senatorial battles with Henry Clay and Daniel Webster, but by 1850 Calhoun was dead and his gift

of compromise became increasingly needed as the country plunged head-long toward civil war. South Carolina did not hesitate, once her "hotheads" were convinced that the triumph of "Black Republicanism" under Abraham Lincoln meant death to her institutions and her way of life. Without a dissenting vote, South Carolina led the parade of seceding states in December, 1860.

The Bitter War

Federal forces under Major Robert Anderson occupied Fort Sumter, guardian of the sea approaches to Charleston. By April, 1861 this fort had become a national symbol — of honor to the North, of insult to the South. Intelligence that a Federal fleet was at sea to reinforce Sumter touched off the explosion that everyone dreaded. Charleston's guns quickly pounded the fort into submission, but the price of the conflict that followed seared South Carolinian hearts. One-fourth of the 63,000 sons that South Carolina sent to fight the battles of the Confederacy died for the cause they held sacred. In 1865, marching north from Savannah, Union troops under General Sherman burned Columbia in a night of horror without peer on the American continent.

Then, in victory, the Federal Government imposed a harsh peace — the only time in history that the United States has done so — and the humiliation of reconstruction saw uneducated Negroes and white carpetbaggers making a mockery of the state's government. Not until 1876, with the election

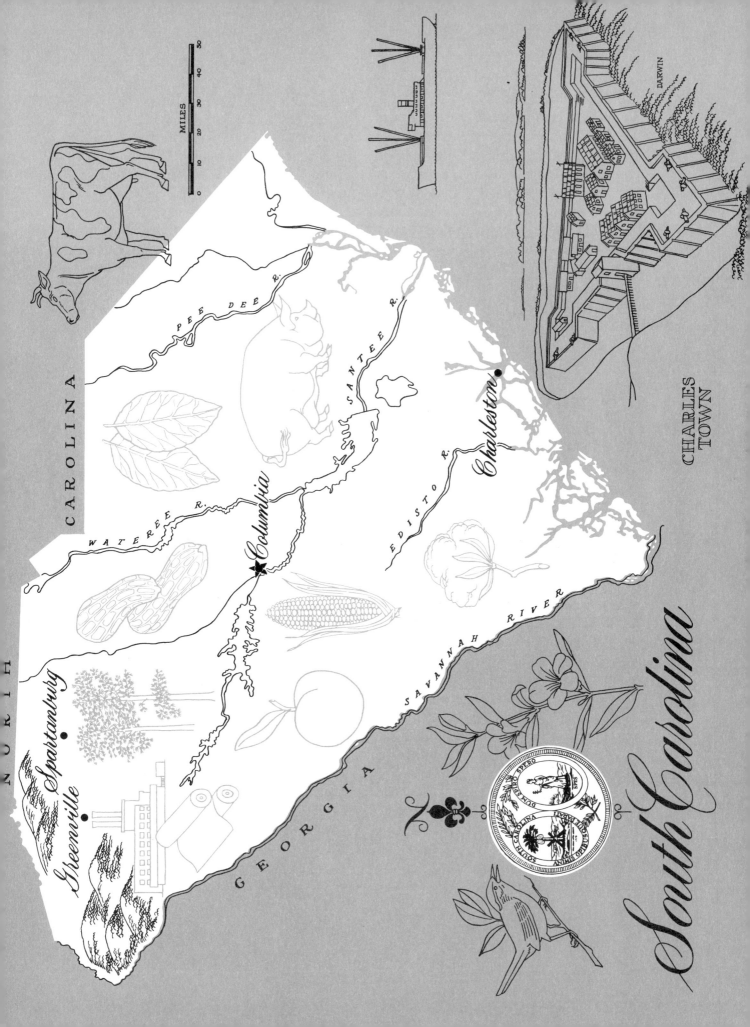

NORTH CAROLINA

NORTH

MILES
50
40
30
20
10
0

PEE DEE R.

SANTEE R.

WATEREE R.

EDISTO R.

Columbia

Charleston

Spartanburg

Greenville

GEORGIA

SAVANNAH RIVER

SOUTH CAROLINA ANIMIS OPIBUSQUE PARATI
DUM SPIRO SPERO
SPES

South Carolina

CHARLES TOWN

DARWIN

The
Palmetto
State

of Wade Hampton as governor, did this twelve-year tyranny end.

Left alone to rebuild their state, South Carolinians put their hearts into the task. The internal problem of conflict between the low-country conservatives and the farmers of the upcountry was worked out by 1890 with the election as governor of Benjamin R. Tillman, who strengthened such democratic institutions as the state's educational system.

The expansion of transportation facilities also quickened the recovery of the Palmetto State. Later, the development of hydroelectric plants encouraged the growth of industries.

Modern South Carolina

Today South Carolina has a vigorous agriculture, and among its chief income producers are corn, tobacco, dairy products, hogs, fruits, vegetables, pigeons and poultry, oats, wheat, peanuts, rice, potatoes, shrubs and flowering plants. Granite, kaolin (a white clay) and phosphates are its principal mineral resources, and its lumber industry uses native cedar, cypress, gum, oak, pine and poplar. From its fisheries come shrimp, oysters and crabs. Manufacturing, which has grown enormously since World War II, includes among its chief products cotton and rayon textiles, yarns, dyed goods, furniture, wood pulp, paper, nonalcoholic beverages, fertilizers, chemicals, canned goods and ships. Charleston and Georgetown are the main seaports on its coastline.

A proud state, South Carolina points to a long list of distinguished sons and

daughters — among them, Washington Allston, the painter whose major work was a portrait of Samuel Taylor Coleridge; Bernard M. Baruch, statesman and financier; Mary McLeod Bethune, Negro educator; James F. Byrnes, Secretary of State; authors Octavus Roy Cohen, DuBose Heyward and William Gilmore Simms; military leaders Andrew Jackson, James Longstreet and Francis Marion; and John Rutledge, the state's poet laureate.

South Carolina breathes the history and atmosphere of the Old South — at Cheraw's St. David's Church, used by the British as a smallpox hospital during the Revolution; along Rainbow Row in Charleston, with its houses painted blue, green, yellow, pink and brown; at Beaufort, with its Arsenal built in 1795 of "tabby" masonry (a concrete of oyster shells); at ancient Mepkin Plantation, with its giant live oaks where Henry Laurens, President of the Continental Congress, once resided; at historic Trinity Church in Columbia; and on King's Mountain, where a monument marks the turning point of the Revolution. From the rolling Piedmont to the mountainous upcountry, South Carolina is past and present blended. The state's motto, *Dum Spiro, Spero,* means "While I breathe, I hope." And the state's spirit is exemplified in the words of its song written by Henry Timrod, a distinguished poet:

Call on thy children of the hill;
Wake swamp and river, coast and rill,
Rouse all thy strength and all thy
skill,
Carolina! Carolina!

Hernando de Soto

GEORGIA

"Empire State of the South"

BEFORE the white man appeared, Creeks and Cherokees came to Warm Springs to heal their wounded bodies in the warm waters and soft mud. Legends told them of fires under the earth, stoked by the Great Spirit, that kept the water warm. Among the red men, Warm Springs was neutral ground where the sick of all tribes could be cured.

Late in the 1700's an epidemic of yellow fever in Savannah led its citizens to discover Warm Springs, and by 1832 the village had become a popular summer resort. Here, after an attack of infantile paralysis, Franklin D. Roosevelt came in 1924, and three years later he organized the Warm Springs Foundation so that persons similarly afflicted could be helped to rebuild their lives. Georgia Hall, the main building, was financed through voluntary contributions from fifty thousand Georgians. On the slopes of Pine Moun-

tain stands the little White House that, during four terms as President, Franklin D. Roosevelt often used as a retreat.

Warm Springs is a monument to the generosity of Georgians, a shrine to a President and a symbol of how free people stretch out their hands to help others in need.

From Piracy to Settlement

Mysterious ceremonial mounds in Georgia tell of Indian civilizations that flourished and died long before the Creeks and Cherokees came into this region. The Creeks pushed to the south, the Cherokees into the highlands, and both built their villages upon sites where once the vanished tribes had lived.

Probably the first white man in Georgia was Hernando de Soto, who, in 1540, found Indians instead of the gold for which he searched. French explorers and trappers, pushing up

Empire
State
of the
South

from the islands of the southeastern coast and building temporary posts, prodded Spain in 1565 into sending a force under Pedro Menendez de Aviles to claim the territory, fortify its coastal islands, and establish missions. Spanish overtures of spiritual salvation and physical domination were bitterly resisted by the Indians, and the white man's control over the region became so slipshod that during the next century and a quarter French and English pirates constantly harried the coast.

A change came on February 12, 1733 when the ship *Anne* landed some 125 English settlers about eighteen miles up the Savannah River. Tomochichi, chief of the Yamacraw (an outlawed tribe of the Creeks), deeded a site on the bluff for a town intended to be unlike any other in the New World.

A Noble Experiment

A noble man, James Edward Oglethorpe, and a noble idea were responsible for the colony. In those days, in England, persons could be imprisoned for their debts. Oglethorpe's plan was to give these unfortunates a new start in life as colonizers in America. Persecuted Protestants in continental Europe — principally Lutherans and Moravians — were added as a second group of settlers. So George II, after whom the colony was named, granted Oglethorpe a petition "for settling poor persons of London," and in the first eight years about 2,500 emigrants arrived.

Trouble arose in unexpected quarters. The trustees of the colony, believing that its settlers should survive by

their own labor, prohibited slave holding. Only a group of Scotch Highlanders, who looked upon slavery as degrading to both master and vassal, supported the law. Others complained, or smuggled in slaves. A prohibition on the manufacture and sale of rum became another source of irritation and rebellion, and Georgians couldn't remember when they had been so thirsty! Unrest also resulted from a law that allowed only fifty acres of land to a settler brought to Georgia at public expense, and gave him a restricted title to that grant. The liquor law was repealed in 1742. Slaveholding was permitted in 1749. The following year land ownership was liberalized. Thereafter, despite Indian troubles within the colony and strife with the Spanish on its southern border, Georgia forged steadily ahead. In 1754 it became a royal province and a dozen years later its population was estimated at about 10,000 whites and at least 7,800 Negroes. Farming, cattle raising, horse breeding and the fur trade were its sources of wealth.

Saved by a Yankee

Georgians cheered the reading of the Declaration of Independence, but the price of this loyalty to the Continental cause was revealed in 1778 when British forces struck along the coast and overland through Florida. Savannah fell that December. Sunbury and Augusta were seized the next month, and by the end of 1779 every major town, except in northern Wilkes County, had been taken by the British. Torn by conflicts from within — Geor-

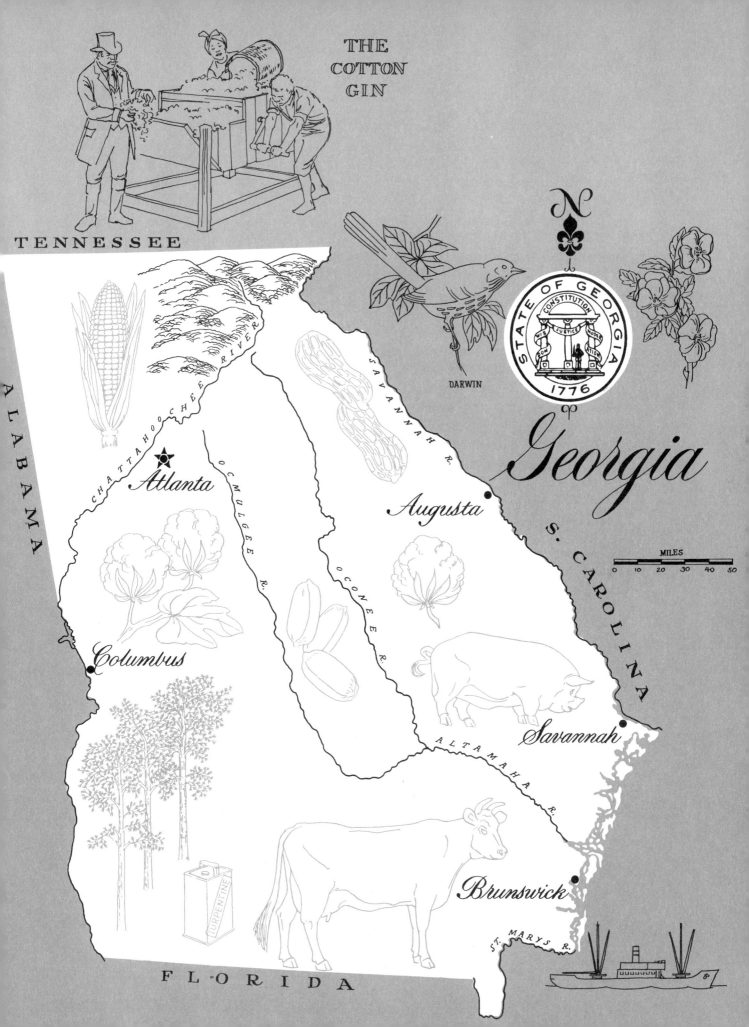

THE
COTTON
GIN

TENNESSEE

ALABAMA

DARWIN

STATE OF GEORGIA
CONSTITUTION
WISDOM · JUSTICE · MODERATION
1776

Georgia

S. CAROLINA

MILES
0   10   20   30   40   50

CHATTAHOOCHEE RIVER

Atlanta

OCMULGEE R.

SAVANNAH R.

Augusta

OCONEE R.

Columbus

TURPENTINE

ALTAMAHA R.

Savannah

Brunswick

ST. MARYS R.

F L O R I D A

Empire
State
of the
South

gia at times was run simultaneously by Tory and Whig governments — guerrilla strife added to the hardships. But ultimately the war ended and in 1788 Georgia, the last of the original thirteen colonies, was among the first in the South to ratify the United States Constitution.

During the Revolution, Eli Whitney had earned his keep making nails by hand. Graduating from Yale College in 1792, this Yankee went south as a private tutor. His job was gone when he arrived, so Eli accepted an invitation from the widow of General Nathanael Greene to be a guest in her spacious home on the Savannah River. In the gadgets he built for her, Mrs. Greene said, it was soon evident that Eli "could make anything." One day the Yankee watched the slow hand labor involved in separating green cotton from its seed. A Negro woman

Eli Whitney

who picked a pound a day did well! For some months Eli worked on building a machine to do this hand labor and when his cotton gin was finished, one person, using the machine, could clean one thousand pounds of cotton in about the time it previously had taken to clean five or six pounds.

Triumph and Disaster

Almost overnight, in Georgia and throughout the "Deep South," Eli Whitney had turned an unprofitable crop into white gold. "King Cotton" had been born! The "institution" of slavery suddenly became "sacred" as plantations increased their acreage and the cotton bales piled higher on the docks, awaiting shipment to mills in both Old England and New England.

Unhappily, Eli Whitney's cotton gin also sowed the seeds of a civil war between the North and South — and the bitter harvest was reaped in the tragic years from 1861 to 1865. Georgia's son and statesman, Alexander H. Stephens, served the Confederacy as Vice President. Her soldiers fought in Southern armies on every front of the war.

On September 19 and 20, 1863 — "the two bloodiest days of the war," some claimed — the scars of conflict came to Georgian soil in the Battle of Chickamauga. The following year, powerful Union armies under General William Tecumseh Sherman fought their way into Atlanta, burned that city, and marched to the sea, leaving in their wake destroyed property valued at $10,000,000. After the war, carpetbaggers gained control of the state and in three years the public debt rose from

$5,000,000 to $16,000,000. Georgia was re-admitted to the Union in 1870.

Modern Georgia

Happier times were ahead. Not only were cotton and cottonseed of prime importance in rebuilding Georgia's agriculture, but also peanuts (explaining why Georgia often is called the "Goober State"). Only California surpasses Georgia as a peach-grower to the nation, and famous varieties of peaches that have been developed in the state include the Georgia Belle, Hiley Belle, Elberta and Hale. Corn, sugar cane, sorghum, tobacco, soybeans, pecans and grains are other leading crops.

With an Atlantic coastline (its chief ports are Savannah and Brunswick), mountains in the north (Georgia has more than twenty-eight peaks exceeding 4,000 feet), and a central section of broad hills, narrow valleys and rolling plains, the state's mineral resources include clay, granite, marble, barite, bauxite, fuller's earth, kaolin, limestone, manganese and ocher. Once Georgia suffered as a "one crop" state and, learning from that lesson, it has encouraged a growth of industries, especially since World War II, in such manufactures as cotton goods and yarn, cottonseed oil, fertilizer, wood products, pulp and paper, and canned food. From Georgia's fisheries come shrimp, crabs, oysters, clams and shad.

In many fields Georgia points with pride to her distinguished sons and daughters, including James Bowie, hero of the Texas revolution; Ty Cobb, all-time baseball immortal known as the "Georgia Peach," who one season batted .420; Jabez Lamar Monroe Curry, educator and founder of Howard University; John C. Frémont, western explorer and first presidential candidate of the Republican Party; Henry Woodfin Grady, editor of the Atlanta *Constitution,* whose editorials and speeches did much in the postwar period to heal the wounds between North and South; Joel Chandler Harris, creator of the immortal Uncle Remus stories; Sidney Lanier, poet of the South; Dr. Crawford Long, first to use ether in performing a painless operation in 1842; Juliette Gordon Low, who began the Girl Scout movement at Savannah in 1912; and Margaret Mitchell, whose *Gone With the Wind,* a novel of Atlanta during the Civil War, ranks as one of America's all-time best sellers.

Empire State of the South

To the Georgian, most of all, his state is an image of eye and mind and heart — of white dogwood and flaming azalea in spring, of the mysterious loneliness of Okefenokee Swamp with its "trembling earth," of the beautiful Blue Ridge Mountains with rainbow trout flashing in their foamy streams, of water-skiing on Georgia waters the year round and of famous old Tybee Light that, built by Oglethorpe in 1753, still guides ships into Savannah Harbor. At Fort Benning there is a monument to Calculator, the crippled dog that was the mascot of the Infantry School. Its bronze tablet reads:

Calculator
Born — ?
Died — August 29, 1923
He made better dogs of us all

FLORIDA

"The Peninsula State"

INDIANS on the island of Puerto Rico spoke glowingly of the land to the northwest. Here gold could be picked from the ground. Here existed a magic fountain that restored youth. Juan Ponce de León, companion of Columbus on his second voyage to the New World, had pondered these stories for a long time before he set out, in 1513, with three flimsy caravels to find fortune and youth in *La Florida* — the Isle of Flowers.

Three weeks of leisurely voyaging carried Ponce de León from Puerto Rico to the Florida coast. On April 2, 1513, he landed a little north of St. Augustine and claimed the land for Spain. Later he sailed south, and, passing the Florida Keys, named them "The Martyrs" because they reminded him of men suffering. Ponce de León never found his gold. And he never found his magic fountain.

But legends of fabulous riches continued to cast their spell, luring other adventurers who, finding no better means to fortune, carried off Indians to sell into slavery in the West Indies. The Spanish tried seriously to make something out of Florida. In 1521 Ponce de León brought two shiploads of cattle and colonists into Charlotte Bay, but his settlement only lasted five months. Two other Spanish expeditions failed before Hernando de Soto landed at Tampa with six hundred foot soldiers and more than a hundred cavaliers and marched north and west, seeking cities made of gold. Three years later de Soto died, and the gaunt survivors of his party buried their leader's body in the Mississippi River to save it from desecration by vengeful Indians.

America's Oldest City

There were other Spanish explorations — under Fray Luis Cancer in 1549, under Tristan de Luna in 1559 — before Spain decided she had sent enough men to rust their breastplates ducking Indian arrows in Florida's swamps. Then French Huguenots under Jean Ribaut planted a colony along that part of the seaboard now belonging to South Carolina, and Spain, a never-failing dog-in-the-manger under such circumstances, came growling back into Florida. The redoubtable Don Pedro Menéndez de Avilés, leader of the Spanish treasure fleet, concluded that to win Florida he needed two triumphs —to rid the land of the French and to convert the Indians to Christianity. Menéndez was more successful at ousting the French then at saving Indian souls. His settlement in 1565 at St. Augustine — so named because Menéndez first sighted Florida on August 28, St. Augustine's Day — would become the country's oldest permanent white settlement.

In succeeding decades, this community could relate the history of Florida by the events that occurred beyond its moated entrance. When England decided to contest with Spain for the Atlantic coast from Virginia to Florida, it was to St. Augustine that Sir Francis Drake, the British admiral, came in 1586, sacking and burning the town. From their forest refuges the Spaniards reappeared to rebuild the settlement, and St. Augustine once more flourished as the headquarters for missionary activities among the southeastern Indians. The English, settled at Charleston, came back in 1702 and 1728, burning, plundering and running off with thousands of Indians that they condemned to slavery. James Oglethorpe, governor of Georgia, next launched the series of attacks that, in 1742, ended the power of Spanish St. Augustine.

The Peninsula State

Tory Hotbed

The Spanish fled to Cuba and, in the decades that followed, the British moved into their empty houses. Beginning in 1763, these slave-owning planters gave St. Augustine twenty years of prosperity. They burned John Hancock and old Sam Adams in effigy, captured three signers of the Declaration of Independence and jailed them in the town fort, all of which served as a springboard for the British in their attacks on the Carolinas. The *East Florida Gazette,* a Tory newspaper, was published here.

American victory in the Revolution restored Florida to Spain, but Americans rather than Spaniards moved into the houses that the British now vacated. For almost forty years, without any form of responsible government, Florida was best described as a hideout for runaway slaves, plundering Indians and nefarious adventurers. The Republic of West Florida, organized by American settlers in 1810, and the Republic of East Florida, organized two years later with the help of two punitive expeditions led by General Andrew Jackson, were the forerunners of the purchase of Florida from Spain for $5,000,000. The land was transferred formally to the United States at Pensacola in 1821, and the territory of Florida was organized the next year.

Osceola

The Seminole Wars

By the thousands, Americans poured into Florida. The best lands were occupied by the Seminoles, who looked upon the invading Americans with a suspicion that grew into outright hatred. The leader of the Indians in the seven-year Seminole Wars that plagued Florida from 1835 to 1842 was tall, arrogant Osceola. The stepson of a white trader, whose wife was captured and carried off to be a slave, Osceola harbored a bitter enmity toward the Americans, which was reflected in a famous message he once sent to the white commander:

"You have guns, so have we. You have powder and lead, and so have we. Your men will fight, and so will ours, till the last drop of Seminole blood has moistened the dust of his hunting ground."

Like so much of Florida's history, St. Augustine had its special chapter in the Seminole Wars as the place of Osceola's imprisonment after his capture. Florida was admitted to statehood on March 3, 1845 — Iowa was admitted as a free state, to keep intact the balance between free and slave states — and it came as no real surprise when, during the years of the Confederacy, Florida was among the first states to secede. About 15,000 Florida troops fought in the Rebel cause. St. Augustine — that doorway through which history seemed so often to enter — did not fail now as Federal forces occupied the city from 1862 to the end of the war. Florida was subsequently readmitted to the Union in 1868.

ALABAMA

GEORGIA

PERDIDO R.

APPALACHICOLA R.

ST. MARYS R.

★ Tallahassee

Jacksonville

St. Augustine

SUWANNEE R.

ST. JOHNS RIVER

Orlando

Tampa

PONCE DE LEON

MILES
0   20   40   60   80   100

N

Miami

GREAT SEAL OF THE STATE OF FLORIDA
IN GOD WE TRUST

Florida

*The
Peninsula
State*

Miracle of Miami

In the 1880's many factors accounted for the astonishing growth of Florida — the reclamation of swampland and the development of fruit-growing were two — but at the top of any list of the men and events that remade Florida must go the name of Henry M. Flagler. This New Yorker and former oil man was fifty-three when he reached St. Augustine to live in retirement. What Florida needed, he could see, was better hotels, better railroads — and Henry M. Flagler set out to prove his point. Among his achievements was Miami, which he helped to build by turning mangrove swamp, jungle and coral rock into a mecca of ornate hotels and dwellings that match the colors of the rainbow. Islands were dredged from the bay and transformed into a winter playground for those who wished to follow the sun — on such feats of engineering and investment would "the Peninsula State" become a national institution!

The year-round Floridian, of course, knows that a great deal more than the hordes of pleasure-bent followers of the sun keeps his state prosperous. The richness of the soil and the long growing season are ideal for truck crops, citrus fruits and field crops like corn, tobacco, sugar cane, cotton, hay and oats — and these, together with a boom in cattle raising, give Florida a vigorous agriculture. Forest products have meant millions of dollars to Florida in lumber, woodpulp and paper. Tobacco products are another chief manufacture, along with canned goods, sugar, chemicals, turpentine, tung-nut prod-

ucts, fertilizers and boats. Phosphate rock, limestone, sand and gravel are important mineral resources. Here more sponges are harvested than in any other state of the Union. Here more fish are caught than in any other Gulf State.

Typically Florida

Living on the Yankee in winter and on fish in summer may be typical of Florida — as pirate stories about Black Caesar and Gasparilla, guaranteed to raise your hair, are typical of Florida — but so, too, is the fact that Ponce de León's "Isle of Flowers" proved worthy of its name. Flatwoods, scrub lands, grassy swamps, salt marshes, hammocks or hardwood forests, high pine lands — you find them all in Florida — each offers its own wonders. Orchids, insect-catchers like pitcher plants and sundews, red lilies and milkwort grow in the flatwoods. In the scrub lands the air is pungent with the blossoms of grapefruit, tangerines, oranges. Yellow American lotus and floating hyacinth can be found in the savannas of central Florida.

Fifteen native palms grow in Florida, including varieties of the palmetto, the royal palm, the coconut palm. "Old Senator," the oldest tree in the Cypress swamps at Longwood, is estimated to be 3,500 years old — give or take a few centuries. About 400 species of birds have been counted in Florida. Native butterflies number more than 300 varieties, and its spiders include the poisonous black widow. Alligators? They're fairly numerous, but only in the brackish coastal inlets from Biscayne Bay to Cape Sable do you find crocodiles.

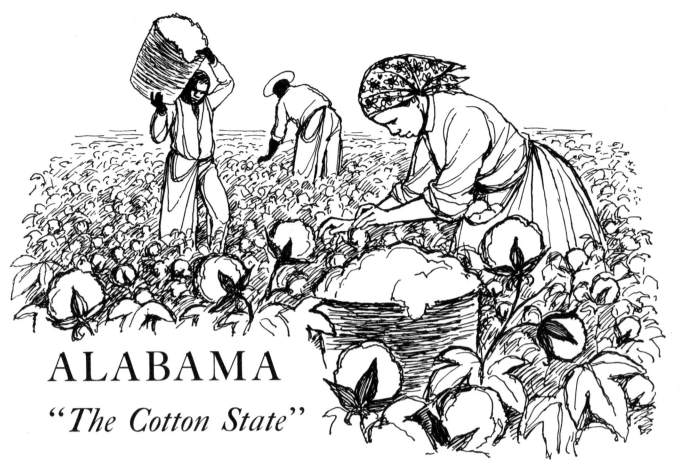

ALABAMA

"The Cotton State"

SOME THINGS never change in 'Bama. Each spring the fields and the roadsides are carpeted with primroses. Green fields turn pale pink, rolling in waves before the wind.

But here in the Deep South, where once King Cotton ruled over every thought and action, there have been deep, radical changes. In Montgomery, Alabama, on January 6, 1861, representatives of six seceding states assembled to establish the Confederate States of America. Jefferson Davis of Mississippi was elected President and Alexander H. Stephens of Georgia Vice President, but the real leaders upon which 'Bama and the Confederacy pinned their faith were cotton and slavery.

How greatly the old can give way to the new strikes the visitor to Enterprise, Alabama, where in 1910 the boll weevil destroyed the cotton. Planters, tired of being enslaved by one crop, turned to cultivating peanuts. Then they erected a monument unlike any in the world — a monument to an insect pest! Its inscription reads:

"In profound appreciation to the boll weevil, and what it has done to herald prosperity, this monument is erected by the citizens of Coffee County and Enterprise."

"Life Is Gay and Luxurious"

"The people wear hats of solid gold and life is gay and luxurious!" Thus seamen who had visited the coast of which Alabama was a part spoke to Hernando de Soto, newly appointed governor of Cuba. In the spring of 1539 de Soto set sail for the mainland, disembarked his soldiers on the shores of Charlotte Bay and began his futile

The Cotton State

march northward in search of golden cities. By 1540 de Soto's band reached Alabama, moving slowly down the valley of the Coosa River. At first the Indians were friendly, for which the Spaniards repaid them with the lash of tongue and whip.

At Mauvila, a palisaded town near present Choctaw Bluff, a great battle between red men and white was fought that autumn. The Indians were defeated and their town burned. Some say as many as 11,000 Indians perished, doubtless a wild exaggeration. The Spanish dead were recorded at 82, but hundreds more were wounded, among them de Soto. The Spaniards pushed on, and again in November there was severe fighting along the Black Warrior River. Gaunt, hungry, staggered, de Soto's band was forced to fight almost step by step through the Choctaw country. The dust of Alabama on their heels was mixed with blood.

Nineteen years later Tristan De Luna, acting under the authority of the viceroy of Mexico, brought the first white settlers to the shores of Mobile Bay. By 1561, when three years of searching for gold and quarreling among themselves were their sole reward, the Spanish colonists abandoned Alabama. A century passed before the French and English began the bitter contest that ultimately decided 'Bama's history.

But She Was "Hard to Please"

In 1702 Jean Baptiste Le Moyne, Sieur de Bienville, was appointed governor of France's vast province of Louisiana and moved the seat of his territorial government to Fort Louis de la Mobile on the Mobile River. A hard year followed, then Mobile was established as a canonical parish by the Bishop of Quebec. Anxious to help in every way, the Bishop in 1704 not only loaded the *Pelican* with food, soldiers, missionaries and nuns, but also with twenty-three "Cassette" girls to become wives to the colonists. Each girl had been provided with a *cassette,* or trunk, and an outfit of clothing, and within a month all had won husbands except one, who was described as "coy" and "hard to please." Before a year passed, little Jean François Le Can became the first white child born in Alabama.

But France found Alabama a disappointing colony, and did not much care whether or not it fared well. The king turned the province over to a private merchant and speculator named Antoine Crozat and then to a Scotch financier and gambler named John Law [see Louisiana, pp. 107-113], with the result that nothing seemed to reap much harvest except the scandalous conduct of these managers. The Seven Years' War in Europe and the French and Indian War in this country gave England, by the Treaty of Paris in 1763, all of France's holdings in America. The British poured in by the hundreds, but poured out again when the end of the Revolution brought northern Alabama, as a part of Georgia, into the United States. Florida, including Mobile, was ceded to Spain. A boundary dispute with Georgia followed, and not until 1817 did Congress establish the Alabama Territory. Statehood was granted on December 14, 1819.

TENNESSEE

MISSISSIPPI

TENNESSEE RIVER

GEORGIA

Birmingham

Montgomery

TOMBIGBEE R.

ALABAMA R.

CHATTAHOOCHEE RIVER

Mobile

FLORIDA

DARWIN

DE SOTO

MILES
0 10 20 30 40 50

N

ALABAMA
GREAT SEAL
TENNESSEE
MISSISSIPPI GEORGIA
FLORIDA

Alabama

The Cotton State

A Scholar and Some Unhappy Noblemen

A remarkable figure during these years in Alabama's history was an Indian named Sequoyah. The son of a white trader and a Cherokee mother, Sequoyah grew up without ever knowing his father. Crippled by a hunting accident in his youth, he still acquired skill as a trapper, a herder of horses and a hunter. Many Indians admired the pictures that Sequoyah painted on bark, smooth boards and bits of tanned deerskin, but his own deep interest was in the "talking leaves" of the white man. How ardently Sequoyah wanted to read! So great was his desire that he began making a sign or symbol for the words he spoke in Cherokee. The fascination grew until his farm and his business were forgotten, and neighbors wondered if he had lost his reason. But he stuck to his "crazy idea," devising in time the Cherokee alphabet — one of the greatest achievements of scholarship in our nation's history.

About the time Sequoyah labored on this enterprise, the strangest colonists ever to penetrate the American wilderness reached Alabama — Napoleonic exiles who, calling themselves the "Association of French Emigrants for the Cultivation of the Vine and Olive," settled in May, 1817 in the Tombigbee country. Women who had enjoyed court life under Marie Antoinette, men who had marched with Napoleon to war in Russia, now settled down to a squatter's life among Indians! Over the puncheon floors of their log cabins they spread luxurious Brussels carpets. They

couldn't grow grapes and olives, for they were not farmers, and they would have starved had not the Indians helped them raise beans and corn. Happily, by the mid-1820's, conditions changed in France and these "growers" could safely return to their homeland.

Cotton is King

As early as 1802 the first cotton gin in Alabama was built by Abraham Mordecai at Coosada Bluff, near Montgomery. In Madison County in the early 1830's Alabama erected its first cotton factory. And 'Bama threw its full support behind the Mexican War for a reason no one ever needed to question — here was a chance to obtain more slave states and thus gain absolute control of the national government. The "Alabama Plan," adopted in 1848 by the Democratic state convention, stated bluntly that only a state could ever determine what to do about slavery. Proudly, Alabamians saw Montgomery made the first capital of the Confederacy when civil war became inevitable.

The war found 'Bama gamely braced for the worst. In most cases, women managed the plantations, for the men were away fighting. Federal raids were frequent, yet not devastating. A combined Union naval and army force did not capture Mobile until the summer of 1864. Alabama could reckon that it had squeezed through the war reasonably well when carpetbagger rule descended from the North. In seven years the public debt leaped from $8,000,000 to $32,000,000. A reasonable form of government was restored in 1874.

On Top of Red Mountain

Before the white man reached Alabama, the Indians were sometimes called "Red Sticks" because they painted their faces and weapons with a substance taken from red rocks. Early settlers around Birmingham knew the rock was red iron ore, but considered it worthless. Not until the early 1860's were a few small furnaces and ironworks in operation, and since these produced rifles and cannonballs, invading Federals burned them down. After the war, when Alabama needed to raise itself by the bootstraps, Birmingham suddenly supplied one bright hope. Its red iron ore, coal and limestone supplied the three essentials for making steel! Today, on top of Red Mountain, stands a sixty-ton statue of Vulcan, the famous blacksmith of Roman mythology. Visible from all parts of the business district, Vulcan reminds citizens of Birmingham that they live in the "Pittsburgh of the South."

So the state where once cotton was king is surpassed today only by Minnesota and Michigan in the mining of iron ore. Since the 1930's, when the TVA (Tennessee Valley Authority) and private power companies began to build dams and electric plants on Alabama's rivers, manufacturing has boomed — especially in cotton goods, cottonseed and peanut products, fertilizer, coke, cement, lumber products, wood pulp and paper, aluminum, turpentine, tar and rosin, tung oil, processed meat, nonalcoholic beverages and prepared foods. Rich soils and a long growing season produce an agriculture distinguished for its cotton and field crops, its nuts, fruits and vegetables, and its livestock and poultry. Mobile, with trade from the Gulf, Montgomery on the Alabama River, and Phenix City on the Chattahoochee are 'Bama's chief ports.

The Cotton State

Strictly for 'Bamians

Alabama's folk heroes all have a Jesse James flavor. Rube Burrow, for example, was a "lone wolf" train robber and murderer, and many songs tell of his daring feats:

He hated work and took the road
To forage for his gains,
And generally obtained a load
By robbing railroad trains.
But justice stern was on his track
With swift and steady tread,
And at the fatal pistol crack
The bandit chief fell dead.

Conceivably Rube was popular in Alabama because all of his crimes seem to have been committed in Mississippi. Rural Alabama, by and large, is a fiddlin', square-dancin' country, fond of old tunes like "Turkey in the Straw" and "Arkansas Traveler," and barn raisings and candy pullings are popular social occasions. The older folk rock in their chairs and enjoy "swapping lies" — Alabamian for making conversation. Farmers have some handed-down superstitions — as, for example, that an "eye crop" like potatoes or sugar cane should never be planted at night. 'Bama Negroes have a legend about the robin. Once caught by the devil, its breast burned red while carrying water to pour onto the eternal fire.

MISSISSIPPI

"The Magnolia State"

OUNDED on the south by the Gulf of Mexico and on the west by the great river whose name it bears, Mississippi touches two of the principal highways by which the Spanish and French sought wealth and empire in the New World. In 1540, as Hernando de Soto and his weary soldiers trudged westward in search of gold, they entered Mississippi and raised the flag of Spain on the banks of the Tombigbee River. Almost a century and a half later — in 1682 — La Salle claimed possession of the Mississippi Valley for France, and seventeen years later at Old Biloxi (now Ocean Springs), a settlement was started by Pierre le Moyne. In 1706 the French, under Jean Baptiste le Moyne, planted a second settlement at Fort Rosalie where Natchez now stands.

The French fared badly with the Indians in the Mississippi country, who called them "the ugly, yellow French."

Though an uprising by the Natchez Indians was subdued in 1730, the French met more than their match against the Chickasaws six years later at the Battle of Ackia. The Chickasaws supported the British in the French and Indian War, keeping the French in the Mississippi Valley from uniting with their countrymen in the Ohio Valley. The British claim to Mississippi dated from the Treaty of Paris in 1763, but the American Revolution provided the opportunity in 1798 for the United States to organize the Territory of Mississippi.

Whereas each of these events changed the history of Mississippi, in 1811 — the year of the earthquake — an incident of an altogether different nature proved equally influential.

Life Along the River

Black smoke billowing from the tall stack of the wobbly little steamer, the

New Orleans — the first to sail down the Mississippi — spread terror along the river that winter of 1811. Backwoodsmen and Indians fled before the "chugchug" of the vessel, convinced that the devil had taken over the river. Others waited breathlessly, expecting the boat to blow up. But with a tremendous blast of her whistle the *New Orleans* came on, conqueror of the Mississippi.

The following year regular steamboat service was started between New Orleans and Natchez, and the pattern of life along the river began to change. Cheap, convenient transportation boomed cotton, and soon the most familiar sight in Mississippi was the streams of cotton wagons pulling up to the wharves. Tyrone Power, a famous Irish actor, described the river scene that met his gaze in the early 1830's: "Walked down to Natchez-under-the-Hill to inquire about a boat to New Orleans [and] saw one monster come groaning downstream looking like a huge cotton bale on fire. Not a portion of the vessel remained above water that could be seen excepting the ends of the chimneys. The hull and all else was hidden by cotton bags, piled high on each other, tier over tier, like bricks."

In 1814 only 20 steamboats arrived in New Orleans, but within two decades the number of river vessels annually reaching this port leaped to 1,200. Rapid improvements in these "palaces on paddle wheels" saw the time of the run from New Orleans to Louisville cut from twenty-five days in the early years to less than four and one-half days in 1853. Explosions and fires took numerous lives — as many

as 4,000 by 1850, according to one estimate. One cause was the fact that when water ran low, the red-hot iron of the boiler turned soft and when cold water was poured in, the quickly forming steam exerted more pressure than the superheated boiler could take.

Negroes were stationed on the decks to watch for sparks from the stacks. With cotton piled everywhere — even against the windows and ventilators — the hazard of fire was constant. Again, rivalries between steamboat captains resulted in frequent races, and tragedies followed as engines were pushed beyond their capacities and precautions were ignored in the excitement of the contest. The greatest battle on the river occurred in 1870 between the *Natchez* and the *Robert E. Lee* when, as Negro roustabouts sang afterward:

De Lee *an' de* Natchez *had a race.*
De Lee *t'rowed water in de* Natchez' *face.*

Soon familiar to river towns was the showboat — "admission, 50 cents; children and servants, 25 cents." Great spectacles floated down river. Aboard the *Floating Palace* in 1855, said the handbill, audiences could visit "a complete zoological exhibition of every wild animal existing in Europe, Asia, Africa and America." Dancing and jigs were featured in Ned Davis' Minstrels aboard the *Banjo*. Van Amburgh's Show offered trained elephants, New Holland ostriches and the "rhinoceros, or unicorn of Holy Writ." Advertisements for Captain Augustus Byron French's *New Sensation* advised Mississippians: "Listen for the toot of the

The Magnolia State

Jefferson Davis

calliope and make a break for the river." Just about everybody did.

Cotton and War

The river packets made the plantation and slavery the foundations of life in Mississippi. An example of a luxurious Mississippi plantation-house was Belle Grove, where fifty house guests were quartered for a week during a wedding. "The great green porticoes of Belle Grove," wrote one of the guests, "were hung with a thousand lights which shone far out into the river, dancing cloths were laid over the lower floors and the chambers were all festooned with flowers." A chef was brought from New Orleans to prepare the food for five hundred persons who attended the festivities and "the feast was so bounteous that the very boatmen on the Mississippi who brought 'the dear five hundred' up the river to Belle Grove landing came in for their share."

As civil war approached, Mississippi stood firmly with the cotton states and followed South Carolina out of the Union. One of her plantation owners, Jefferson Davis, was elected President of the Confederacy. Grim battles were fought on Mississippi soil — at Corinth, Iuka, Port Gibson, Holly Springs, Brice's Crossroads, Jackson and Champion's Hill — but by far the most terrible experience came in 1863 when Union forces under Ulysses S. Grant besieged Vicksburg. Women and children were forced to live in caves, food became so scarce that, by some accounts, even fried rats were eaten, and the city was left a mass of rubble.

Recovering From Reconstruction

Bitter years of reconstruction followed, stemming from the "Black and Tan Convention" of 1868 that took the vote away from many leading white citizens. Carpetbaggers ruled until 1875, but finally justice and reason were restored and the people permitted to manage their own political affairs. Flood control along the Mississippi, a child labor law in 1912, the Industrial Act in 1936 to encourage manufactures

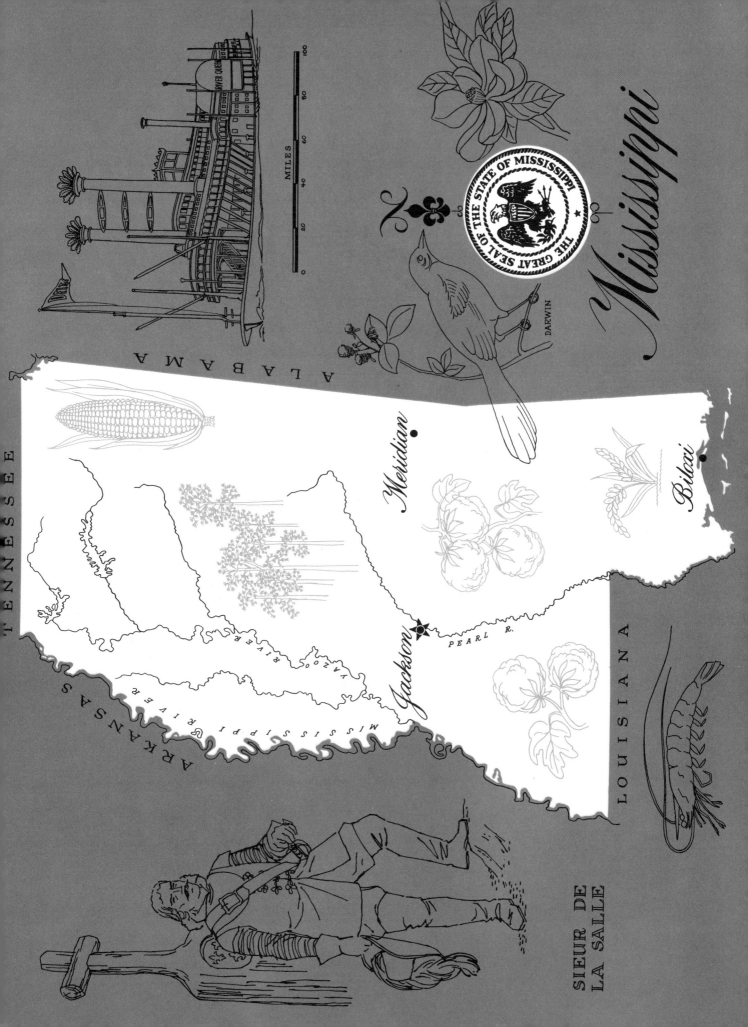

Mississippi

ALABAMA

TENNESSEE

ARKANSAS

LOUISIANA

DARWIN

MILES
100
80
60
40
20
0

Meridian

Jackson

PEARL R.

YAZOO RIVER

MISSISSIPPI RIVER

Biloxi

SIEUR DE
LA SALLE

THE GREAT SEAL OF THE STATE OF MISSISSIPPI

The Magnolia State

are examples of the progressive legislation that has built the modern state.

Farming remains the principal source of wealth in Mississippi, which is sometimes called the "Dairyland of Dixie." Among its chief crops are cotton, corn, alfalfa, oats, cowpeas, wheat, rye, barley, soybeans, peanuts, rice, sugar cane, pecans, vegetables and fruits. The discovery of petroleum at Tinsley in 1939 and at Vaughan in 1940 have added greatly to the state's natural resources that include lumber, sand and gravel, clay, bauxite, limestone and sandstone. With ports on the Gulf at Biloxi and Gulfport, and on the Mississippi at Natchez and Vicksburg, the state's growing manufactures include lumber products, fishing boats, fertilizers, textiles (cotton and silk), newspapers, cottonseed oil, tung oil, soybean oil, peanut oil, sweet-potato starch, glass bottles, brick, tile and canned foods.

Virtute et Armis — "By valor and arms" — reads the motto of Mississippi, and the Stars and Bars of the old Confederate flag are retained in its state flag. The glories of past history and tradition are scrupulously preserved in Mississippi — at the Mardi Gras in Biloxi, held the second week before Lent; at the Azalea Trail and Spring Festival along the Gulf coast in March; at Vicksburg, where the battlefield of 1863 has been restored as a national shrine; at the garden pilgrimages to the beautiful old homes in Natchez, Holly Springs, Port Gibson, Jackson, Aberdeen, Columbus, Meridian and Greenwood; and at the Delta Staple Cotton Festival in Clarksdale, held in late August or early September. Confederate Memorial Day is observed throughout the state each April 26.

Shrimp boats setting out from Biloxi, Spanish moss on the giant oaks along the Gulf coast, the grand view of the old river at Natchez, oystermen off the shores of Pass Christian, cotton pickers in the Delta country — such images belong to modern Mississippi. And if you listen hard some nights, down by the banks of Old Miss', maybe you'll hear from bygone days one of its Negro songs:

I fink I hea'd de preacher say
  Oh how, how oh!
You never git to heben less you pray,
  Oh how, how oh!
W'en Satan come into de room,
  Oh how, how oh!
We'll bang him wid a hick'ry broom,
  Oh how, how oh!
'Roun' de room we'll gibe him chase,
  Oh how, how oh!
And frow de kittle in he's face,
  Oh how, how oh!
De w'ile temptation we defy,
  Oh how, how oh!

LOUISIANA
"The Pelican State"

THE ROMANCE and mystery of Louisiana are in the words one hears spoken in this land so well described as "a boot with its frayed toe dipping into the Gulf of Mexico."

From the Choctaw *bayuk,* meaning river or creek, comes the word *bayou,* which is a sluggish stream or natural canal rising from the overflow of a river or the draining of a marsh.

From the Spanish *coriollo,* meaning native to the locality, comes the term *Creole,* used to describe a white descendant of the French or Spanish settlers in Louisiana.

From the French *brûlant,* meaning burning or hot, comes *café brûlot,* a festive concoction of coffee, spices, citrus peel and burning brandy; and *praline,* which is a confection made of pecans browned in sugar, is derived from Maréchal du Plessis Praslin, whose cook is believed to have invented the candy.

From the Angolan *kingombo,* Negro-French influences have created the word gumbo to describe a thick soup prepared with okra and crabs, shrimp, oysters, chicken, ham or veal. It is a local joke that any Louisianian who cannot get his gumbo in heaven returns to earth.

From the jungles of Africa come words like *voodoo,* describing a cult practicing forms of sorcery; *wanga,* meaning a spell; and *zombi,* meaning a spirit.

The Spanish, first on the Louisiana scene, arrived in the early 1500's. They came seeking fortunes in gold, and lost interest when the gold did not tumble down on them from the branches of the live oaks. A century later the French appeared, and largely in spite of themselves became the true settlers of Louisiana. Even today, in some communities, French-speaking natives can be found who do not understand English.

ARKANSAS

MISS.

LOUISIANA

The South

W. VA.

VIRGINIA

KENTUCKY

NORTH
CAROLINA

TENNESSEE

SOUTH
CAROLINA

GEORGIA

ALABAMA

FLORIDA

The
Pelican
State

A King Loses Interest

In 1682 the French explorer, Robert La Salle, solved a great mystery by proving that the Mississippi emptied into the Gulf of Mexico. Three leagues from the Gulf, La Salle climbed the river bank and planted a cross and a column bearing the arms of France with an inscription claiming the territory in the name of King Louis XIV. In February, 1698 a French expedition under Pierre Le Moyne, Sieur d'Iberville, reached Mobile Bay and journeyed overland to the mouth of the river. The party started upstream on March 2, 1699, and the next day (Shrove Tuesday) they named Mardi Gras Bayou. The following Friday they reached the site of New Orleans, where they killed a buffalo and erected a cross, then they explored as far north as Baton Rouge (so named for the red stick that marked the boundary between the Houma and Bayogoula hunting grounds). In succeeding years Catholic missionaries and traders were the principal explorers of the region. Like the Spanish emperor, Louis XIV had hoped for a fortune in gold and when it was not forthcoming his taste dulled for colonizing the province named in his honor.

The French government in 1712 consigned to Antoine Crozat, a wealthy merchant, trading rights in the territory, in return for which Crozat was supposed to encourage the establishment of settlements. By 1717 Crozat's Company of the West had suffered all the financial reverses it cared to withstand, and the remarkable John Law, a Scottish financier in high favor in France, took over. With such canny devices as descriptions of Louisiana that made it seem a paradise, Law lured settlers to the wilderness and investors to his Company of the Indies. But the quick profits that Law had promised did not materialize, the investors began dumping their stock for anything they could get, and the resulting collapse of the venture was known, picturesquely, as the "Mississippi Bubble." Moreover, the large number of Negro slaves who had been brought in worried Governor Bienville, and in 1724 he established the *Code Noir*, which inflicted severe penalties for endangering the lives of whites. Jews were expelled from the colony and the Catholic religion was made the state faith.

Back Under Spain

France lost Canada to England in the Seven Years' War (1756-63). Rather than see its other New World possessions snatched away, Louis XV preferred to give his cousin, Charles III of Spain, the "Island of New Orleans" and all of Louisiana lying west of the Mississippi. This gift Louis XV made in 1762, though the deal was kept secret for two years. In March, 1766, Antonio de Ulloa, the Spanish commandant, arrived with ninety soldiers to take over the colony. A revolt followed and a republic under a "Protector" was proposed, but in August, 1769 Count Alexander O'Reilly arrived with twenty-four men-of-war and some two thousand soldiers to enforce the rule of Spain. By the time he had executed the leaders of the rebellion, he was

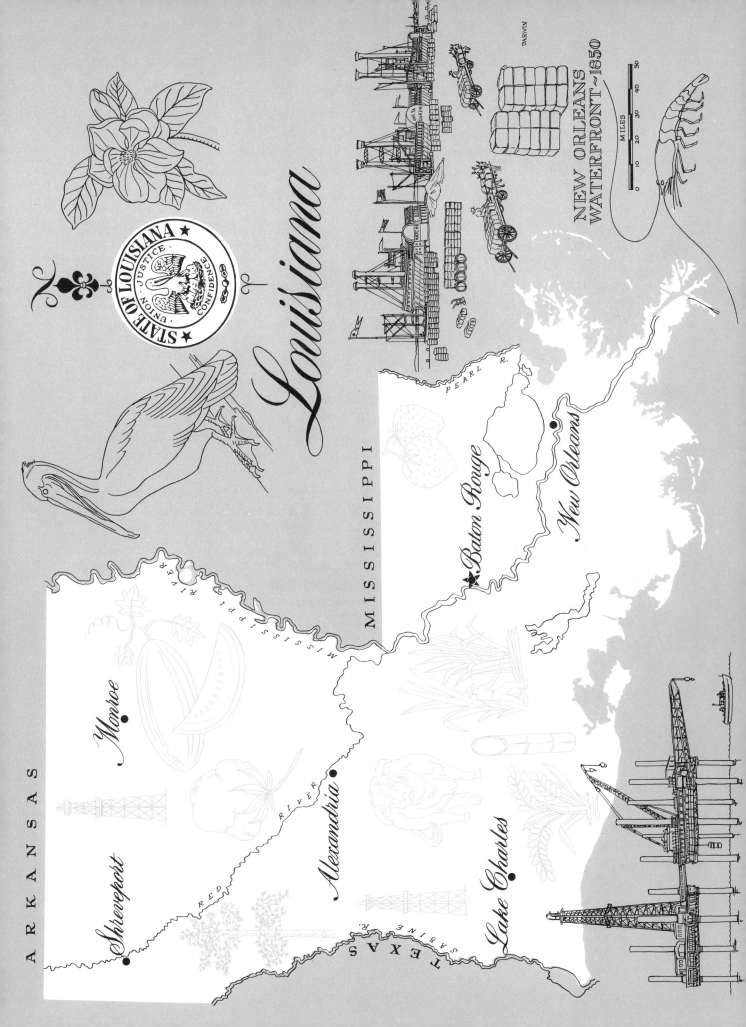

Louisiana

STATE OF LOUISIANA

JUSTICE · UNION · CONFIDENCE

NEW ORLEANS
WATERFRONT ~ 1850

MILES

0 10 20 30 40 50

DARWIN

ARKANSAS

MISSISSIPPI

TEXAS

MISSISSIPPI RIVER

RED RIVER

SABINE R.

PEARL R.

Shreveport

Monroe

Alexandria

Lake Charles

Baton Rouge

New Orleans

The
Pelican
State

"Bloody" O'Reilly, but Spain's claim was firmly anchored. During the American Revolution the rebelling colonists received credit and supplies through New Orleans, which was also the base whence forces under James Willing sallied forth to pillage and terrorize British Loyalists in West Florida.

In the years after the Revolution, Spain began to blow hot and then cold over permitting free navigation on the Mississippi, and the seizure of cargoes riled American tempers as far up-river as Kentucky and Tennessee. Napoleon, taking advantage of Spain's weak position in Europe, forced her to return the colony to France in 1800. If this was a surprise that pleased no one, Napoleon's decision in 1803 to sell his Louisiana holdings to the United States for $15,000,000 — or about 2½¢ an acre, the biggest real estate bargain in history — came as an even greater shock. Actually it was not until 1803 that the Spanish in Louisiana learned officially that their province had been transferred to France, and now, in another twinkling, their land was not French, but American!

Unrest, War, Progress

No one seemed happy, least of all those Louisianians who had rubbed elbows with the tough American river boatmen who had drifted into New Orleans from time to time. The winter of 1806 brought wild tales of Aaron Burr coming down-river with an army to capture the territory and take over New Orleans, but Burr and his band — never more than from sixty to eighty men — were arrested and dispersed at

Bayou Pierre, above Natchez. On April 8, 1812, Louisiana was admitted as our fifteenth state, and the war with England that broke out this same year brought a British force under General Sir Edward Pakenham to New Orleans in December of 1814. With a ragtag army of Kentucky and Tennessee riflemen, pirates, Choctaw Indians and free Negroes, General Andrew Jackson taught the Redcoats warfare, frontier-style. The British killed numbered 700 — Jackson's, 13. The British wounded numbered 1,400 — Jackson's, 30.

American enterprise saw Louisiana leaping ahead in the years that followed. In 1814 only 20 river boats had docked at New Orleans. By 1840 that figure became 1,573. Cotton, sugar and slaves made Louisiana's plantations as prosperous as any in the South until the War Between the States changed everything. Among seceding states, Louisiana was next in line behind South Carolina. In April, 1862, a Union fleet under David G. Farragut captured New Orleans, and after 1864 the state was divided between two governments — one Federal, one Confederate. Reconstruction was a time of particular hardship in Louisiana, and Federal troops were not entirely withdrawn from its soil until 1877.

The New — and Always the Old

Louisiana began to recover, especially after the completion of the Panama Canal in 1914 brought the markets of the world closer to its chief ports — New Orleans, Baton Rouge, Lake Charles. Today Louisiana's farms lead the nation in growing sugar and rice.

Among all the states, more shrimp, more diamondback terrapin come out of Louisiana waters. The country's leading fur producer, Louisiana is also one of the nation's best mineral-producing states, fourth in the production of petroleum, fifth in wood products. But though one enters Louisiana over fine modern highways, crossing bridges as long as any in the world and whizzing by new factories, refineries, markets and housing developments, the charm of "the Pelican State" is that never far away is a strange, romantic world unlike any other part of America.

Take the Cajun country, for example — around New Iberia, St. Martinsville. In the three decades from 1760 to 1790 about 4,000 Acadians, expelled by the British from their homes in Nova Scotia, came to Louisiana to start life anew. In *Evangeline,* Henry Wadsworth Longfellow tells a part of their story — and, indeed, a statue to Evangeline stands in St. Martinsville. Gentle, honest, industrious, the descendants of these Acadian exiles cling to an Old World atmosphere and attitudes. A rule in an Acadian home is to keep the coffeepot always partially full and warm. A mixture of laundry soap, mutton tallow, sugar, wood ashes and turpentine (one of many home remedies) has the expressive name of *onguent-des-pauvres* — ointment of the poor. A country dance is still called a *fais-dodo,* meaning, literally, go to sleep. Perhaps a visitor to a Cajun village in 1876 gave as good a reason for this name as any: "The balls are generally made up of the sons and daughters of small Creole farmers who work all day

and dance at night. There are not less than sixty fiddlers in this district. They are a merry people."

Voodoo and Pirates

In and about Buras, many say, are believers in voodooism who still consult "remedy men" for cures for toothache, backache, bellyache, or for instruction in how to unhaunt a haunted house (take a frizzly chicken, walk backward to the river, and throw the fowl over the left shoulder).

Any visitor to New Orleans' Vieux Carré, as the French Quarter is called, may admire the old buildings with their iron balconies, but he stops for his picture to be snapped in Pirate's Alley. The pirate, of course, was the notorious Jean Lafitte and legend insists that the old cutthroat crept along this alley en route to a secret meeting at the Absinthe House with Andrew Jackson to plan the defense of New Orleans. Well, maybe. For the part he did play in the Battle of New Orleans, Lafitte and his Baratarian outlaws were fully pardoned for all crimes by President Madison. And what good did it do? Off they skipped to Galveston Island, embarking on new piratical deviltry while flying the Venezuelan flag, until Lafitte died of fever off the Yucatan coast (or so says *one* story).

The mystery of Lafitte belongs in Louisiana, where the unexpected is more or less what one should expect. Gay, carefree — land of the Mardi Gras — land where the blues and jazz were born — Louisiana, be it remembered, *is* the state of the pelican, whose bill holds more than its belly can!

The Pelican State

ARKANSAS

"The Wonder State"

ARKANSAS, which claims the only diamond mine in North America, decided by official legislative action in 1923 that its proper designation should be "The Wonder State." If the legislators had selected as Arkansas's nickname "The Bit of Everything State" that title also would have been appropriate. Where eastern Arkansas touches the Mississippi, cotton plantations suggest the life and customs of the Deep South. Moss-hung trees and sluggish cypress swamps in southeastern Arkansas seem like part of Louisiana. Irrigated rice fields dot the east-central region, and even the drawling speech of southwestern Arkansans belongs to the Old Southwest. Northward are the hills of the Ozarks and Ouachitas — homeland of mountain people such as one finds in Tennessee and Kentucky — and these hills level off into farmlands like those in Indiana and Illinois. Sometimes Arkansas is aptly described as the land "where the Old South meets the West."

A Ragged Lot

In 1541 the first white men to behold Arkansas were a ragged lot — the remnant of that weary group of fortune-seekers who had trudged from Florida with Hernando de Soto. Two years later, with at least two hundred of them dead, the survivors stood in their rusty armor and looked across the wide Mississippi at the shore of Arkansas. Some wore raccoon and wildcat furs under their armor, and at least one, said an eye-witness, "was barefoot and without breeches." Before them stretched a river a mile wide. Within a month they constructed boats and ferried across.

De Soto's reception was hardly cordial — first a deserted Indian village, and then, after a three-day ordeal crossing swamps, a chief who listened with suspicion to the claims of the Spaniards that they were divine creatures. The Indian ordered lame and blind people brought before these self-styled children of the sun. Cure them, he bade the bearded de Soto. The Spaniard erected a cross and told the chief to kiss it, but that cunning fellow suspected a ruse and resorted to a trick of his own, speaking of other Indian villages far more prosperous than his — the old lure by which de Soto was led to quit one region in the hope of finding fortune elsewhere. That night, however, a long-awaited rain fell, convincing the chief that the cross was "good medicine."

But in the weeks that followed de Soto became involved in a succession of Indian quarrels. Whereas he found a "very warm and brackish lake" that was probably Hot Springs, the gold he sought was as elusive as ever. A winter in Arkansas, eking out an existence on corn, beans, pecans and dried persimmons grudgingly supplied by Indians who had their own troubles, shattered the health of de Soto. His body was buried in the great river that he had crossed as the first white man.

Coming of the French

A hundred years passed before other white men appeared in Arkansas. Then in 1673 those indefatigable French explorers, Father Marquette and Louis Joliet, came paddling down the Mississippi in search of the place where the river flowed into the sea. At the mouth of the Arkansas River, Marquette and his good-humored friend Joliet won the

friendship of the Indians, who feasted them on such wilderness delicacies as roast dog and convinced the travelers that the hostility of tribes to the south made it unwise to continue the journey. That night, while mosquitoes plagued them, the two explorers made a shrewd guess that the river flowed into the Gulf of Mexico rather than into the Gulf of California. Since this information was what they had come to learn, they started back to Canada at daylight.

The next French party in Arkansas was that of La Salle, almost ten years behind Marquette. In March, 1682, La Salle and fifty-four followers landed in dense fog with war drums rolling and Indians yelping in a scalp dance, but the Indians proved extremely friendly. La Salle erected a cross and claimed the land in the name of the king of France, and the Indians carefully protected the cross by building a neat cane palisade around it. On another expedition La Salle took part of his party in search of the mouth of the Mississippi, hoping to found a colony there. Before he could return to Arkansas, death at the hands of a mutinous faction befell him [see Texas, pp. 177-184] and so he never saw the first white settlement that his faithful lieutenant, Henry de Tonti, established in 1686 at Arkansas Post.

Territorial Years

The scheme of John Law in 1717 to help solve France's financial difficulties through colonizing Louisiana produced the scandal of the Mississippi Bubble [see Louisiana, pp. 107-113], yet before Law's company collapsed, a number of colonists had arrived at Arkansas

The Wonder State

Robert E. Lee

lina mountains, or the Quapaws, heavy whiskey-drinkers already declining as a nation. There was not yet a grist mill in the territory — hand-ground flour sold for twelve dollars a barrel — but already at Arkansas Post there was a printer who had floated a hand press and types down-river in two log dug-outs and who, on November 20, 1819, published the first issue of the *Arkansas Gazette*. Rough-and-ready pioneers continued to pour in — from Virginia, the Carolinas, Tennessee and Mississippi — and hard on their heels came the land speculators and ambitious politicians. The only effective law seemed to be a pair of dueling pistols.

War and Reconstruction

By 1821, with the capital moved from Arkansas Post to Little Rock, and the Cherokees migrating into the Indian Territory that later became Oklahoma, Arkansas was taking shape as a future state. Steamboats began hauling cotton, hides and lumber on the Arkansas, Ouachita, St. Francis and White rivers. By 1836 Arkansas, a slave state, was ready for admission to the Union (Michigan came in that year as a free state), and when the following year brought hard times to the East, the rush of pioneers westward increased. Vigilante groups, called Regulators, organized to curtail the reign of law by dueling pistol. A stagecoach line was completed through western Arkansas in 1858, and two years later a telegraph line linked St. Louis and Fayetteville.

As the Civil War approached, Arkansas voted down secession, but after the attack on Fort Sumter, when Presi-

Post. The give-and-take of international diplomacy in later years saw Arkansas bartered with the rest of the Louisiana territory — from France to Spain in 1763, from Spain to France in 1800, then from France to the United States in the Louisiana purchase three years later. At first, Arkansas was part of the Louisiana Territory, in 1813 it was included in the Missouri Territory, and in 1819 it was organized as a separate territory.

By now there were 14,255 settlers in Arkansas, not counting the peaceful, intelligent Cherokees who were being moved westward from their original homelands in the Tennessee and Caro-

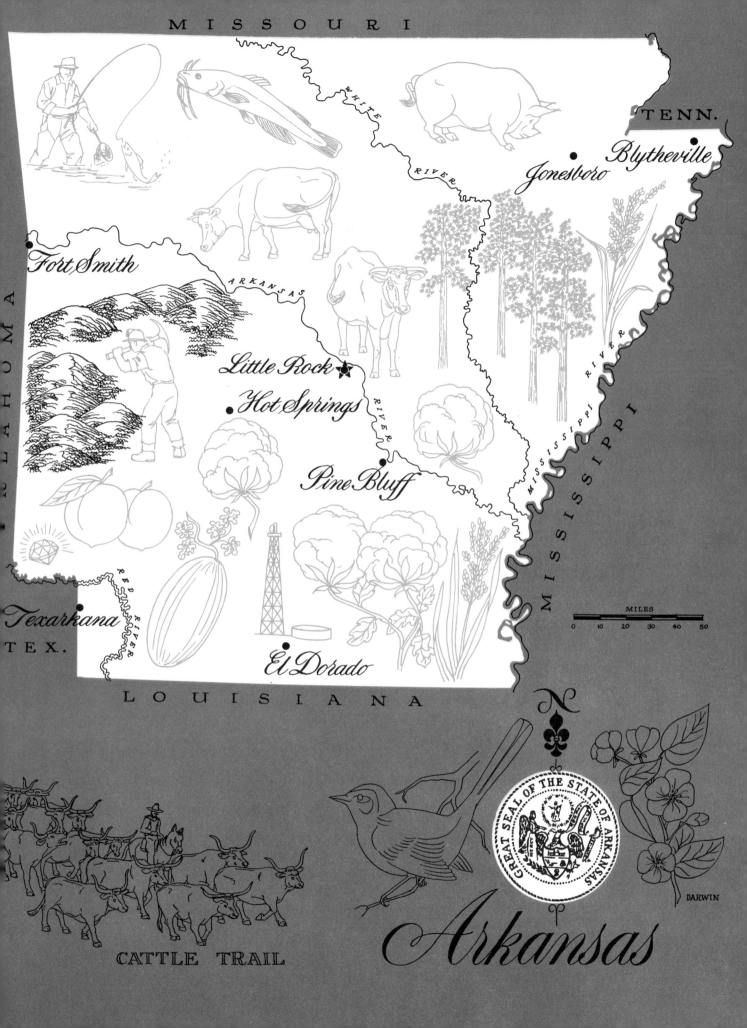

MISSOURI

TENN.

Blytheville

Jonesboro

WHITE RIVER

Fort Smith

OKLAHOMA

ARKANSAS

Little Rock

Hot Springs

RIVER

Pine Bluff

MISSISSIPPI RIVER

MISSISSIPPI

Texarkana

TEX.

RED RIVER

El Dorado

MILES

0 10 20 30 40 50

LOUISIANA

GREAT SEAL OF THE STATE OF ARKANSAS

DARWIN

CATTLE TRAIL

Arkansas

*The
Wonder
State*

dent Lincoln called for troops to suppress the rebellion, Arkansas joined the Confederacy by a vote of 69 to 1. Bloody battles were fought on its soil at Pea Ridge and at Prairie Grove in 1862, and at Arkansas Post and Helena in 1863. With the fall of Little Rock to Northern forces on September 10, 1863, a pro-Union governor, Isaac Murphy, who had cast the lone vote against secession in 1861, was placed in power. A Confederate governor, Harris Flanagin, ruled from the provisional state capital at Washington. The end of the war brought bitter years of reconstruction.

Modern Arkansas

The aluminum-bearing ore called bauxite was discovered near Little Rock in 1887 and Arkansas today mines about ninety per cent of the nation's yield of this ore. The state's richness in such natural resources as petroleum, natural gasoline, gas, coal, limestone, manganese and other nonmetallic minerals accounts in no small measure for Arkansas's present economic stability. The unique "Crater of Diamonds" near Murfreesboro, the only spot in North America where genuine diamonds of volcanic origin are found, was discovered by John Huddleston in 1906. Since then, more than 100,000 diamonds have been recovered, and whereas most of the stones are used industrially, gems of rare beauty sometimes are found. The notable example is the Star of Arkansas, a diamond that weighed 15.33 carats and which was valued after cutting at $75,000.

Primarily an agricultural state, mod-

ern Arkansas's most important crop remains cotton, with rice, corn, hay and soybeans ranking next in dollar value. The state is also one of the country's leaders in forest products and supplies some 2,000 wood-using factories with pine, white oak, gum, red oak, non-pulping hardwoods, ash and hickory. Other chief manufactures include cottonseed and vegetable oils, beverages, canned goods, petroleum refinery products, aluminum, pottery, bricks, fertilizers, paper and textiles.

The name Arkansas comes from an Indian word, *Ugakapah,* which means "downstream people." The early French inhabitants found the Indian word hard to pronounce and changed it to its present form. Arkansas's people— downstream or upstream — vary with where you find them. The cotton planter lives differently from the rice grower, and even tends to dress differently.

The Ozarker is another breed, independent as the day is long, who very likely still grinds his own corn and whittles his own furniture. His lonely, unpainted two-room cabin, with its "dog-run" between rooms, clings to the steep hillside. How far apart the cotton planter is from the Ozarker comes out in his folk heroes. Down in the plantation country no better man ever lived than Robert E. Lee, while up in the mountains a man handy with a gun — even a Jesse James — is more likely to have a following. Yet the state's motto, *Regnat Populus,* fits all groups. It means "The people rule," and in their own bailiwicks they surely do!

TENNESSEE

"The Volunteer State"

A CHEROKEE legend tells of a time when all Tennessee was flat, wet and very soft. The Great Buzzard — the ancestor of all buzzards living today — flew over the land. The journey tired him and his wings began to flap and strike the ground, with the result — or so said the Cherokees — that wherever his wings struck the earth a valley was formed and wherever his wings turned upward a mountain arose.

Whatever the cause, from the lofty peaks in the east to the Mississippi bottomland in the west, Tennessee surely has its share of mountains and valleys. It is not by accident that "no such animal" as a Tennessean exists. The independent mountain man calls himself an *East* Tennessean, the man from the plains who raises some of the best beef and dairy cattle in America is known as a *Middle* Tennessean, and the plantation owner with his cotton fields overlooking the Mississippi is distinctly a *West* Tennessean.

The state that one day would count among its distinguished residents Daniel Boone, Davy Crockett and Andrew Jackson was first visited by the white man in 1541 when the soldiers of Hernando de Soto camped near the site of present-day Memphis. Not until 1673 is there a record of another white visitor — then two parties appeared. From Virginia, under James Needham, came woodsmen to scout the valleys of the Little Tennessee and Tellico rivers, and down the Mississippi came the French missionaries, Joliet and Marquette, to visit among the Chickasaw tribe that lived along the river banks. La Salle established Fort Prudhomme on the Chickasaw Bluffs in 1682, but the place

*The
Volunteer
State*

was soon abandoned. A decade later the French had their first trading post at French Lick, near the site of Nashborough (Nashville).

"Dark and Bloody"

With Spain, France and England each claiming the territory, a Cherokee leader, Dragging Canoe, warned a band of North Carolinians in 1775: "You have bought a fair land, but will find its settlement dark and bloody." By now the British reckoned their fur trade in the territory as worth a million dollars a year, and men have risked their necks for far less. With the Cherokees for allies, the British had gained the upper hand over the French and hundreds of settlers had poured into the region in the fifteen years since Boone blazed the Wilderness Road.

But troubles remained. Though the territory belonged to North Carolina, no official in that colony paid the least heed to the needs of the region. In 1772, sick of the neglect, the settlers took matters into their own hands, establishing the Watauga Association and drawing a code of laws that many historians call America's first written constitution.

With Dragging Canoe remaining loyal to his British friends, open warfare between the settlers and Cherokees broke out during the Revolution. The woodsmen of Tennessee had a natural commander in John Sevier — the renowned "Nolichucky Jack" of legend — who, in 1780, led the Tennesseans across the Smokies to help deal the British regulars a stinging blow at King's Mountain and then hastened home to handle the Indian menace at

their backs! American victory in the Revolution did not end the dog-eat-dog struggle for Tennessee. Now with Florida fully owned by Spain, a new conspirator eagerly whispered into Indian ears that only through attack by ambush and horse-stealing could these invaders be expelled.

North Carolina still wished to wipe its hands of these problems, and in 1784 offered the territory to the Federal government. Pioneers in northeastern Tennessee that December organized the "State of Franklin" with John Sevier as governor, but Congress ignored this self-styled state, and in 1790 recognized Tennessee as the "Territory South of Ohio." Six years later Tennessee was admitted to the Union as our sixteenth state.

Opening the State

By treaty with the Cherokees in 1805, roads were planned across the Cherokee country to open communication between the states of Tennessee and Georgia. Two years later the roads were in use, and an eyewitness described the changes they brought: "Enterprising men soon established stands on the road and built good frame houses and clusters of log houses, also stables and stake-and-rider fence lots. They made provision for the traveling public. At first most of the traveling was on horseback. A strong horse, with a good, roomy saddle, stirrups the right length, and going in a fox trot, will easily carry a rider forty miles a day. Sometimes . . . people met at one of these stands. They found plenty to eat, and around a wide fireplace good cheer prevailed."

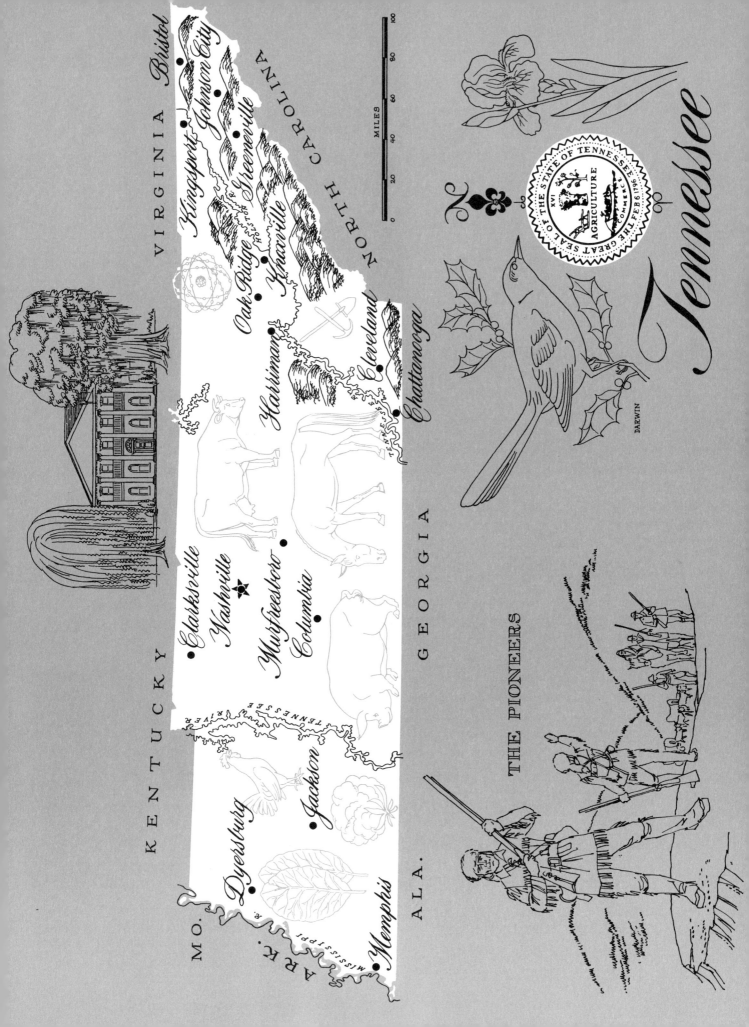

Tennessee

THE GREAT SEAL OF THE STATE OF TENNESSEE · AGRICULTURE COMMERCE · XVI · FEB. 8, 1796

DARWIN

THE PIONEERS

VIRGINIA

Bristol
Johnson City
Kingsport
Greeneville
Oak Ridge
Knoxville
HOLSTON R.
Harriman
Cleveland
Chattanooga
TENNESSEE R.

NORTH CAROLINA

GEORGIA

MILES
0   20   40   60   80   100

KENTUCKY

Clarksville
Nashville
Murfreesboro
Columbia

TENNESSEE RIVER

Dyersburg
Jackson

Memphis

MISSISSIPPI R.

MO.
ARK.
ALA.

*The
Volunteer
State*

The drovers soon appeared on the roads, driving herds of fine beef cattle, horses and mules, and finally hogs to markets in Georgia. Wilderness trade called for organization: "The manager went forward a day or two ahead to engage corn and lots for his hogs. Often there was a purveyor, who came early in the afternoon to stop at the place where they were to spend the night. He commenced cooking for the hands that drove the hogs, and also prepared an early breakfast in the morning. Usually the cooking was done in a little house for their use. The hallooing of the drivers could be heard from morning till night."

Another type of settler also was needed. In 1792 Gideon Blackburn, a Presbyterian missionary, reached East Tennessee. He served as pastor of two churches near Maryville, then in 1804 established a school among the Cherokees on the Hiwasse River. Exercises were held the following Fourth of July and Blackburn could report with feeling on what he had accomplished: "Each scholar read such a portion, as was requested. The different classes then spelled a number of words without the books. Specimens of their writing and ciphering were shown, and the exhibition closed by the children singing, with a clear and distinct voice, a hymn or two, committed to memory. The scene was very impressive. Few of the spectators were unmoved, and many shed tears plentifully. The Governor, a hardy man who had often braved the dangers of war in the same forest, said to me: 'I have often stood unmoved amidst showers of bullets

from the Indian rifles; but this effectually unmans me. I see civilization taking the ground of barbarism, and the praises of Jesus succeeding to the war-whoop of the savage.' All this time the tears were stealing down his manly cheeks."

Andy Jackson's State

With the road-builder, trader, drover, missionary and teacher, Tennessee still had a place for the soldier, and the age would produce none better than the state's own Andy Jackson, who led Tennessean troops to victory over the British in the final battle of the War of 1812 at New Orleans. Jackson, during his lifetime, was a dominant figure in the growth of the state.

And grow Tennessee did, as a leader in commerce and industry. A steamboat reached Nashville in 1819, and within another decade the state was setting aside $15,000,000 to develop road and river transportation. Wheat and cotton became highly profitable crops, and a popular ditty around 1825 proclaimed:

*All I want in this cre-a-tion
Is a pretty little girl
And a big plan-ta-tion
'Way up yonder in the Cherokee
nation.*

Tennessee had a spirit, a drive, that was revealed in unexpected ways. During the Mexican War the state was asked to supply the Federal army with 2,800 volunteers; 30,000 responded and henceforth Tennessee was "The Volunteer State."

The last state to secede from the Union at the outbreak of the Civil War

— and the first to be readmitted afterward—only Virginia felt more severely the impact of that tragic conflict. Over four hundred engagements were fought on the soil of Tennessee, including major battles at Fort Henry, Fort Donelson, Shiloh, Murfreesboro, Chattanooga, Lookout Mountain, Missionary Ridge, Franklin and Nashville. Since there was virtually no sympathy for secession in the eastern mountains of the state, Tennessean often fought against Tennessean in this brother's war.

Andrew Jackson

Modern Tennessee

Readmitted to the Union in 1866, the state faced a bitter struggle, for the war had destroyed homes, businesses, highways and railroads. Really not until 1900 did Tennessee seem to be firmly started down the road that has led to its present prosperity.

Today about two-thirds of the people of Tennessee are farmers, and whereas corn, cotton and tobacco are far and away the leading crops, other important products of Tennessee's farmlands are cattle, chickens, hogs and pork, horses, mules, milk, butter, eggs, grapes, grass seed, hay, peaches, peanuts, strawberries, sweet potatoes, walnuts, wheat and wool. Among its chief mineral resources are clays, coal, lead, marble, oil, phosphate rock, sandstone and zinc. Manufacturing grows annually in Tennessee and chief products include aluminum, automobile equipment, chemicals, cement, clothing, fertilizer, footwear, flour, furniture, iron products, lumber, nonalcoholic beverages, tobacco (snuff and cigars), textiles (cotton, silk, rayon and wool),

and books, newspapers and periodicals.

Another "chief product" of Tennessee appears to be statesmen, including three Presidents of the United States — Andrew Jackson, Andrew Johnson and James K. Polk — and Sam Houston, first President of the Republic of Texas. Great warriors, too, have come from Tennessee — the Confederate cavalry leader, Nathan Bedford Forrest; the first man ever to hold the rank of admiral in the United States Navy, David Glasgow Farragut; and the symbolic hero of World War I, Sergeant Alvin York.

Anyone who ever has smelled the fragrance of balsam in the air in the Great Smokies of Tennessee, glimpsed the beauty of redbud along the state's fine highways, fished its twenty-two lakes for smallmouth bass, stood atop Lookout Mountain or admired The Hermitage, where Andrew Jackson lived northeast of Nashville, nods when he hears the opening lines of the state song:

The land of pure and balmy air,
Of streams so clear and skies so fair,
Of mountains grand and fountains
* free,*
The lovely land of· Tennessee.

KENTUCKY
"The Bluegrass State"

NAMES like the "Long Hunters" and the "Red Horses" reveal the hardy breed of men who followed Daniel Boone into Kentucky. In April, 1775 Boone brought a band of thirty through the Cumberland Gap. The Warriors Path marked fifty miles of the way for him, from the Shawnee villages on the Ohio to the Cherokee country of the south. Here he branched westward along a buffalo trace—to Rockcastle River, up Roundstone Creek, through the gap in Big Hill—until Otter Creek led him to the Kentucky River. A plain south of that stream, near a salt lick frequented by buffalo herds, was the spot he picked for Fort Boonesboro.

When Boone looked back, he counted eight years since he had first come over the mountains from North Carolina into that unexplored part of the royal colony of Virginia now known as Kentucky. The men who had hunted with Boone in those days — Uriah Stone, John Finley, Henry Skaggs—each was a legend in his own right. As woodsmen, if circumstances forced them, they could track down and trap the devil. The tales they carried back to North Carolina started the settlers moving into Kentucky.

Meanwhile authorities in North Carolina and Virginia pinched their mouths at the way these pioneers were striking off into the wilderness without asking anyone's by-your-leave. Trouble was brewing. Sullen Indians, watching, also pinched their mouths. When they thought the time was right, they intended to turn Kentucky into "the dark and bloody ground."

Boonesboro Days

Boone's employer was Judge Richard Henderson of North Carolina, who had made a treaty with the Cherokee Indians to secure all land south of the Watauga River, north of the Cumberland River, and west of the Appalachian ranges. Rival Harrodsburg — of Virginia origin — was established that same spring. But Daniel Boone did the sensible thing, calling together the people from Harrodsburg along with those in the forts at St. Asaph and Boiling Springs, to form a kind of government. Under the "divine elm," where the first religious service in Kentucky was held, nine laws were agreed to.

As fall came on, part of the settlers began to drift away. Some simply couldn't buckle under to the hard work that went with pioneering, and others — a gifted few, maybe — possessed noses that smelled out Indians a hundred miles off. But Daniel Boone and his older brother, Squire Boone, were stickers — especially after their women arrived in September. They grinned, hearing the hum of the spinning wheel or watching the soap kettles over the fire. A Boone kept his wilderness home snug and neat.

On July 14, 1776 Boonesboro was roused by cries from the river. The Indians, striking quickly, were gone in almost the next wink. Three girls were missing, Daniel Boone's daughter with them. But it was Elizabeth Callaway who kept her head, leaving behind a trail of bent twigs, torn bits of clothing and deep-dug heel prints to follow. The girls were rescued, unharmed.

The Dark, Bloody Ground

The warning had been sounded. Boone and fifteen companions were salt-making in 1778 when the Shawnees appeared and captured the group. Boone spent that winter in Detroit as the adopted son of Chief Black Fish. What he heard, principally, was talk of raids to come.

In June, Boone escaped. His wife, believing him dead, already had left Boonesboro, but Boone stayed on, waiting for the attack that could come at any hour. On September 7, about four hundred Indians — and forty French-Canadians — came whooping out of the forest. Within the fort not more than sixty could bear arms, but they stood off a ten-day siege, backed only by a steady aim and courage.

But politics played its part, as Judge Henderson ruefully discovered when the Virginia Assembly refused to recognize the judge's Boonesboro claim (although they gave him 200,000 acres in the "new country" between the Ohio and Green rivers). Yet Kentucky benefited, since Virginia's governor, Patrick Henry, sent George Rogers Clark to look out for Virginia's interest in the territory. Clark launched an expedition against the British and Indians that carried him in 1779 to victory at Vincennes [see Indiana, pp. 139-143]. The American frontier was opened to the banks of the Mississippi.

From 1784 onward, Kentuckians agitated for separation from Virginia, giving good reasons — the refusal to permit Indian forays beyond the Ohio, the need to travel to Richmond for a

The Bluegrass State

*The
Bluegrass
State*

trial whenever a legal dispute was appealed to a higher court. There was talk of forming an independent state called Transylvania. Some urged throwing in with the Spanish in Louisiana. On June 1, 1792 the issue was settled and Kentucky joined the Union as our fifteenth state.

War Hawks and Neutrals

Quickly Kentucky showed her vitality as leaders like Henry Clay emerged to take their place in Congress among the "War Hawks" who talked the country into the War of 1812. Above all else, Kentucky had her eye on her trade to the south. It was no happenstance that 5,500 Kentucky riflemen were present when the Battle of New Orleans showed, conclusively, who controlled the traffic on the Mississippi.

Although Kentucky counted many slaveholders, between 1820 and 1835 the president of the American Colonization Society, which sought to abolish the "institution," was Kentucky's own Henry Clay. In the election of 1860, as civil war impended, Kentuckians had the unique chance of choosing between two native sons for President — Abraham Lincoln and John C. Breckinridge — and chose neither, giving their major vote to John Bell of Tennessee.

Despite the fact that another native son, Jefferson Davis, became President of the Confederacy, Kentucky remained neutral throughout the war. Her troops, like her loyalty, divided almost equally between North and South. Kentuckians Albert Sidney Johnston and John Hunt Morgan were Rebel generals and Kentuckians Don Carlos

Buell and Jeremiah Boyle were Union generals. Major battles were fought on Kentucky soil at Mill Spring and Perryville.

Bluegrass and Thoroughbreds

Millions of years ago, when the Kentucky around Lexington was an ocean floor, nature left behind a shell deposit that has become the rare layer of limestone on which twelve hundred square miles of Kentucky bluegrass grow. For horses who graze on this grass, or drink from the ponds and streams in the area, this deposit provides a rich phosphorus and calcium content, building light, solid bones, strong tendons and elastic muscles. As early as 1775 Daniel Boone walked into the Virginia Assembly with a resolution urging the improvement of the breed of horses in Kentucky. Perhaps it was an omen that the first court held in Kentucky (1781) tried one Hugh McGary for playing the races and found him "an infamous gambler."

In the years since, a great many others like Hugh McGary have risked the shirts on their backs on the running qualities of the Kentucky thoroughbred, as fine as any racing horse in the world. To develop the thoroughbred, Virginia and Carolina horses were crossbred with such fine English stock as Diomed, winner of the first English Derby in 1799. From Messenger, brought to America in 1768, has come the standard-breed (or light-harness horses known as trotters and pacers). A third breed, the American Saddle Horse, developed after Denmark (an American thoroughbred, foaled in

Kentucky

DARWIN

COMMONWEALTH OF KENTUCKY
UNITED WE STAND
DIVIDED WE FALL

FORT HARRODSBURG

W. VA.

BIG SANDY RIVER

OHIO

Covington

INDIANA

Louisville

KENTUCKY RIVER

Lexington

Frankfort

OHIO RIVER

Owensboro

VIRGINIA

TENNESSEE

CUMBERLAND

TENNESSEE R.

MISSISSIPPI R.

MO.

ILLINOIS

MILES
0   10   20   30   40   50

The Bluegrass State

1839) is entirely a Kentucky product. For beauty and intelligence, the American Saddle Horse is the pride of the show ring.

Cavalry demands during the Civil War depleted the stock of thoroughbreds and brought Kentucky horse-breeding to its chilliest hour. Colonel Lewis Clark revived the majesty of the bluegrass-bred thoroughbred with the establishment of the Kentucky Derby, first run at Louisville in 1875. A Kentuckian takes pride in the fact that two Kentuckians, Abraham Lincoln and Zachary Taylor, became President of the United States, but if the same Kentuckian knows horse-racing — and he *sure* does — he'll also ask: "And how about those other great Kentuckians — Man o' War, Equipoise, Gallant Fox, Seabiscuit?"

What's Kentucky Like?

Bluegrass and thoroughbreds are just one part of Kentucky. The Eastern Mountains and Western Kentucky — well, they're each different, yet when you add them all together you get some idea of what the preacher meant when he told his congregation, "Heaven is a Kentucky of a place."

The only large industrial center in Kentucky is Louisville. The state's manufactures include iron and steel products, beverages, tobacco products, machinery, furniture, baseball bats, clothing, textiles, synthetic rubber, paints, flour, hemp products, lumber, and stone, clay and glass products. About one-third of Kentucky's farm income is derived from the sale of its light-colored burley tobacco, and other principal agricultural resources are corn, dairy products, hogs and pork, cattle and hay, in about that order. Coal and natural gas make Kentucky one of the nation's leading fuel producers, while other mineral resources include petroleum, crushed stone, fluorite, clays, limestone, rock asphalt and gravel.

And, of course, Kentucky has *all* the nation's gold bullion — safely stored in a vault on the Fort Knox Military Reservation about thirty miles south of Louisville. This national treasure is kept in a bomb-proof structure, one hundred feet square, the walls and roof of which are faced with granite blocks. Machine-gun turrets guard each corner of the treasure house. Mirrors and brilliant lights make every corner within the vault visible at all times. Supersensitive microphones can pick up any sound.

But Kentucky's lack of hospitality ends at Fort Knox. Even in the country of the mountaineer, a typical greeting is, "Welcome, stranger, light and hitch." If the Kentucky mountaineer is a species all his own — whose "buss" for kiss, and "pack" for carry are out of the England of Robin Hood, like so many of his manners and attitudes — he remains an intensely likable, kind human being. His log cabin and farm-patch often provide a tight-fisted existence, and that struggle is in the names he gives to the hollows where he lives — Lonesome, Troublesome, Peevish. He is a fiddler and a singer, and his humor is in his love for such old songs as "Give the Fiddler a Dram" and "Pa's Done Et the Shotgun."

WEST VIRGINIA
"The Mountain State"

WEST VIRGINIA is no more the most northern of our southern states than it is the most southern of our northern states. "Mountaineers are always free," boasts the motto of West Virginia. And also stubborn, two-fisted individualists.

John Henry, the Negro steel driver who, twenty-pound sledge in hand, pitted his skill against a newfangled steam drill, is West Virginia's folk hero. A ballad sung around the world celebrates this heroic contest during the construction of the Big Bend Tunnel in 1872. He would drive the six-foot steel faster, John Henry promised, "or hammer my fool self to death," and sure enough —

The men that made that steam drill
Thought it was mighty fine;
John Henry drove his fourteen feet,
While the steam drill only made
*   nine, Lawd, Lawd,*
While the steam drill only made
*   nine.*

West Virginia has its special home remedies, handed down by the mountain folk. For coughs and colds, you can't beat horehound tea. For intestinal disorders, slippery elm tea is best. To heal chapped lips, nothing works like kissing the middle rail of a five-rail fence.

After a century and a half, the ancient sport of riding "tournament," where perfect horsemanship is required

The Mountain State

to spear the ring on the lance, is still practiced in West Virginia. To a West Virginia logger, cooks are "stomick robbers" and coffee is "jerkwater." In Smoke Hole — off the beaten trail in a canyon of the South Branch of the Potomac — descendants of Hessian soldiers talk in such redundancies as "rifle-gun," "ham-meat," and "tooth-dentists." In brief, a great deal more than the "West" makes West Virginia different from neighboring Virginia.

From Mound Builders to Colonists

The first inhabitants of West Virginia, an ancient Indian people known as the Mound Builders, have left the remnants of their civilization in the Great Kanawha Valley. Here are found the crude weapons of flint and bone with which they hunted, the pipes of clay they smoked and the rude pottery with which they cooked. About the neck of the skeleton of one woman were seventeen hundred ivory beads and five hundred shell ornaments. The skeleton of a man measured seven feet. Walls, often three or four miles in length, protected their villages.

By the time the white man reached North America, Indians looked upon mountainous, virtually uninhabited West Virginia as a mere crossroads. Here the trail from Pennsylvania to the Ohio River intersected that from Maryland to Virginia — forest paths for hunting and fishing parties, for Indians gathering salt or for braves on the warpath. In 1670 John Lederer, coming from coastal Virginia, crested the Blue Ridge Mountains and looked upon West Virginia, but not until

1726 did a white settler — Morgan ap Morgan, a Welshman — build a log cabin in the region. The following year thrifty Germans followed the valleys from Pennsylvania and settled at Mecklenburg (Shepherdstown).

The ring of striking axes was heard through the forests as other cabins rose during the next thirty years in the valleys of the Greenbrier, New and Tygarts rivers. Over the mountains came young George Washington, surveying the land for Lord Fairfax and persuading his patron in 1756 to grant "ye Fam'd Warm Springs" (Berkeley Springs) to the colony "to be forever free to the publick for the welfare of suffering humanity." However, more than health-bathing drew the Scotch-Irish into West Virginia. Watching sullenly, the Indians resolved to end this invasion of their hunting grounds.

By Tomahawk Rights

Wisely, in 1763, George III tried to halt further colonizing until treaties could be reached with the Indians to acquire title to the land. But the Dutch and Germans, who couldn't read the king's proclamations in English, and the Scotch-Irish, who could but took no heed, pushed on into the wilderness. With axe or tomahawk they made their marks on the trees, claiming the territory by "tomahawk rights." Then they built blockhouse and fort and defied the Indians to do anything about it. Raids, murders, little wars became the rule. And short truces, too, as occurred in 1768 when the Iroquois ceded all claims to land between the Alleghenies and the Ohio River.

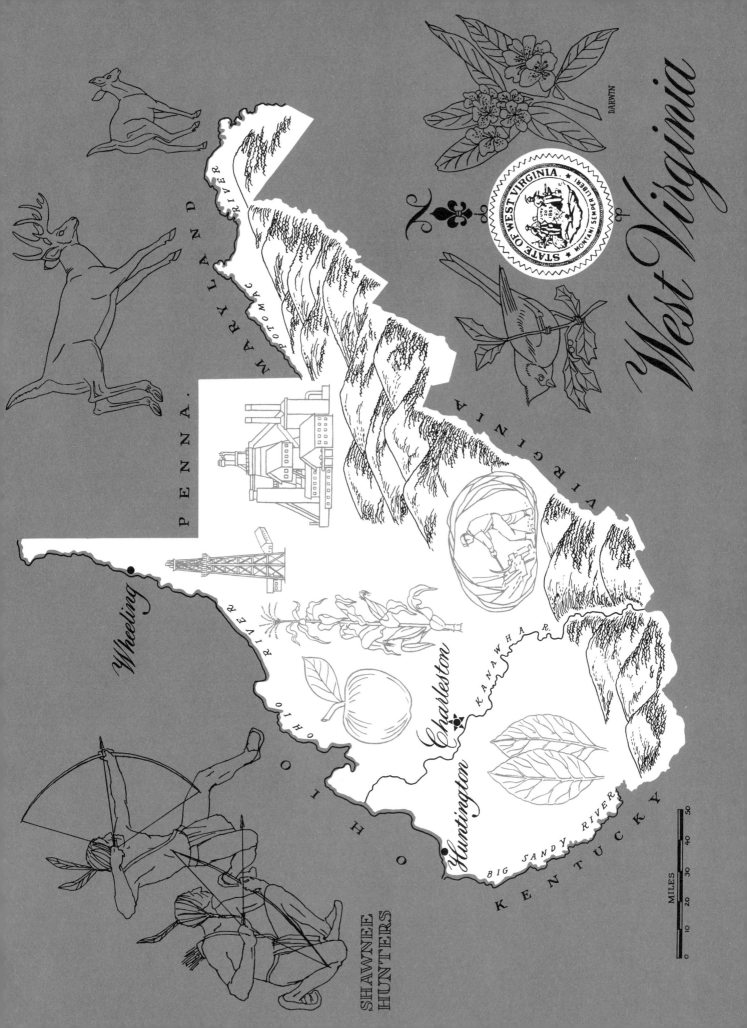

West Virginia

DARWIN

STATE OF WEST VIRGINIA · LIBER · MONTANI SEMPER · 1863

PENNA.

MARYLAND

POTOMAC RIVER

VIRGINIA

OHIO

OHIO RIVER

Wheeling

Charleston

Huntington

KANAWHA R.

BIG SANDY RIVER

KENTUCKY

SHAWNEE HUNTERS

MILES
0 10 20 30 40 50

The Mountain State

A movement to make West Virginia a separate colony to be called Vandalia gathered momentum in 1771, and a principal supporter of the proposal was Benjamin Franklin. The bubbling of the political pot that ultimately stewed up the Revolution thwarted the idea. Then in 1774 some drunken whites senselessly murdered the family of a friendly Mingo chief, again setting the Indians to war-dancing. Lord Dunmore, royal governor of Virginia, led the frontier army in the all-day battle at Point Pleasant that crushed the red men. Sometimes this fight is described as the "first battle of the Revolution," since it restored peace along the frontier until "the bloody years of the three 7's." For the next five years — until September, 1782, specifically — British-led Indian armies launched three major invasions. But these West Virginians proved equal to the emergency, and while Washington's ragged Continentals won in the East, the mountaineers kept the country's back door securely closed to the invaders.

The Changing Frontier

The first Federal census taken in 1790 — about the time Daniel Boone was a leading citizen in the Kanawha Valley — gave the population in what is now West Virginia as 55,873. Ten years later the figure was 78,592. A settler of the time remembered how the youngsters watched the potato tops growing, the corn ripening, and added: "How delicious was the taste of young potatoes when we got them. What a jubilee when we were permitted to pull the young corn for roasting ears." Mountain settlers lived for simple pleasures, making their own rules of proper conduct and "hating out" of the village those who didn't measure up. Old-timers in the hills around the 1800's complained that life had been better when there were no courts and sheriffs.

The completion of the National Road from Cumberland to Wheeling, the coming of the steamboat and the railroad made the difference. By mountain wagon (called, so appropriately, a "shake-gut") or afloat, progress kept edging west to the Ohio River — and beyond.

The more West Virginia grew in size and economic strength, the more it resented being part of Virginia. Mountain people worked their own farms, and had no mind to be taxed to support the slaveholding crowd along the tidewater. Long before John Brown dumped the impending conflict into West Virginia's front yard by raiding the arsenal at Harper's Ferry, there was no doubt how these mountain people leaned. And when, after the attack on Fort Sumter, Virginia called its convention to vote on secession, the delegates from West Virginia stood 9 for, 7 absent, 1 excused, 29 against. In the popular election held that October the vote in favor of becoming a new state carried 18,408 to 781. By mid-1863, when President Lincoln proclaimed West Virginia our thirty-fifth state, Federal forces had already routed the Rebs west of the Alleghenies. In round figures, West Virginia sent 36,000 troops into the Union Army and 7,000 into the Army of the Confeder-

acy, and the figures tell why — though Virginia wanted to patch up the split after the war — the people reckoned they had already picked the winning side.

Typically West Virginia

West Virginia has a character as native as the great growths of oak and hickory that dominate its forests. Go into any part of the state and, with pride and a grin, a West Virginian has a story to tell. South from Parkersburg, set in the Ohio River, is the island where that eccentric Irishman, Harman Blennerhassett, and Aaron Burr reputedly plotted to set up their own empire in the Southwest — a plot for which Burr stood trial for treason. Shepherdstown on the Potomac recalls that Monday in December, 1787 when James Rumsey — "Crazy" Rumsey, they called him then — launched a steamboat twenty years before Robert Fulton sailed his *Claremont* on the Hudson.

A pioneer named Van Bibbers found natural gas bubbling through the waters at Burning Spring, and all through the salt-mining country in those days the salt-makers complained bitterly when they struck oil. They'd just let the stuff float down the Kanawha in big patches, until folk began calling the river "Old Greasy." Some enterprising pioneers remembered that the Indians used to rub themselves with the stuff, so they bottled it as "Rock Oil" or "Seneca Oil," an early stock-in-trade for the medicine peddler.

Any number of West Virginia stories like these add up to only one conclusion — the natural resources of the "Mountain State" held the key to its prosperity. One of its other nicknames is "The Coal Bin of the World." Oil production reached its peak about 1901 and has since declined. The natural gas fields cover most of the western half of the state. Sand and gravel, limestone, sandstone, glass sand, salt brine and iron ore round out West Virginia's chief mineral resources.

Wheeling is known as the "Steel City" and West Virginia's manufactures are topped by its iron and steel production, then its chemicals. Other typical West Virginia industries include tableware, glazing and structural glass, chinaware, pottery, lumber and textiles. The state's farms produce cattle, dairy products, sheep, chicken and eggs, corn, hay, buckwheat, peaches and apples, vegetables and tobacco. Farming around a mountaintop has led to a West Virginia joke about the careless farmer who fell out of his corn field.

Mountain people — in West Virginia and elsewhere — tend to cling to old ways, to old beliefs, to live in the tradition of the great John Henry:

John Henry had a little boy,
This is all the children he had.
John Henry is now at rest,
But his boy is driving steel like his dad,
    Lawd, Lawd,
But his boy is driving steel like his dad.

Lakes and Prairies

OHIO
"The Buckeye State"

A COFFEE SACK with holes cut in it for arms once served for his garment, and for a hat he wore a stew kettle. When first he led his pack horse into Ohio in 1801, pioneers knew him as John Chapman. He stopped finally along Licking Creek, west of the Ohio River. The burlap bags he carried contained apple seeds, which he carefully planted. He built a fence around his wilderness orchard, then disappeared into the forests of buckeye trees that covered the land.

In succeeding years this eccentric fellow — some called him "the nursery man" — was a frequent visitor to Ohio. His fame as Johnny Appleseed grew into a legend, and pioneer families loved this man who planted his apple trees so that the fruit would provide a preventive for scurvy. Stories about him emphasized his great goodness. Sometimes he distributed religious tracts, saying that he "brought news from Heaven." If Johnny Appleseed met anyone in need, he gladly gave that person the food in his pack or the clothes off his back. Once he put out a fire so that the insects would not perish in its flames, and he was welcomed in Indian country where other white men traveled at considerable peril.

Among the famous men Ohio would give to the nation in future years were seven Presidents — Grant, Garfield, Hayes, Benjamin Harrison, McKinley, Taft and Harding. But in Ohio history and legend, no figure surpasses Johnny Appleseed, who lived to serve others.

Wilderness Battleground

Some hundred and thirty years before Johnny Appleseed appeared in Ohio, the French explorer, La Salle, probably was the first white man to penetrate the region between Lake Erie and the Ohio

River. The French king, Louis XIV, was inclined to shrug off as virtually valueless any lands west of the Alleghenies, and Britain's monarch, Charles II, clung to much the same notion. Fur traders and trappers of both countries knew better. This country was the crossroads of an expanding empire, and for almost a century the rival fur trappers turned Ohio into a wilderness battleground.

By 1745 the British had a fort on Sandusky Bay, and five years later, with the organization of the Ohio Land Company of Virginia, they sent explorers into the region. Indian scalpers, emboldened by French whiskey, greeted these British "interlopers," and the French were not impressed when young George Washington brought them warning that, unless they stopped this deviltry, trouble must result. The six bloody years of the French and Indian Wars followed before, finally, France ceded to England all land east of the Mississippi.

Soon the British were quarreling among themselves over the Ohio lands, with Virginia and Pennsylvania competing for title to them. Under the Quebec Act of 1774, England sought to make the Ohio lands part of Canada, which hardly pleased any American claimant. With the frontier conquests of George Rogers Clark, the United States won Ohio as part of the Northwest Territory.

Victory at Fallen Timbers

After the passage of the Land Ordinance of 1785, Congress began disposing of the Ohio lands to the highest

Ulysses S. Grant

bidders in the hope of obtaining funds for a treasury flattened by the cost of the war for independence. A permanent settlement — the first in the Northwest Territory — was established at Marietta in 1788 and New Jersey emigrants founded Cincinnati the following year. The wave of settlers into Ohio swelled.

Outraged Indians, seeing their hunting grounds invaded, their villages pillaged, their corn fields snatched away, retaliated. With musket, firebrand, scalping knife, they fashioned a bloody story of wilderness savagery and re-

*The
Buckeye
State*

venge. To save Ohio against these depredations, General "Mad Anthony" Wayne was sent to the territory. Wayne looked over the raw recruits that he must whip into an army, and devoted months to training them in the art of fighting Indians. By the spring of 1794 he was ready to advance into the Indian country between the Auglaize and Maumee rivers. Deserted villages were all that greeted him until he came to a region where a tornado had uprooted the trees.

And here the Indians were — Miamis under Little Turtle, Shawnees under Black Wolf, Ottawas and Chippewas and Potawatomis under Blue Jacket. Here were Sauk and Fox from Lake Superior and a small band of Iroquois. Wayne's cavalrymen hurdled the felled trees. Wayne's infantrymen charged with fixed bayonets. After forty minutes Wayne turned the Battle of Fallen Timbers into a rout, bringing peace to the Ohio country.

"Half Cockeyed Alligator"

Organized as a territory in 1799, Ohio was admitted to the Union four years later as our seventeenth state. A decade of growth followed, then the War of 1812 posed the danger of a British invasion across Lake Erie. On September 10, 1813 spunky Oliver Hazard Perry, who never had commanded at sea, left Put-in-Bay to turn back the British fleet. When Perry's flagship, the *Lawrence,* was destroyed, the commodore coolly rowed to the *Niagara* and carried on the battle. Two British warships became entangled, and the *Niagara* raked both with

broadsides. Doom approached the British flotilla of six vessels and Perry dispatched a famous message: "We have met the enemy, and they are ours."

Bright days were ahead for Ohio. In October, 1811, the *Orleans* swept down the Ohio River to herald the age of the paddle-wheeler. Along the rivers of the state — and later over the Miami and Erie Canal — prosperity journeyed into Ohio by flatboat, keelboat, raft and steamer. By the mid-1830's floating palaces, like the *Jacob Strader,* became familiar sights. A contemporary account describes the *Jacob Strader* sailing "along the starlit river" with "all her windows blazing with lights, her furnace fires throwing their glare forward, the black smoke, filled with sparks of fire, whirling from her tall stacks, steam roaring from her escape pipes, perhaps a band playing, and a gay party dancing on her lofty promenade deck."

King of Ohio River boatmen was Mike Fink, who declared that he was "half wild horse and half cockeyed alligator." Boasted Mike: "I can out-run, out-jump, out-shout, out-drink, an' out-fight — rough-an'-tumble, no holts barred — any man on both sides the river from Pittsburgh to New Orleans an' back ag'in to St. Louie." At the same time, Mike and his breed hauled the food, dry goods, furniture, coal, timber and livestock that was making Ohio a seambursting part of the new Empire of the West. "Come on, you flatters, you bargers, you milk-white mechanics, an' see how tough I am to chaw!" sang out Mike, a symbol of the undaunted spirit building that empire.

OHIO
RIVERBOAT

DARWIN

THE GREAT SEAL OF THE STATE OF OHIO

Ohio

PENNSYLVANIA

WEST VIRGINIA

OHIO RIVER

MILES

Cleveland

Youngstown

Akron

Canton

Sandusky

Marietta

Columbus

SCIOTO RIVER

Toledo

MAUMEE RIVER

Lima

Springfield

Dayton

Cincinnati

MICHIGAN

INDIANA

KENTUCKY

The
Buckeye
State

Wars — Private and Otherwise

A private war between Ohio and Michigan broke out in 1835. Called the Toledo War, this boundary dispute found both states arming for battle, and even after President Andrew Jackson intervened as peacemaker, some two hundred Michiganders invaded Toledo, ripped down the Ohio flag and dragged it through the streets. Ohio struck back by organizing the disputed territory into a county, sending in three judges under an armed escort to hold a session of court by candlelight, and thus claiming that Ohio had "exercised jurisdiction" over the region. In the end Michigan surrendered claim to the land as a provision of admission as a state.

Ohio's strong antislavery feeling in the decades before the Civil War was influenced by Lane Seminary in Cincinnati, a training school for Presbyterian ministers. The institution's militant leader, Theodore Weld, was author of a pamphlet about slavery that inspired Harriet Beecher Stowe to write *Uncle Tom's Cabin*. Ohio also gave to the abolitionist cause Levi Coffin, known as "the president of the underground railroad," and a runaway slave, reaching Ohio, invariably believed that his freedom had been secured.

A strong peace movement in Ohio, led by Clement L. Vallandigham, divided the state into hostile political factions during the years of war, yet Ohio remained a tower of strength to the Union. Two of Ohio's sons served in Lincoln's cabinet — Salmon P. Chase as Secretary of the Treasury and Edward Stanton as Secretary of War.

The three generals most responsible for Northern victory were Ohio-born — Ulysses S. Grant, William Tecumseh Sherman, and "Little Phil" Sheridan.

A Get-Up-and-Go State

Iron ore and coal, coming across Lake Erie into ports like Cleveland, Toledo, Lorain, Ashtabula, Conneaut, Fairport Harbor, Sandusky and Port Clinton brought boom years to Ohio in the age of steel that followed the Civil War. A wide range of manufactures was developed, including, in addition to iron and steel, rubber goods, motor vehicles, machine tools, glass, meat packing, flour, grist, cereals, clay products, clothing, oil refinery products, paints, varnishes, electrical equipment, textiles and chemicals. The state's mineral resources, in addition to iron ore and coal, include natural gas, limestone, oil, clay, sandstone, shale, sand, gravel, salt and gypsum. Prosperous farms are producers, notably, of corn, dairy products, hogs and pork, wheat, eggs and cattle.

Ohioans have gained distinction in many fields — Wilbur and Orville Wright in aviation, William H. McGuffey and Horace Mann in education, B. F. Goodrich and Harvey Firestone in industry, to cite a few. To the Indians, living along the river, *Ohio* meant *great,* and modern Ohio certainly lives up to its Indian name. "I can hit like fourth-proof lightnin' an' every lick I make in the woods lets in an acre o' sunshine," bragged Mike Fink. But gentle, noble Johnny Appleseed endures as the man who touched the hearts of Ohioans, and they have erected three monuments in his honor.

INDIANA
"The Hoosier State"

THE WHITE MAN'S story in Indiana begins with Father Marquette, the Jesuit missionary who crossed the dunes of Lake Michigan as early as 1675, and with that indefatigable explorer, La Salle, who appeared soon afterward, following the St. Joseph and Kankakee rivers into Indiana. Yet in those years a much wilder breed of man was needed to bend the Indiana wilderness into an empire.

Shouting and cursing, paddling the rivers with bold strokes, so came these reckless fellows — the *voyageurs,* who were traders traveling under permit from the king of France, and the *coureurs de bois,* who were best described as wandering smugglers and outlaws. Were they not the red man's good friend? Look there — at the beads, the trinkets they brought for the women. And for the men — here, such whiskey as this was worth the few pelts they asked!

The early years of the eighteenth century found dozens of French traders scattered through the Indian villages. French forts at Miami, Ouiatenon and Vincennes guarded these rough-and-tumble fellows, who often took Indian squaws for wives and raised families of noisy half-breed children. Thus France gained her powerful Indian allies for the savage wars with the British that made both Ohio and Indiana bloody ground until 1763, when the Treaty of Paris gave all land east of the Mississippi to England.

At the outbreak of the Revolution there was no English garrison in Indiana, but in Detroit Governor Henry

*The
Hoosier
State*

Hamilton moved swiftly to correct this error by rebuilding the fort at Vincennes — and, enlisting the Indians as allies, to win his nickname as "Henry the Hair-buyer."

March to Vincennes

In raw, wet February of 1779, George Rogers Clark and his band of American rangers reached the Little Wabash River at that point where the stream divided into two branches, encircling about five miles of ground.

"There's no hope of going on," discouraged rangers growled. "Every inch of that land is under at least three feet of water! Here we wait."

But young Colonel Clark shook his head. Wait for spring and the Indians to renew butchering American settlers? Not one bit of it! They had come to win the Northwest and there could be only one decision:

"March on to Vincennes!"

In water to their hips, feet pawing in the slime, the rangers followed their jaunty, stubborn leader. Muscles stiffened, a rifle came to feel like a cannon. Clark pushed on relentlessly — snatching sleep whenever a spot of high ground permitted, then plunging on to the Wabash where the water covering the surrounding ground was now neck-deep.

For a time the rangers seemed to lose heart, but Clark ordered the men nearest him to begin singing and soon a cheer went through the ranks. Men who were too weak to slosh on, held onto logs and floated! Single file, in torment, on legs with swollen veins, gasping, reeling, often seeing images

that didn't exist, Rogers and his rangers did the impossible — they reached Vincennes! The battle with the British was almost an anticlimax, yet though it was swiftly over, Clark and his men had won Indiana — and a great deal more — for the United States.

A Future President

After the Revolution, raids by Indians continued to bedevil settlers in Indiana until General "Mad Anthony" Wayne crushed the Miamis and their confederates at the Battle of Fallen Timbers [see Ohio, pp. 134-138]. In 1800 the Indiana Territory was created and included not only the present states of Indiana, Illinois and Wisconsin, but also parts of Michigan and Minnesota. To the capital at Vincennes to serve as first territorial governor came a future President of the United States — William Henry Harrison.

In 1811 the great Shawnee leader, Tecumseh, traveled among the Creeks, Choctaws and Cherokees, organizing a revolt against the white settlers. Harrison rallied his ragtag frontier army and marched against the Indian stronghold at Tippecanoe on the upper Wabash. The Indians asked for a truce and a parley and Harrison, though he assented, expected trickery.

The governor had guessed wisely. Before dawn shrill war whoops signaled an Indian attack.

"Boys," sang out Harrison, "keep your aim low!"

Gun flashes through the darkness held the Indians at bay. Harrison waited eagerly for daylight, then threw his cavalry into the attack. The frontier

MICHIGAN

OHIO

ILLINOIS

•Gary

•South Bend

Fort Wayne

WABASH

RIVER

Muncie

Indianapolis

Terre Haute

OHIO RIVER

KENTUCKY

Evanston

MILES

0   10   20   30   40   50

INDIAN WAR COUNCIL

DARWIN

SEAL OF THE STATE OF INDIANA

1816

N

Indiana

*The
Hoosier
State*

horsemen roared to the charge. With slashing sabers, clubs, hunting knives, they ripped their foes to shreds.

But defeat at Tippecanoe only rallied the tribes in the Indian Territory to bitterer rebellion, and with the outbreak of the War of 1812 Tecumseh gained a powerful ally in the British. Doggedly Harrison pursued his old enemy and in December, 1813 clashed in the Battle of Thames. This time, when Harrison's cavalrymen turned the tide, among the dead was the mighty Tecumseh.

Young Abe Lincoln

With a constitution that recognized an obligation to educate all citizens, Indiana became our nineteenth state in December, 1816. Among those who moved into Indiana at this time were Tom and Nancy Lincoln, their daughter Sarah and eight-year-old Abe Lincoln, who "was large for his age." The family settled, Abe remembered, in "an unbroken forest" where there were "many bears and other wild animals," and Dennis Hanks, a cousin, added: "We lived the same as Indians, 'ceptin' we took an interest in politics and religion."

Breaking a wilderness to a plow was hard work the future President never forgot, and often it seemed as though the only time there wasn't an ax in his hand was when he ate and slept. The death of his mother within two years brought Abe Lincoln his first heartbreak. Once, using his father's "rifle-gun," he aimed through a crack in the cabin at a flock of wild turkeys and fired, but he was aghast when one of

the turkeys fell dead and never again "pulled a trigger."

Other settlers, coming into the Indiana wilderness, attracted itinerant schoolmasters who set up "subscription schools." Young Abe attended for short periods, learning to read and write and mastering the elements of grammar and arithmetic. During the Indiana years, he grew tall, muscular and capable of doing a man's work. He "hired out" to neighbors, clerked in a store, and ferried passengers from a landing on the Ohio to passing steamers. By firelight he read such books as trickled into the frontier, and his friends marveled at the way he could tell a story or mount a stump and make a speech. No one else had his ability, they all admitted.

Good Times and Bad

The scarcity of settlers and the lack of flourishing communities posed many problems for Indiana. Whence was coming the trade, the taxes to support a government? In 1818 the central part of the state was purchased from the Indians and for decades was called the "New Purchase." Borrowing heavily to build roads and canals (many of which were never finished), Indiana experienced a giddy wave of land speculation, then financial collapse and depression. By 1850, however, the railroads were reaching into Indiana. Commerce increased steadily. Cities began to grow.

In 1861 the lad who once had plowed fields in Indiana became President and the country erupted into civil war. The Hoosier State loyally supported the Union, and only once — in 1863, when the Confederate cavalry leader, John Morgan, crossed the Ohio River from Kentucky — did the war touch the soil of Indiana. Afterward, like so many neighboring states, Indiana experienced rocky times as farmers fretted over debts, low prices and high freight rates. Meanwhile, industries were creating a new set of problems — strikes, slums, labor unions. Thousands of immigrants arrived from Europe to work in the factories and mills.

Modern Indiana

In time, Indiana took in stride this industrial challenge. Her "Cities of the Calumet" — Gary, Hammond, East Chicago, Whiting — lying in an area that follows the curve of Lake Michigan for sixteen miles, probably contain as great a concentration of diversified industry as any comparable area in the world. In these seventy square miles are great steel and rail mills, cement plants, soap factories, oil refineries and large electric generating plants. At night the glow of blast furnaces illuminates the sky with a strange, breathtaking beauty. Forges clang, wheels roar, and slag is dumped to its own great thunder.

Across Lake Michigan, into the ports at Gary and Indiana Harbor, come the raw materials needed to keep factories and blast furnaces, rolling mills and equipment shops at peak production — iron ore, gypsum, wood pulp, coal, limestone from Baltic ports, palm oil from Africa. To these Indiana adds its own mineral resources — coal, limestone, sand and gravel, petroleum and clay. And behind the mill and factory worker stands the Indiana farmer, one of the nation's leading producers of mint, potatoes, onions and tomatoes, in addition to corn, hogs and pork, dairy products, beef and dairy cattle, wheat, eggs, hay, oats, soybeans, sheep and wool.

Among Indiana's points of pride is its wealth of literary giants — Civil War General Lew Wallace, who wrote *Ben-Hur;* James Whitcomb Riley, creator of *Little Orphant Annie, The Raggedy Man* and *The Old Swimmin' Hole;* Booth Tarkington, George Ade, and a dozen others equally famous. Battleground where George Rogers Clark became immortal, boyhood home where Abraham Lincoln grew to manhood, Indiana has built monuments to these past glories. But Indiana has another claim to fame: on June 2, 1883, in the old League Park at Fort Wayne, electric lights were strung around the field as a professional team from Quincy, Illinois defeated the Methodist College nine, 11 to 10, in America's first night baseball game.

And speaking of famous folk in Indiana, how about Bill Stafford in Morgan County, who was picking raspberries one June day when a bear surprised him. Bill took flight, with the bear in hot pursuit, but luckily Bill escaped across the ice cakes in the White River.

"How could you ever do that during the month of June?" skeptics often prod Bill.

"Well, you see," Bill tells them, "we'd done a heap of runnin' and by the time I got to the White River, it was December."

The Hoosier State

ILLINOIS
"Land of Lincoln"

FROM RELATIVES in Illinois the Lincolns received letters describing black soil of fabulous fertility. So, after fourteen years in Indiana, Tom Lincoln moved his family in the spring of 1830. Abe, now twenty-one, drove one of the ox teams on the ten-day journey to the unbroken prairie on the Sangamon River. Ten miles west of the new town of Decatur, he helped to plow the prairie, to plant the first crops and to split rails for fences.

When another spring came, young Lincoln decided to strike out on his own. On a bluff of the Sangamon River, twenty miles northwest of Springfield, he settled in the rude frontier hamlet of New Salem. Here he fumbled along as a store clerk and mill hand, an unsuccessful candidate for the state legislature, local postmaster and surveyor, until finally he turned to the study of law. In the spring of 1837 he was admitted to the bar. New Salem, declining rapidly in population and importance, offered no future for a lawyer.

Abe Lincoln, his meager belongings in his saddlebags, rode off to Springfield, hoping for the best. A merchant named Joshua F. Speed gave him lodging that first night, and they became lifelong friends. It was, of course, this gift of winning people that explained the future greatness of the young man from New Salem. When for the final time he departed from Springfield, it was to become President of a nation threatened by civil war.

"We Have Seen Nothing Like This River"

Today Illinois calls itself the "Land of Lincoln," yet its proud history under the white man's influence reaches back to the spring of 1673 when Jacques Marquette and Louis Joliet, with five *voyageurs,* navigated the Illinois River. "We have seen nothing like this river," Father Marquette wrote, "for the fertility of land, its prairies, woods, wild cattle, stag, deer, ducks, parrots, and even beaver." The friendliness of the

Kaskaskia Indians in their village near Starved Rock so won the heart of Father Marquette that he paddled back the following year to found a mission near the present city of Utica. He was canoeing up the eastern shore of Lake Michigan when in May, 1675 illness cut short his life.

In the century that followed, the Illinois story differed only in detail from the stories of neighboring states — French missionaries converting Indians to the Christian faith, French traders and trappers seeking to monopolize the fur trade, British interlopers fomenting the brew of massacre and jealousy that finally boiled over into the French and Indian War and the loss of the land for France.

On October 10, 1765 the British flag was raised over Fort de Chartres, but for the next two decades the English phase of the Illinois story followed a familiar pattern — the great march to Vincennes of George Rogers Clark and his rangers [see Indiana, pp. 139-143], and the establishment of the authority of the United States with the passage of the Ordinance of 1787. That act created as Federal property the Northwest Territory, consisting of the present states of Illinois, Indiana, Michigan, Ohio and Wisconsin. Except as a punishment for a crime, slavery was prohibited in the territory.

The Black Hawk War

Illinois was included in the Indiana Territory from 1800 to 1809 when the Illinois Territory was established. Along the highway of the Ohio River, in flatboats and keelboats, settlers poured into the prairies where, one observer declared, all that existed was a "wilderness of flowers and grass." In "Hints to Immigrants," pioneers in Illinois were advised to bring a pair of good horses, a wagon, a cow, "a couple of pigs," domestic fowl, two plows — "one for breaking the prairie, and the other for tillage" — and "a few other tools and implements." In order to brighten the prospect for the future settler, this tract advised: "A log house can soon be erected."

After the victory of "Mad Anthony" Wayne at Fallen Timbers and William Henry Harrison at Tippecanoe [see Ohio, pp. 134-138 and Indiana, pp. 139-143], Indian troubles subsided for a time. Statehood was granted in 1818. Frontier villages sprang up, trading in fur, corn, whiskey, venison, beef, pork and other staples of life—villages much like the New Salem where Abraham Lincoln settled in 1831.

The following year, like many young volunteers, Lincoln marched off to war against Black Hawk and his Sauk and Fox Indians, who were determined that no longer should the white man plow up ancient burial grounds or take over tribal corn fields. Lincoln's war experiences, by his own account, were hardly glorious, consisting of "charges upon the wild onion" and "a good many bloody struggles with the mosquitoes," but the white men were ingloriously routed at Stillman's Run before hunger led Black Hawk to surrender. Afterward, dictating his *Autobiography*, the chief spoke poignantly: "That you may never experience the humility that the power of the American Government

Land of Lincoln

Land of
Lincoln

has reduced me to, is the wish of him, who in his native forests was once as proud and bold as yourself."

"Saw, Saw, Bang, Bang"

A great peace pow-wow was held in Chicago in 1833. That year, with a population of less than 200, the town that is today America's second largest city was incorporated. By the Erie Canal through the Mohawk pass to Buffalo, thence by lake to Chicago, the settlers came. That first year — 1833 — 20,000 persons arrived. An exuberance of growth was in the air, and no one experienced it more keenly than Joseph Jefferson, an actor, who described his arrival in Chicago in 1838:

"Off we go ashore and walk through the busy little town, busy even then, people hurrying to and fro, frame buildings going up, board sidewalks going down, new hotels, new churches, new theaters, everything new. Saw and hammer — saw, saw, bang, bang — look out for the drays! — bright and muddy streets — gaudy-colored calicos — blue and red flannels and striped ticking hanging outside the dry goods stores — bar-rooms — real-estate offices — attorneys-at-law — oceans of them!"

In Springfield, lawyer Abe Lincoln was beginning to win a solid reputation. An Eastern lawyer, visiting the Sangamon County Courthouse at about this time, pictured the judge presiding "with his chair tilted back and his heels as high as his head." A rail divided court and spectators, "outside of which smoking and chewing and spitting tobacco seemed to be the principal employment." In this easygoing en-

vironment the lanky Lincoln fitted like a pea in a pod. He liked people and their problems, large and small. He became in time one of the best lawyers in the state. As a member of the state legislature and, for one term, the United States Congress he became one of Illinois' most respected political thinkers.

To Save the Union

In 1858 Abraham Lincoln's debates with Stephen A. Douglas in a campaign for election to the United States Senate identified clearly how the issue of slavery was dividing the nation. As a true son of the old Northwest Territory, where slavery had been prohibited by the Ordinance of 1787, Lincoln came to the gist of the question when he said: "It is the eternal struggle between these two principles — right and wrong — throughout the world." Raised to national prominence by the debates, Lincoln was nominated for President when the Republicans held their convention in Chicago in May, 1860. The city on the shores of Lake Michigan now had a population of 110,000.

The tragedy of four years of war between the North and South followed. When statehood was granted to Illinois, she was given an outlet on Lake Michigan so that closer relations would be established with the northern and middle states as "additional security for the perpetuity of the Union." Now that foresight was justified. Since Illinois held sacred the memory of her six regiments that fought in the War with Mexico, the first regiment she sent to fight in the Civil War was designated

WISCONSIN

IOWA

MARQUETTE
and
JOLIET

Rock Island

Rockford

DES PLAINES R.

ROCK RIVER

Chicago

Joliet

INDIANA

Galesburg

Peoria

ILLINOIS RIVER

MISSISSIPPI RIVER

MISSOURI

Bloomington
Danville

Decatur

Springfield

Alton

MILES
0   20   40   60   80   100

N

DARWIN

SEAL OF THE STATE OF ILLINOIS
AUG. 26TH 1818

Illinois

MISSOURI

WABASH RIVER

OHIO R.

KENTUCKY

the Seventh Illinois, and during the four years Illinois contributed 255,092 men to the Federal armies. With Lincoln of Springfield at the head of the civilian government, and Ulysses S. Grant of Galena becoming commander of all the Northern armies, Illinois took pride in supplying the two great architects of ultimate victory. Yet, as the war dragged on, a strong opposition movement developed and at one time the Illinois membership in the Sons of Liberty, a copperhead organization, was estimated at 50,000. Still, first among the states to ratify the Thirteenth Amendment, freeing the slaves, was Illinois.

Industrial Growth

Railroads connecting in Chicago so that it became the "hub city" of the nation were responsible for Illinois' industrial growth after 1865. In 1871, within twenty-four hours, the Chicago Fire, one of the greatest tragedies of its kind in America, left 300 dead and 90,000 homeless while property dam-

age was estimated at $200,000,000, but such was the vitality of the people that within two short years the prairie city had been largely rebuilt. Labor disputes, culminating in the Haymarket Riot in 1886, were symptoms of the unrest that resulted as a once predominantly agricultural economy gave way to dependence on industry. Illinois cities became famous for their markets and products — Chicago for livestock and grain, Elgin for watches, Rockford for furniture, Decatur for corn products, Peoria for distilleries, Kewanee for boilers, Moline, Springfield and Peoria for farm machinery.

After 1900, Illinois' manufacturing flourished, particularly in such fields as machinery, food, fabricated metals, printing and publishing, chemicals, transportation equipment, apparel, and products derived from stone, clay, glass, petroleum and coal. Illinois likewise is an important mining state, especially of coal, and its other chief mineral resources include clay, limestone, dolomite, lime, cement, sand, gravel, fluorspar, tripoli (dustlike silica), lead and zinc. Illinois farms are among the nation's leaders as producers of cereals and corn, and milk, eggs and livestock are also abundantly raised on the rolling prairies.

Any proud Illinoisan will tell you that, in addition to Lincoln and Grant, his state is noted as a producer of famous men and women and on his list of such personages would be newspaper publishers Victor Fremont Lawson and Robert R. McCormick, inventor John Deere, who perfected a steel plow for turning over the gummy soil of the prairies, poet Carl Sandburg and lawyer Clarence Darrow, historian Allan Nevins and mail-order merchandiser Montgomery Ward, social worker Jane Addams and master sleuth Allan Pinkerton, showman Florenz Ziegfeld and preacher Dwight L. Moody, among a great many others.

The Windy City

"Hog Butcher, Tool Maker, Stacker of Wheat, Player with Railroads and Freight Handler to the Nation" — thus a poet described Chicago. The origin of the name is uncertain, although, possibly, it is derived from the Ojibway word *she-kag-ong* meaning "wild onion place." Thirty-two trunk lines feed into its railroad terminals. Set upon the shores of Lake Michigan, it is a city of swiftly changing moods and within an hour, if the wind shifts over that sparkling body of blue water, the temperature can drop twenty degrees or more. Divided into a North Side, West Side and South Side by the branches of the Chicago River, the city is different in

character wherever one approaches it.

Chicago, in a real sense, is all things to all men, depending on whether one refers to German Chicago or Polish Chicago or those areas inhabited by Swedes, Italians, Yiddish-speaking Jews, Lithuanians, Czechs, Greeks, Negroes or Chinese. It is a city where slums rub elbows with the "gold coast," where honky-tonks screech loud music and fine museums house many treasures. It is a city of business streets jammed with traffic and quiet parks and university campuses, of noisy orators in "Bug House Square" and bums sleeping off a bad night along Skid Row. It is a city of mixed memories — of the crime and lawlessness when the mob of "Scarface" Al Capone was in its heyday, of the 27,539,521 visitors admitted in 1892 to the World's Columbian Exposition celebrating the four hundredth anniversary of the discovery of America, and of 22,320,456 in 1933 and the 16,314,480 in 1934 who saw "A Century of Progress," celebrating the city's incorporation as a municipality.

Visitors come to Chicago for many reasons. They find a city laid out, prairie-style, in a rigid gridiron pattern. Business, pleasure or politics may bring them — politics more than many suspect until they realize that from nominating conventions here Lincoln, Grant, Garfield, Cleveland (twice), Harrison, Theodore Roosevelt, Taft, Harding, Franklin D. Roosevelt (twice) and Eisenhower went on to become President of the United States. So to Chicago's distinction as Hog Butcher, Stacker of Wheat, perhaps we should add President Maker.

Land of Lincoln

Mark Twain

MISSOURI

"The Show Me State"

"S-T-E-A-M-BOAT a-comin'!"

How well Sam Clemens remembered what happened when that cry rang through the town of his boyhood — Hannibal, Missouri:

"The town drunkard stirs, the clerks wake up, a furious clatter of drays follows, every house and store pours out a human contribution, and all in a twinkling the dead town is alive and moving. Drays, carts, men, boys, all go hurrying from many quarters to a common center, the wharf. Assembled there, the people fasten their eyes upon the coming boat as upon a wonder they are seeing for the first time."

What a picture Sam recalled — the boat with her two tall, "fancy-topped" smokestacks, pilothouse, paddle-boxes, white railings, flag flapping on the jack-staff — and:

"The upper decks are black with passengers; the captain stands by the big bell, calm, imposing, the envy of all; great volumes of the blackest smoke are rolling and tumbling out of the chimneys . . . the crew are grouped on the forecastle; the broad stage is run far out over the port bow, and an envied deck-hand stands picturesquely on the end of it with a coil of rope in his hand; the pent steam is screaming through the gauge-cocks; the captain lifts his hand, a bell rings, the wheels stop; then they turn back, churning the water to foam, and the steamer is at rest."

When Sam Clemens wrote this description of how backwoods Missouri reached out to clasp the hand of the world, Sam had gained his own world-wide fame under the pseudonym of Mark Twain, author and wit.

The
Show Me
State

Under Three Flags

Missouri's story began when in 1673 Louis Joliet and Father Marquette, journeying down the Mississippi, discovered the mouth of the Missouri River, and their hope that here was the Northwest Passage to the Orient was strengthened by the stories Indians told La Salle when he explored the region in 1682. La Salle paddled on to the mouth of the Mississippi, claiming the entire valley of that great river for France. Fur traders and missionaries came into the region, seeking profits and converts, and in 1700-03 the mission of St. Francis Xavier was founded within the limits of the present city of St. Louis. Another half century passed before a group of Creole families — from Kaskaskia, in Illinois country — gave Missouri permanent settlement on the west bank of the Mississippi at Ste. Geneviève.

By secret treaty in 1762, France ceded the territory to Spain and two years later a French trader, Pierre Laclède Ligueste, and his fourteen-year-old stepson, René Auguste Chouteau, founded St. Louis. Although Spanish was now the official language, even Spaniards coming to take over the offices of government did not change the French habits and customs of the people. Meanwhile, with the end of the French and Indian Wars, the land east of the Mississippi was transferred to Britain and British settlers rushed into the territory secretly ceded to Spain. Spanish stockades and forts sprang up none too soon, for a combined British and Indian attack was launched on St. Louis in 1780. That affair fizzled out, however, and Missouri was part of the region Spain ceded back to France in 1800. Then came the biggest surprise of all — the Louisiana Purchase of 1803 — and the following year Missouri came under its third flag. Eight years later the Territory of Missouri was organized.

The Missouri Compromise

In 1812 the population of the territory was about 20,000 and by 1820 it had grown to 66,586. What had caused the boom? The answer in no small degree belonged to the arrival of the first steamboat at St. Louis, the territorial capital, in 1816. Missouri farmers had many products to ship down the river — wheat, corn, tobacco, meat products and, far from least, Missouri mules. The entire fur trade on the upper Mississippi soon was centered in St. Louis, and by 1818 the territorial legislature petitioned for statehood.

But stormy days were ahead. With the admission of Alabama as a slave state, the division of slave and free states in the Union was exactly even. Missouri, a slave state, was balanced off against Maine, a free state, setting the stage for the Missouri Compromise of 1820 whereby the southern boundary of Missouri — 36°30′ north latitude — was made the line between slavery and freedom in all territory acquired through the Louisiana Purchase. Deeply offended, Missourians wrote into their constitution a provision that no free Negro could enter the state and no slave ever could be freed without the consent of his master. A second Missouri Compromise, worked out by

Pony Express

the astute Henry Clay, finally forced upon Missouri an agreement that it could never deny to Negro citizens of the United States their constitutional rights.

Good Times and Bad

Slavery as an institution was never of very great moment in the history of Missouri, but the two compromises were of vast significance in emphasizing the deep conflict developing within the nation between states' rights and Federal rights. Yet *that* trouble belonged to the future. With statehood, the influx of settlers from Kentucky and Tennessee and from the back country of Pennsylvania, Virginia and the Carolinas continued at a quickening

pace. In 1836 the purchase from the Indians of the region known as the Platte Country added six northwestern counties.

Quickly Missouri assumed national significance as a gateway to the Rocky Mountains and California. The city of Independence, Missouri, became the starting point for three overland trails and St. Joseph was selected for the eastern terminus of the Pony Express. By 1860 St. Louis had grown to a city of 160,000 as steamboats gathered along its docks. Flour mills, tobacco factories, foundries, and cotton and woolen industries, among others, gave promise of making "St. Looy" the principal city of mid-America. About 30,000 Germans, exiles of revolution, had made St. Louis their new home by 1850, and even that highly critical visitor, finicky Charles Dickens, had to admit that the Planter's Hotel was "an excellent house" where "the proprietors have most bountiful notions of providing the creature comforts."

The Civil War divided Missouri, as it did the nation, into two hostile camps and even into two hostile state governments. Missourians who fought for the Union numbered 109,111 and as many as 50,000 may have shouldered arms for the Confederacy. The first land battle of the war was fought on Missouri soil at Booneville in June, 1861 and was followed by a fierce engagement at Wilson's Creek. Roving bands of guerrilla raiders harassed Missouri throughout the bitter years of conflict, and among the most notorious were the bushwackers under the bandit chief, Billy Quantrill. From this band in later

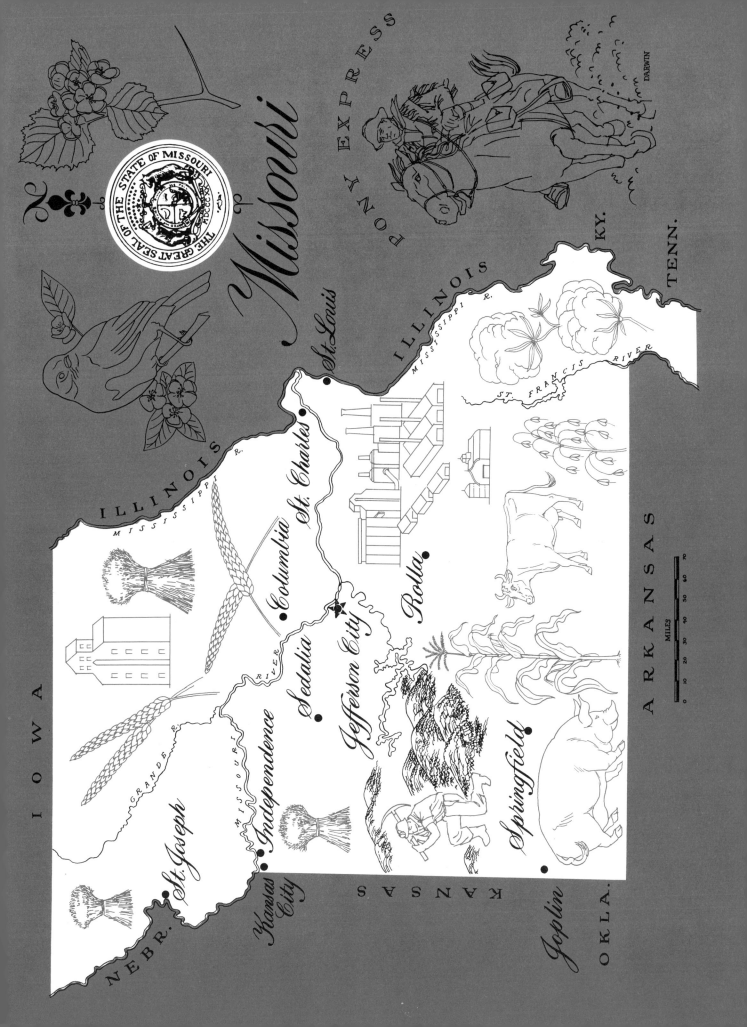

Missouri

PONY EXPRESS

DARWIN

THE GREAT SEAL OF THE STATE OF MISSOURI

MDCCC

UNITED WE STAND DIVIDED WE FALL

ILLINOIS

KY.

TENN.

St. Louis

ILLINOIS

MISSISSIPPI R.

ST. FRANCIS RIVER

ST. CHARLES

St. Charles

Columbia

Rolla

MISSISSIPPI R.

IOWA

ILLINOIS

MISSISSIPPI R.

MISSOURI RIVER

GRANDE R.

Sedalia

Jefferson City

ARKANSAS

MILES
0 10 20 30 40 50 60 70

St. Joseph

Independence

Springfield

NEBR.

Kansas City

KANSAS

Joplin

OKLA.

ARKANSAS

years came such legendary outlaws as Frank and Jesse James.

Modern Missouri

In 1865 a new constitution abolished slavery, and with the development of railroads both St. Louis and Kansas City became important centers of transportation. The mining of lead and zinc also gave great stimulus to the growth of the state, especially in the "Joplin district" of southwestern Missouri.

Today lead and zinc remain two of Missouri's principal mineral resources, along with cement, bituminous coal, stone, lime, sand, gravel and clay. With the exception of California, Missouri is the leader of states west of the Mississippi in manufactures and mechanical pursuits, and its chief industries are food products (including malt liquors and meat packing), transportation equipment, clothing, chemicals, leather and leather products, printing and publishing, fabricated metals and all types of machinery.

As an agricultural state, Missouri shows a proud record of production of corn, hay, soybeans, cotton, winter wheat and oats. It is a large producer of chicken and turkeys, eggs, cattle, hogs and pigs, sheep and lambs, horses and colts — and mules.

A State of Many Moods

To the Missourian, his state has many moods and he loves them all — the wild crabapple blooming in May, the tasseled corn that means July, the pumpkins that go with Indian summer. Missouri is river smells and mountain scents — the lakes of the Ozarks, the land of Mark Twain along the "wide Missouri," the scenic beauty of the Big Springs country, the rivers and caves of Meramec Valley, the Daniel Boone country where the great frontiersman spent the last twenty years of his life (his original grave is near Marthasville), the green hills of North Missouri with large farms dotting the rich prairies and, spreading fanlike from the confluence of the Ohio and Mississippi, the Delta of southeastern Missouri famous for its cotton, melons, sweet potatoes and peaches.

The "Show Me State" probably takes its nickname from the Missouri congressman who told a Philadelphia convention in 1899: "I come from a country that raises corn, cotton, cockleburrs, and Democrats. I'm from Missouri, and you've got to show me." Meanwhile Missouri, through its native sons and daughters, has shown the rest of the world what its best qualities can produce — in Harry S. Truman, thirty-third President of the United States; in George Washington Carver, renowned Negro scientist; in John J. Pershing, commander of the American Expeditionary Forces in World War I; and in operatic stars Gladys Swarthout and Helen Traubel.

Missouri — a native pronounces the word "Mi-zur-a" — has for its proud motto the Latin words *Salus Populi Suprema Lex Esto,* meaning "The welfare of the people shall be the supreme law." Missouri's most articulate son, Mark Twain, was thinking in this very vein when he advised: "Let us endeavor so to live that when we come to die even the undertaker will be sorry."

IOWA

"The Hawkeye State"

HUNDREDS OF thousands of years ago a great glacier covered Iowa. Three more glaciers pressed down upon the land, accounting for the soils, sands, gravels, silts and clay that give Iowa its splendid rich, rolling prairies for which many a proud native raises his right arm as he sings:

We're from Ioway, Ioway,
That's where the tall corn grows.

Early French explorers, pronouncing the name of the Sioux Indians living here, sometimes said "Ay-u-vois" (I-u-wa) and sometimes "Ay-u-ou-ez" (I-u-oo-ay), so that it always has been touch-and-go whether to call the region Iowa or Ioway. The state's official translation from the Sioux dialect of its name is "beautiful land," but other possible interpretations are "dusty-faces," or "dust-in-the-faces," or "drowsy ones," or "here is the place."

The state's nickname honors Black Hawk, famous chief of the Sauk Indians.

An Incident on Catfish Creek

One hundred eighty-one years after Columbus stumbled upon America — on June 17, 1673, to be precise — those indefatigable French explorers, Louis Joliet and Father Marquette, entered the Iowa country, and seven years later that equally determined French priest, Father Hennepin, traveled along the eastern border. For the next century, except for a few fur traders and missionaries, the Iowa country remained an undisturbed wilderness, even after France ceded this region as part of its holdings west of the Mississippi to Spain in 1762.

Iowa's history really begins in 1788 when a French-Canadian who would give his name to a city paddled down Catfish Creek to the bluffs near an In-

Black Hawk

dian village. Julien Dubuque asked permission to mine the lead ore here, and the Fox Indians, who called Dubuque "Little Night," took a real shine to him.

Yet the Indians had their streak of obstinacy, and legend insists that they once refused Dubuque a request even after he threatened to burn the entire Mississippi if he didn't get his way. Secretly, Dubuque emptied a barrel of oil into Catfish Creek, then, calling the Indians, seized a brand from the fire and threw it upon the oil-smooth surface of the water. A sheet of flame shot into the air. Terrified, the Indians gave in to Dubuque's demands. Seemingly at his wish, the fire went out. When this first white settler died in 1810, the Indians buried him with honors befitting a chief.

By then, of course, Iowa had been acquired by the United States as part of the Louisiana Purchase. The American Fur Company at St. Louis began

stringing its posts through the country — at Council Bluffs, Sioux City, Eddyville, Muscatine and Keokuk — and on November 22, 1829 the first white child, a girl, was born in Iowa. The following October, in a crude log structure, Isaac Galland opened Iowa's first school.

Toward Statehood

In the years from Julien Dubuque's "fire water" on Catfish Creek to the establishment of Isaac Galland's school, Iowa's territorial status made a muddled story. First included in Indiana Territory (1804) and then Louisiana Territory (1805), when Louisiana was made a state in 1812, Iowa became part of Missouri Territory. In 1821 Missouri became a state and for the next thirteen years Iowa existed as an unorganized territory of the United States. From 1834 to 1836, Michigan Territory claimed it and from 1836 to 1838 Iowa belonged to Wisconsin Territory.

In 1832 not more than fifty persons lived in Iowa country, but during the next eight years, from south and east, the settlers seemed to come as though human flood gates had been opened. The population passed 43,000. Farmers, millers and millwrights, driving their wagons over the old Indian trails to Captain Ben Clark's ferry across the Mississippi at Buffalo, made up the bulk of this horde. Linking six or seven yoke of oxen, they broke the tough prairie sod. On July 4, 1838 Iowa became a territory in its own right, and the following year became embroiled in a quarrel with Missouri that was given the name of the Honey War.

WISCONSIN

MINNESOTA

S. DAKOTA

ILLINOIS

MISSOURI

NEBRASKA

Dubuque

Cedar Rapids

Davenport

Des Moines

Sioux City

MISSISSIPPI RIVER

DES MOINES R.

MISSOURI RIVER

BIG SIOUX R.

Iowa

BUFFALO HUNT

THE GREAT SEAL OF THE STATE OF IOWA

MILES
0 10 20 30 40 50

DARWIN

The
Hawkeye
State

An early government survey, fixing the northern boundary of Missouri at "the rapids of the River Des Moines," led Iowans to claim that the reference was to rapids by that name in the Mississippi River and not, as Missourians contended, to rapids in the Des Moines River above the present site of Keosauqua. Some two thousand square miles of land were involved, but it was the destruction of bee trees in the disputed areas that found tempers exploding into calls for volunteer militia in both states. Luckily saner counsel prevailed, and it was decided to permit the United States Government to decide the argument. In 1851 the Supreme Court sustained Iowa's case.

Skunk River War

Cash was never plentiful among pioneer farmers, and the increased taxation that would come with statehood found voters delaying the admission of Iowa to the Union until 1846 (Florida, a slave state, was paired with Iowa to keep the national balance intact). The wave of settlers into the new state swelled steadily and by 1850 the population showed a four-year increase of 90,000. Life in Iowa followed a pleasant, self-sufficient pattern. Towns like Fort Madison, Burlington and Dubuque began to thrive and wherever farms dotted the countryside, schools and churches appeared. Pioneering, though hard work, also supplied many good times — annual fairs, hunting parties, sleigh rides and quilting and husking bees.

In 1854 Iowa's first locomotive was ferried across the Mississippi to Davenport, and by 1856 the Mississippi and Missouri Railroad (today the Chicago, Rock Island and Pacific) completed laying its tracks to Iowa City. Towns followed the railroads. Long before the Civil War no one could question where Iowa stood on the slavery question, for the Quakers in the state were busy transporting runaway slaves over its Underground Railroad and the abolitionist, John Brown, for three years made Iowa one of the mustering points for his supporters.

During the years of conflict, Iowa sent 72,242 soldiers into the Union army, yet in Keokuk County the issue wasn't all one-sided, for here a faction under Cyphert Tally, a young Baptist preacher who had come from Tennessee, vigorously opposed the war against "states' rights." When Tally was shot in the head during a political rally, 2,000 sympathizers from Wapello, Mahaska and Poweshiek counties organized the "Skunk River Army." Governor Samuel Kirkwood ordered eleven companies of militia to Keokuk County, but happily future hostilities were confined to a series of arguments.

Modern Iowa

Inflated prices, panic and unemployment following the Civil War stimulated the growth of the Grange movement, which forced sensible regulations upon the high-handed practices of the railroads. Then in the 1880's Iowa farmers found a better income producer than wheat — hogs fattened on home-grown corn. Today Iowa ranks first among the states in growing corn, oats, popcorn and timothy grass, and in the number of hogs, horses, chickens and eggs.

Yet Iowa's industrial development also has been tremendous. At Muscatine, the "Button City," clam shells from the Mississippi have built a prosperous business. An enormous breakfast food mill at Cedar Rapids, meat packing plants at Sioux City and Ottumwa, washing machine factories at Newton, printing presses at Des Moines are other examples of Iowa's industries. Coal, limestone, clay, gypsum, sand and gravel are its chief mineral resources. It has port cities on two great rivers — Dubuque, Clinton, Davenport and Burlington on the Mississippi, and Sioux City, Council Bluffs, Muscatine, Keokuk and Fort Madison on the Missouri.

Number one among Iowa's famous sons and daughters is Herbert Clark Hoover, thirty-first President of the United States, and some of its other "immortals" include Carrie Chapman Catt, a leader in gaining the right to vote for women; William Frederick Cody, who became the famed "Buffalo Bill"; Lee De Forest, whose inventions greatly advanced the development of wireless telegraphy, sound pictures and television; William Daniel Leahy, one of America's distinguished admirals during World War II; John L. Lewis, labor leader; those renowned builders of shows under the big top, the Ringling brothers; evangelist Billy Sunday, who, as a professional baseball player, set a record by circling the bases in fourteen seconds and who claimed credit for inventing the bunt; and Grant Wood, one of America's foremost artists.

Strictly Iowan

The real spirit of Iowa is in its state motto: "Our liberties we prize and our rights we will maintain." A verse of the state song — sung to the tune of *O, Tannenbaum* or *My Maryland* — fills many hearts with pride:

The Hawkeye State

See yonder fields of tasseled corn,
  Iowa, in Iowa,
Plenty fills her gold horn,
  Iowa, in Iowa,
See how her wondrous prairies shine,
To yonder sunset's purple line,
O! happy land, O! land of mine,
  Iowa, O! Iowa.

Tulip time in Pella, the Little Brown Church at Nashua that became immortalized in the hymn, *The Little Brown Church in the Vale,* the famous band of "Scottish Highlanders" parading at a University of Iowa football game, the gold dome of the State Capitol at Des Moines, the old Block House in Fort Defiance State Park, the Woolen Mill at Middle Amana — Iowa is many pictures of the heart and mind. Open corn cribs. Threshing time. A cooperative grain elevator. Corn-husking contests with the ears slamming up against the "bang-boards" of the wagons. Hog calling. Sauerkraut Day in Ackley. These pictures, too, flash before the Iowan, singing:

You ask what land I love the best,
  Iowa, 'tis Iowa,
The fairest State of all the west,
  Iowa, O! Iowa.
From yonder Mississippi's stream,
To where Missouri's waters gleam,
O! fair it is as poet's dream,
  Iowa, in Iowa.

MICHIGAN

"The Wolverine State"

FOUR OF THE five Great Lakes — the exception is Lake Ontario — touch the shores of Michigan, and the state takes its name from an Ojibway word meaning "big water." The fact that mid-America contains a state with twenty-four hundred miles of shore line surprises most nonresidents of Michigan. The Marylander with his Chesapeake Bay or the Down Easter of Maine, with a tradition of the sea going back to the days of the whaling fleets, hardly expects to encounter between the Alleghenies and the Rockies a hardy breed of sailor who splashes himself awake humming:

Rain before wind, take your topsails in,
Wind before rain, hoist 'em up again.
Or:
When the clouds appear like rocks and
  towers,
You may expect light wind and showers.

No state in the Union, east or west, outmatches Michigan for its lore of life upon the waves. Schoonermen from the age of the fore-'n'-afters, the steamboatmen who came later, the modern navigators of bulk-carrying freighters on the Great Lakes — each has left tales of adventures on storm-ridden waters and of ships that sailed away and vanished, crew and cargo. Old superstitions that seemingly should belong alone to our ocean-bound states are deeply woven into Michigan's folk history. Never start a voyage on Friday — it will bring bad luck. Rats leaving a ship foretell disaster. Only a fool sails on a vessel with a woman cook or a cross-eyed sailor.

Whence came the Great Lakes in the first place? Any well-informed Michigander can supply that answer. Paul Bunyan dug 'em, throwing the dirt over his shoulder. Where did the dirt land? Why, in the Dakotas, for how else can you account for the Black Hills?

Cadillac Founds Detroit

The first white men to reach Michigan were Frenchmen from Quebec, who came looking for the Northwest Passage to the Orient. Etienne Brulé probably visited Michigan as early as 1618, discovering the falls of St. Mary's River. Returning three years later, Brulé found Hurons mining copper along the shore of Lake Superior. In 1634 another Frenchman, Jean Nicolet, also seeking a passage to the Orient, passed through the Straits of Mackinac and sailed along the northern shore of Lake Michigan. Next came Frenchmen of quite different stripes — the licensed traders known as *voyageurs* and the unlicensed seekers after fortune called *coureurs de bois,* who came to set up their fur trade with the Indians, and devoted missionaries like Fathers Marquette, Hennepin, Claude Allouez and René Mesnard, who sought to bring the blessings of Christianity to the 15,000 Indians then inhabiting Michigan.

France's failure as a successful colonizer in Michigan followed the old pattern. Neither missionaries nor *voyageurs* brought farming or permanent homes into the wilderness. Meanwhile British frontiersmen began worming their way into the territory, striking what bargains they could with Indians or unscrupulous *coureurs de bois.*

To offset this English intrusion, Antoine de la Mothe Cadillac, the French commandant, established in July, 1701 a fortified settlement at the "place du détroit" — the place of the strait — and many look upon this event as beginning the white man's effective history in Michigan. The result for France, however, ended no more happily in Michigan than elsewhere in the old Northwest Territory. Wars with Britain, in America and Europe, culminated in the loss of the land by France under the Treaty of 1763.

Indians, Rum and Statehood

British high-handedness in managing the territory won few friends among the Indians — most of all, after a decree prohibited the sale of liquor to the tribesmen. Pontiac, chief of the Ottawa Confederacy, sensed the ripeness of the moment for a conspiracy to overthrow the British interlopers. Pontiac's supporters appeared in the fort at Detroit on May 7, 1763. Beneath their blankets they carried sawed-off muskets. Warned at the last moment, the British thwarted this surprise, but they were not so lucky elsewhere. Between the Straits of Mackinac and western New York every post fell to Pontiac's raiders. Detroit held out through five bitter months of siege, finally forcing Pontiac to fail through the loss of patience of his followers.

The Treaty of 1763, ending French domination, had made Michigan part of Quebec Territory, and not until the Treaty of Paris at the close of the Revolutionary War, twenty years later, did the region come under American control. Even then, Detroit remained under British administration for another thirteen years before General "Mad Anthony" Wayne, the hero of Fallen

The Wolverine State

Pontiac

Timbers, raised the Stars and Stripes above the fort on July 11, 1796. Along with Ohio, Indiana, Illinois and Wisconsin, Michigan ultimately would be one of the states carved out of the Northwest Territory, although from 1800 to 1805 Michigan was split — with part belonging to Indiana Territory and part to Ohio Territory.

Organized as a separate territory, with Detroit as capital and General William Hull of Massachusetts as governor, Michigan began its independent existence in 1805. Michigan's real growth began with the governorship of General Lewis Cass, who brought vision and intelligence to administering the territory. In his dealings with the Indians, he also brought all the rum they could drink, increasing his effectiveness in persuading them to migrate peacefully into the western lands.

A belligerent boundary dispute known as the Toledo War [see Ohio, pp. 134-138] delayed Michigan's statehood for some months. Ultimately, by agreeing to surrender some 470 square miles around Toledo to Ohio in return for the Upper Peninsula, Michigan was admitted to the Union in 1837 as our twenty-sixth state.

Doorway to the World

A year earlier the approximately thirty-five miles of the Erie and Kalamazoo Railroad, running from Toledo to Adrian, became the first railroad west of the Alleghenies. So was forged the link — sailing vessels on lakes and rivers, railroads running inland — whence would come the great strength of mid-America. Thus the wilderness gained its doorway to the world — for the work it performed, for the thoughts it pondered. Detroit became the busy terminus for one of the chief routes on the Underground Railroad. And at Jackson, Michigan, in 1854 the name Republican was given to the new political party that only six years later elected Abraham Lincoln sixteenth President of the United States.

"The higher the clouds, the fairer the weather," sang sailors on the Great Lakes, and in the years following the Civil War the economic clouds began to climb higher and higher over Michigan. For twenty years, beginning in 1870, each spring found men who belonged in the legends of Paul Bunyan untangling the log jams along the Muskegon and Saginaw rivers that made Michigan the nation's leading producer of lumber. Then in 1893 Henry Ford appeared on the streets of Detroit in America's first practical motorcar. This two-cylinder vehicle, mounted on twenty-eight-inch bicycle wheels, looked like a buggy that had lost its horse. People gaped — laughed — and soon wanted one just like it.

*The
Wolverine
State*

America on Wheels

The future history of Michigan — and of America — was being shaped by the spurts and sputters of that motorcar bouncing over the dusty thoroughfares of Detroit. On June 12, 1903 the Ford Motor Company was organized. Ford, then forty years of age, served as vice president, designer, master mechanic and general manager. There were thirteen shareholders. "A silly fad," skeptics sneered, but in the first three years the company produced 5,002 vehicles. The following year 14,887 cars were manufactured and by 1908 stockholders were receiving profits of 10,000 per cent on their investments.

How well America liked the horseless buggy — and the practical, inexpensive model that Ford continued to make — would be demonstrated by the fact that one day investors in the Ford Motor Company would receive profits of 300,000 per cent! Ford was not the first American to build a carriage driven by a gasoline engine, but he was the first to manufacture automobiles on a mass production basis. More so than any other one man, Henry Ford put America on wheels.

"Look About You . . ."

Automobiles, and later airplanes, provided a solid basis for Michigan's fame today as an industrial leader. Yet the state is almost equally renowned as a manufacturer of furniture (Grand Rapids is called the "Furniture City of America") and of food products (Battle Creek, the "health city," is known around the world for its break-

fast cereals). Other Michigan products that are widely used include iron and steel, tools, paper and pulp, chemicals, drugs and medicines, and refrigerators.

From the Upper Peninsula, once despised as a poor bargain for the land the territory was forced to cede to Ohio, has come the ore that has made Michigan one of the nation's principal producers of iron, and other profitable mineral resources include petroleum, copper, cement, salt, gypsum, clay and building stone. Dairy products and grains for breakfast cereals give Michigan a prosperous agriculture, and the state also is known for such fruits as apples, peaches, grapes, cherries and berries. Its chief ports on the Upper Peninsula are Houghton, Marquette, Escanaba and Sault Sainte Marie, and on the Lower Peninsula the port cities are Detroit, Muskegon, Bay City, Port Huron and River Rouge.

Si quaeris peninsulam amoenam, circumspice reads the motto of Michigan, meaning "If you seek a pleasant peninsula, look about you." From the wolverine, an animal that helped lure the first fur trappers into the territory, the state takes its nickname. Since those days Michigan has come a long way, and at times you may well hear ghostly voices singing in the wind:

*Up the river on a towline,
Passed the city of Detrite,
The cinders fall upon the deck
All day and half the night.*

*When up the length of old St. Clair,
And at Port Huron we let go;
We'll hoist the canvas on the forestick,
On the main and mizzen too.*

WISCONSIN
"The Badger State"

WHEN IN 1634 the French explorer, Jean Nicolet, sighted the shores of present-day Green Bay, Wisconsin, he was so confident he had found the Northwest Passage to the Orient that he donned a beautifully embroidered mandarin robe. Friendly Winnebago Indians greeted him with appropriate ceremony, preparing a feast with a main course of 120 beavers. The very name that the Indians had given to this region, *Wishkonsing,* probably meaning "hole of the muskrat" (or "beaver"), spoke of the abundance of this fur-bearing animal for which there was so great demand.

Other Frenchmen — explorers, trappers, missionaries — following Nicolet into Wisconsin would reveal their influence in the history of the state by the names they gave to many communities. Prairie du Chien, Eau Claire, St. Croix, Lac Vieux Desert — behind these names, and others like them, stand the images of those soldiers of New France who sought fortunes from furs in the wilderness across Lake Superior and Lake Michigan. Conversion to Christianity was one gift they offered in return. As for material goods to pay for the furs they took, the French policy was to get off as cheaply as possible. In theory, this policy may have seemed sound. In practice, it led to their undoing.

*The
Badger
State*

The Foxy Fox Strikes Back

Scarcely a mile of portage separated the Fox River and the Wisconsin River, and the French did not wish to lose control over this waterway that, joining Lake Michigan and the Mississippi, linked all the great centers of New France — Quebec and Montreal to the north, New Orleans to the south. But the waterway was part of the domain claimed by the Fox Indians who held two grudges against the French. British traders, pushing into the territory, offered far better prices for furs than the French. Again, the men from Quebec had neither taste nor sense, but traded with and supplied arms to the Sioux, mortal enemies of the Fox. Almost a half century of conflict resulted, including high toll charges for the use of the waterway, closing the waterway, massacre, alliances with other tribes against the French, open warfare — and if finally the soldiers of New France subdued the Fox Indians, the cost of the victory was loss of face, broken defense lines, and a steady improvement of the British position.

France's downfall in Ohio and Indiana, Illinois and Michigan, followed a similar course in Wisconsin. By 1763, with defeat in the French and Indian War, the end had been reached. England consolidated her fur trade under the Northwest Fur Company, and even though the territory nominally came under American control with the close of the Revolutionary War, British traders managed to run this business almost as they pleased until 1816. Then, the War of 1812 over, Americans be-gan occupying the Northwest and built Fort Crawford at Prairie du Chien and Fort Howard at Green Bay.

Toward Statehood

From these two forts the military governed Wisconsin for the next two years. Then, as Brown and Crawford counties, Wisconsin was incorporated into Michigan Territory. Fur trading, the bulwark of Wisconsin's economy from the days of the first white man, began gradually to give way to lead mining. But new Indian troubles were brewing, and not until the Black Hawk War was settled [see Illinois, pp. 144-149] did Wisconsin begin to grow.

The call of cheap, fertile land reached to New England and Pennsylvania and New York, for easy water transportation now existed along the Erie Canal (completed in 1825), across the Great Lakes, into Green Bay and up the Fox-Wisconsin Waterway. In December, 1833, the appearance of the Green Bay *Intelligencer,* Wisconsin's first newspaper, spoke of the change that had come. And still the settlers arrived — from Canada, from Ohio — lead miners and land speculators, putting up a cry for a separate government and winning their point with the organization in April, 1836 of the "Territory of Wiskonsan" — an empire that included present day Wisconsin, Iowa, Minnesota and part of the Dakotas. That year banks were established at Dubuque, Mineral Point and Milwaukee, but the government land offices, doing a boom business, were shot through with fraud. The bust came in 1837 — banks failing, debts unpaid.

Wisconsin

GREAT SEAL OF THE STATE OF WISCONSIN

MICHIGAN

MINNESOTA

ILLINOIS

IOWA

Superior

Eau Claire

Wausau

La Crosse

Green Bay

Appleton

Oshkosh

Madison

Milwaukee

Racine

Kenosha

MENOMINEE R.

ST. CROIX R.

WISCONSIN RIVER

FOX R.

MISSISSIPPI RIVER

MILES
0 10 20 30 40 50

Wisconsin Goes Ahead

Illinois, wanting a port on the Great Lakes, nibbled at the boundary of Wisconsin and gained a strip of lake front, including Chicago. Michigan, quarreling with Ohio over boundaries, had to be mollified, so Congress generously offered it Wisconsin's copper- and iron-rich northern peninsula. Trimmed thus to present size, Wisconsin was admitted to the Union on May 29, 1848 as our thirtieth state.

German and Scandinavian immigrants pouring into the state increased its population tenfold during the 1840's. A sign on the tavern at Janesville gave a picture of the life of the steamboat and stagecoach traveler in Wisconsin at this time:

Four pence a night for a bed,
Six pence with supper,
No more than five to sleep in one bed,
Organ grinders to sleep in Wash House,
No dogs allowed upstairs,
No beer allowed in the kitchen,
No Razor Grinders or Tinkers taken in.

Railroads began to open the interior of Wisconsin at about the time lead mining was weakening as the prop under the state's economy, but now the wheat growers emerged to save the situation. In the Fox River Valley flour mills soon dotted the countryside and wheat shipments built Milwaukee into an important port. Elsewhere shadows of the future were being cast — in a decision of the State Supreme Court in 1854 that declared the Fugitive Slave

Law unconstitutional, and in a meeting at Ripon that same year that led to the formation of the Republican Party. More than 91,000 men from Wisconsin fought for the Union during the Civil War.

Meanwhile the mileage of railroads in Wisconsin continued to grow, and by 1880 there were 2,960 miles of track in the state. A combination of factors — worn-out soil, the chinch bug, competition from Minnesota and the Dakotas — was forcing wheat growing into a serious decline. At this critical moment William Dempster Hoard stepped forward, determined to give Wisconsin's wheat growers an entirely new source of agricultural strength. He founded the Wisconsin Dairymen's Association. And, as so often happens, one good idea produced others — in 1882 William Horlick invented malted milk, in 1890 a butterfat tester was invented at the University of Wisconsin.

"Dairyland of the Nation"

Today, practically any town or city in Wisconsin — indeed, almost any crossroads — contains at least one of the small cheese factories that have made famous this "Dairyland of the Nation." But quite apart from producing more than half of all the cheese made in America, Wisconsin has other claims to national leadership. Here started the American farmers' cooperative movement. Here under the leadership of liberal statesmen like Robert M. La Follette, Sr. many acts of progressive legislation were passed at early dates — workmen's compensation and teachers' pensions in 1911, minimum

wage laws in 1912, old-age pensions in 1931, unemployment compensation in 1932. At Appleton on the Fox River in 1882 was built the first plant in America using water power to generate electricity.

The Badger State

Bounded on the north by Lake Superior and on the east by Lake Michigan, Wisconsin's busy ports at Milwaukee, Manitowec, Superior, Ashland, Green Bay and La Crosse reflect the Badger State's modern industrial prominence in such branches of manufacturing as motor vehicles and parts, paper and pulp, furniture, malt liquors, tractors, footwear, internal combustion engines, construction machinery, electrical apparatus, beet sugar, stoves, leather and leather goods, polishes and waxes, ships and the various by-products of its agriculture — condensed and evaporated milk, cheese, butter and canned vegetables. In addition to dairying and livestock, hay and forage, Wisconsin farms are noted for their potato crop and canning peas, for apples and cherries (chiefly in Door County), for grain crops and for ginseng, a herb used in medicine. Mineral resources include stone, iron ore, clays, sand and gravel.

Each year Wisconsin gains in reputation as a vacation land, and no wonder — it has 10,000 miles of trout streams, thirty-one state parks, 8,500 lakes filled with sturgeon, muskellunge, pike, bass, perch and smelt, and seven state forests where hunters can find deer, bear, red fox, raccoon, partridge, geese and ducks.

"Forward!" urges the motto of Wisconsin. The spirit of the state is well expressed in that cry.

MINNESOTA
"The Gopher State"

NEAR KENSINGTON, southwest of Alexandria, Minnesota, a Swedish farmer named Olof Ohman dug a stone from beneath the roots of a poplar tree in 1898. There were inscriptions on the stone that Ohman could not read, but at least the stone served him as a prop to hold open the door of a shed. Later, experts in runic writing, puzzling out the inscriptions, deciphered the message on the stone:

"Eight Goths [Swedes] and 22 Norwegians upon a journey of discovery from Vinland westward. We had a camp by two skerries [islands] one day's journey north of this stone. We were out fishing one day. When we returned home we found ten men red with blood and dead. A V M [Ave Virgo Maria] save us from evil."

Along the edge of the stone was another inscription:

"[We] have ten men by the sea to look after our vessel fourteen days' journey from this island. Year 1362."

Is the stone fake or genuine? On this point authorities disagree. Yet if the stone is a hoax, then how long ago must that spoof have been planned for the roots of the old tree to grow around it? Anyhow, if you like mysteries, Minnesota offers this first-rate baffler!

Some Things We Do Know

Three centuries passed before there was a record of another white man in Minnesota. Then the French — trader and trapper, soldier and priest — came into the lands held by the Sioux and Chippewa. In 1680, ascending the upper Mississippi from the Illinois country, Father Louis Hennepin discovered and named the Falls of St. Anthony, and nine years later Nicholas Perrot claimed all the upper river for France.

Wars in Europe and North America between France and England in 1763 finally brought that part of Minnesota east of the Mississippi under British control, but this claim only lasted twenty years until, defeated in the Revolution, Britain surrendered the area to the United States.

Western Minnesota followed another pattern. France ceded it to Spain, which ceded it back to France, which sold it to the United States in 1803 as part of the Louisiana Purchase. President Jefferson, curious about what he had bought, sent Zebulon Montgomery Pike as leader of an expedition to explore the upper regions of the Mississippi. The resourceful Pike — among his many achievements, Pike's Peak would be named in his honor — set out from St. Louis in August of 1805. For sixty gallons of whiskey and baubles worth perhaps $200 he bought military sites at the mouths of the St. Croix and Minnesota rivers and his explorations carried him northward.

A busy fellow, Pike claimed a string of trading posts for the United States, but this accomplishment was rather an empty one, since without an established authority on the scene trappers and traders behaved as they pleased. A second defeat for the British in the War of 1812 strengthened America's hold on its wilderness empire, especially after 1816, when John Jacob Astor's American Fur Company, coming into Minnesota, was in no mood to countenance competitors.

The Gopher State

Shadows of the Future

Statehood was still forty years away for Minnesota. In 1819 Colonel Henry Leavenworth arrived with troops to police the borders, bringing permanent American authority into the region, and the following year Colonel Josiah Snelling supervised the building of Fort St. Anthony (afterward renamed Fort Snelling). A trickle of Swiss immigrants now came into Minnesota to establish its earliest farms, and a grist

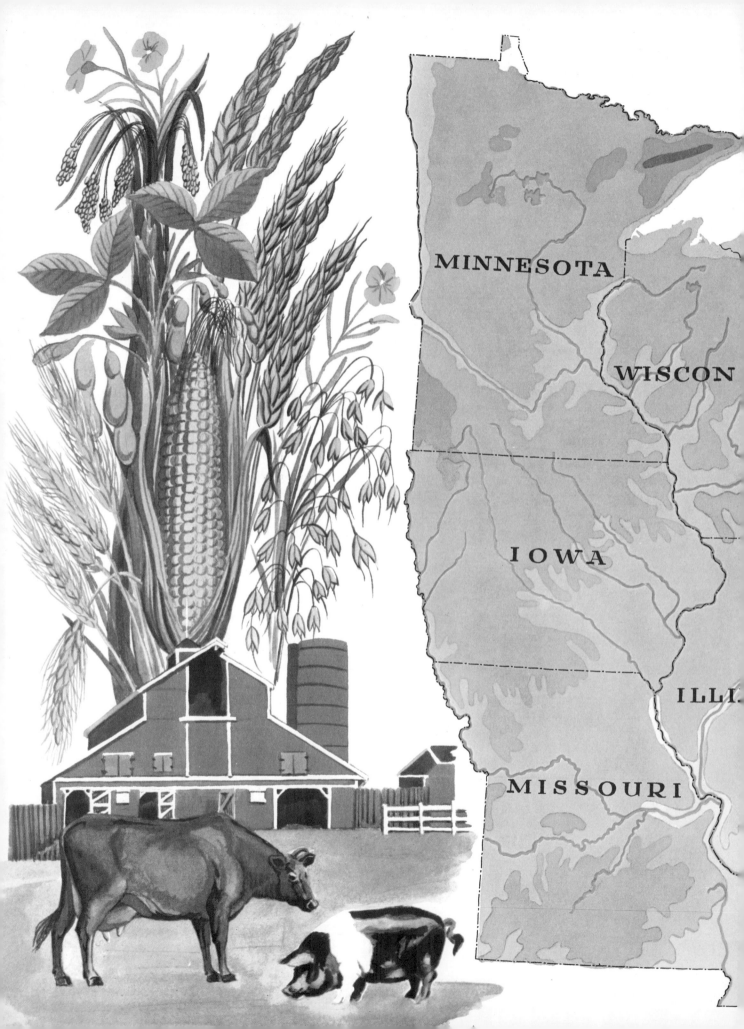

MINNESOTA

WISCON

IOWA

ILLI.

MISSOURI

MICHIGAN

IS INDIANA OHIO

DARWIN

Lakes and Prairies

The
Gopher
State

mill and sawmill built at Fort St. Anthony sometime after 1821 were the first shadows of the future city of Minneapolis. Henry Schoolcraft's explorations in 1832 to the headwaters of the Mississippi and Lake Itasca, which he named, greatly increased the white man's knowledge of the resources of the northwest country. At Mendota (then called St. Peter's) two years later, Henry H. Sibley took up residence as partner and manager of the American Fur Company, and his name dominated Minnesota's history over the next three decades.

Five hundred Red River oxcarts bumped in and out of Mendota, bringing furs to Sibley's company, but Minnesota's future also rested in other events — in the establishment of lumber towns along the St. Croix River, in the first public school that started in a St. Paul blacksmith shop in 1847. Up to now, parts of Minnesota had been sprinkled like salt from a shaker over the territories of Louisiana, Indiana, Michigan, Missouri, Iowa and Wisconsin, but in 1849 a separate Minnesota Territory was organized. That same year the *Minnesota Pioneer,* the territory's first newspaper, began publication at St. Paul.

In 1851 a treaty with the Sioux secured 28,000,000 acres of land west of the Mississippi. News of the deal with the Sioux spread on the wind. A stampede into the territory followed.

The Boom is On

By steamboat up the Mississippi, the Minnesota, the St. Croix, or overland in prairie schooners, hordes of settlers

came, eager to snatch up some of the finest farm land in the world at $1.25 an acre. Dust clouds rose from the herds of cattle they drove into the territory. Hammers and saws broke the wilderness silence as homes, grist mills, whole villages sprang up, sometimes overnight. Soon the steamboats that brought settlers hauled off wheat and flour. On May 11, 1858 Minnesota was admitted to the Union as our thirty-second state and the following year its population was estimated at 172,023.

The Sioux, however, sulked over the treaties they had made, not only believing that they had been deceived as to the white man's terms, but also that the traders were cheating them out of what little compensation they had obtained. With the outbreak of the Civil War, Minnesota stood stanchly by the Union, sending the first boatloads of the more than 22,000 men that she contributed to the Federal armies — even though it meant sending forces needed for defense against possible Indian uprisings. The Sioux found new fuel for their smoldering resentment when, during the summer of 1862, a delay occurred in paying the annuities due them.

That August four Indians killed three white men and two women. This completely unplanned act was like one stroke of summer lightning setting a forest ablaze. Within two weeks 1,500 braves were on the warpath in the Great Sioux Uprising. The Minnesota River ran red with the blood of more than 400 white men, women and children who were killed. Entire families were wiped out in a twinkling. Cold terror hung over Minnesota until,

MILES

0   20   40   60   80   100

CANADA

RAINY R.

International Falls

Bemidji

Hibbing

Moorhead

Duluth

Brainerd

Little Falls

Sauk Centre

St. Cloud

St. Paul

Minneapolis

Red Wing

Winona

Rochester

Austin

NORTH DAKOTA

S. DAKOTA

RED RIVER

MINNESOTA RIVER

MISSISSIPPI R.

ST. CROIX R.

MISSISSIPPI R.

WISCONSIN

IOWA

PAUL BUNYAN

N

DARWIN

THE GREAT SEAL OF THE STATE OF MINNESOTA
L'ÉTOILE DU NORD
1858

Minnesota

*The
Gopher
State*

finally, forces under Sibley defeated Little Crow's warriors at Wood Lake. Sioux braves who escaped into the Dakotas and Missouri were pursued through 1863 and 1864.

The Bread and Butter State

Though the bloody Sioux uprising haunted dreams for a generation, the future was now secure. Old Sioux hunting grounds ripened into wheat fields waiting for the harvest. Railroad construction, beginning with a line between St. Paul and St. Anthony in 1862, went steadily forward so that by 1870 almost one thousand miles of track had been laid. In 1884 the mining of iron ore in the Vermilion range — and the discovery in 1890-91 of larger deposits in the Mesabi range — gave new force to Minnesota's economic growth.

Sometimes called "the bread and butter state," Minnesota today is, first of all, an agricultural state that derives its principal farm income from livestock, milk, butter and such crops as flaxseed, oats, rye, corn, barley, spring wheat, hay and soybeans. The open-pit iron mine near Hibbing is the world's largest — two and one-half miles long, three-quarters of a mile wide, four hundred feet deep. Sight should not be lost of Minnesota's other mineral resources, including granite, marble, limestone, jasper, sandstone, mica, feldspar and clay. Carelessness in exploiting its lumbering resources has cost Minnesota some of the leadership it once held as a timber producer, but today scientific forestry is correcting old errors.

Manufacturing in Minnesota is distinguished by the meat-slaughtering and packing industry, centered in South St. Paul and Austin, and the flour milling industry, which has made Minneapolis famous. Machinery, chemicals, paper, printing and publishing are other industries for which the state is noted.

Characteristically Minnesota

The name Minnesota is taken from two Sioux words, probably meaning "sky-tinted water." Often Minnesota is called "the land of 10,000 lakes," which is an understatement, since the state has more than 11,000 lakes. A concrete statue of Paul Bunyan, eighteen feet high, standing beside his pal Babe, the blue ox, is on the shores of Lake Bemidji.

Fabulous though the deeds of Bunyan were, native and adopted sons of Minnesota often have claimed achievements that have seemed equally spectacular. Railroader James J. Hill, who won fame as the "Empire Builder," is one of these, and aviator Charles A. Lindbergh, the first man to fly nonstop from New York to Paris, is another. At Rochester stands the Mayo Clinic, built by William and Charles Mayo. Patients come from around the world to this clinic where, it has been said, the aim is "to make surgery as accurate and as dependable as bookkeeping."

To those who live and work in Minnesota — and to the tens of thousands more who come here on vacations — the state's motto, *L'Etoile du Nord,* is certainly appropriate. "The Star of the North," those words mean — Minnesota, a shining star among the fifty that make up our nation's firmament!

Great Plains

TEXAS

"The Lone Star State"

SIX FLAGS have flown over Texas. Hard-whipped by breezes across the Gulf, the first banner bore the castles and lions of Spain. In 1519 — twenty-seven years after Columbus reached the New World — the explorer Alonso Alvarez de Pineda mapped the coast of Texas, and, spending forty days at the mouth of the Rio Grande, recommended that a settlement be planted there. Nine years later an expedition under Alvar Núnez Cabeza de Vaca, shipwrecked off the coast of Texas, waded ashore with three fellow-survivors to spend nearly six years as captives of the Indians. In an adventure equaling a tale from the *Arabian Nights,* these Spaniards wandered hundreds of miles before reaching the outpost of Culiacán, near the Gulf of California, on May 18, 1536, where they repeated reports of cities to the north whose wealth exceeded the riches of Peru.

De Vaca's stories revived a long existing belief among the Spaniards that somewhere in the New World existed the fabulously rich Seven Cities of Cibola. With 300 horsemen, 70 footmen and more than 1,000 Indians, Francisco Vásquez de Coronado set out in 1540 on a futile quest that carried him across the plains of Texas and as far as east central Kansas before he turned back, convinced that he had chased a rainbow. Hernando de Soto, who explored the southwestern United States on the same fool's chase, died on the lower Mississippi and the tattered remnant of his party in 1542 struggled

*The
Lone Star
State*

across eastern Texas, no more successful than Coronado's men in finding "glory, God and gold."

The Lilies of France

In 1683 the Spanish established a mission among the Jumanos Indians near El Paso, just two years before a second flag bearing the lilies of France appeared over the soil of Texas. The bearer of this proud banner was Robert Cavalier Sieur de La Salle, who dreamed of a series of forts from the mouth of the Mississippi to Canada as the guardians of a vast empire for France in the New World. In 1685 La Salle founded the colony of Fort St. Louis upon the shore of Matagorda Bay, and set out to find the Mississippi. A mutiny among his own men near the site of Navasota in 1687 brought death to the courageous nobleman. The settlement he built was destroyed and its inhabitants slain.

The Spaniards, learning of La Salle's activities from French pirates, were suddenly on the alert and in 1690 declared that Texas was a province of Spain. Missions began to dot eastern Texas — at present-day Nacogdoches in 1716, at San Antonio in 1718, at Goliad in 1749. After the Louisiana Purchase, the United States claimed the territory as far south as the Rio Grande, but by treaty in 1819 accepted the Sabine River as its southwestern boundary.

Meanwhile Americans had pushed into Texas, gathering herds of wild horses and trading with the Indians. Spain's rule was cruel and severe, a kind of pig-headed, far-off government that had no understanding of the problems of the people in Texas. Rebellion, seething beneath the surface, burst forth in short-lived revolutions at Dolores in 1810 and at Bexar in 1811.

The following year an American soldier of fortune, Augustus W. Magee, led a conglomerate army of Mexican revolutionists, Indian allies and Americans and Frenchmen from the Louisiana-Texas frontier in an uprising. Magee died before this motley force had defeated a Spanish army on April 1, 1813, captured Bexar and, five days later, issued a "Declaration of Independence of the State of Texas." Spain struck back that August in a battle on the Medina River, west of San Antonio, slaying most of the Americans who had aided the Mexican revolutionists. But the spirit of revolt lingered — the more so after Napoleon dethroned Ferdinand VII and placed Joseph Bonaparte in power — and on February 28, 1821 Mexico declared its independence as a constitutional monarchy that protected the Catholic religion and guaranteed racial equality.

Under the Eagle, Cactus and Serpent

So Texas came under its third flag — Mexico's banner of the eagle, cactus and serpent. And now appeared two Connecticut Yankees with a large dream — Moses Austin and his son, Stephen Fuller Austin — who offered to establish a colony of 300 families in Texas. Moses Austin died before he could fulfill this dream, but twenty-seven-year-old Stephen carried on and by 1821 had established his first settlement, San Felipe de Austin.

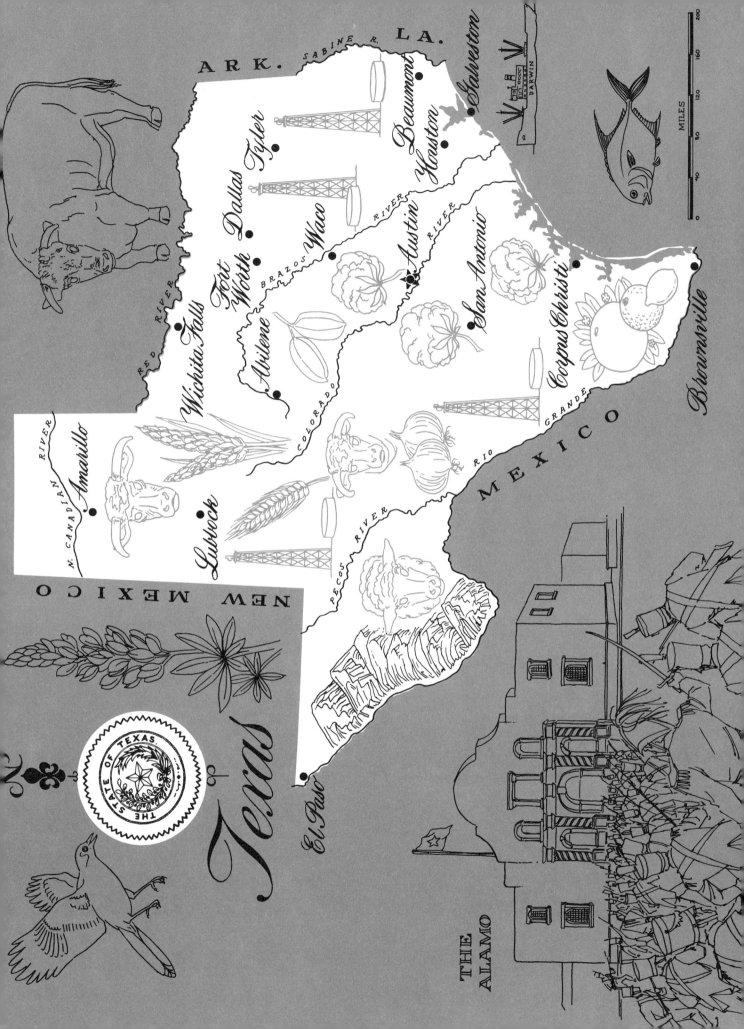

ARK.

LA.

SABINE R.

Galveston

Beaumont

Houston

Tyler

Dallas

Fort Worth

Waco

BRAZOS

RIVER

Austin

RIVER

San Antonio

RED RIVER

Wichita Falls

Abilene

COLORADO

Corpus Christi

RIVER

RIO

GRANDE

Brownsville

N. CANADIAN RIVER

Amarillo

Lubbock

PECOS RIVER

MEXICO

NEW MEXICO

El Paso

Texas

THE STATE OF TEXAS.

MILES

0 40 80 120 160 200

DARWIN

THE ALAMO

Great Plains

DARWIN

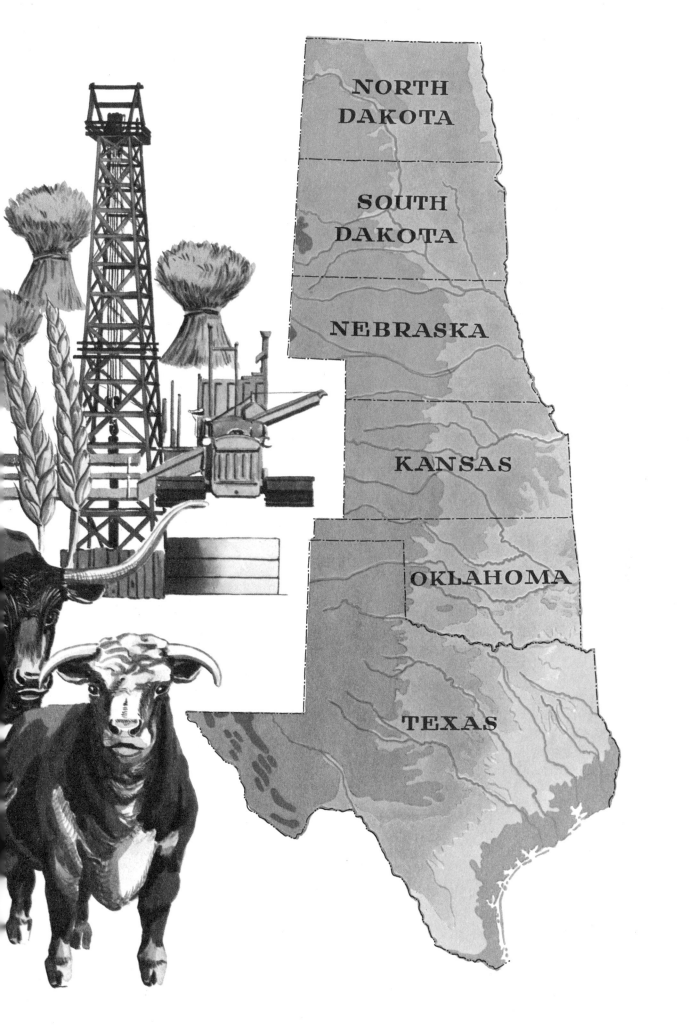

NORTH
DAKOTA

SOUTH
DAKOTA

NEBRASKA

KANSAS

OKLAHOMA

TEXAS

The
Lone Star
State

By 1830 more than 20,000 Anglo-Americans had settled in Texas and the Mexican authorities grew alarmed. A law that year forbade further settlement by Americans. Insofar as Mexicans had little wish to live in Texas, this decree virtually ended the growth of the province — a far cry from the ambition of the American settlers to build here an "abode of civilization, of abundance and happiness, and by that means to repay themselves, their wives and children for the hardships and sufferings of the early settlement." The conflict deepened with other decrees until, by the close of 1835, Texans said to one another: "Boys, rub your steels and pick your flints."

The strutting Santa Anna, as dictator of Mexico, sent his brother-in-law, General Martin Perfecto de Cos, to drive rebellious Americans out of Texas. Instead, the Texas Rangers soundly trounced de Cos at every point. Enraged, Santa Anna led an army of many thousands into Texas, and in February, 1836, trapped 183 Americans under William Barret Travis within the Alamo, an old mission in San Antonio. A hard-headed, two-fisted lot were these Americans who stood with Travis — men like James Butler Bonham, Jim Bowie and Davy Crockett, who once said "If there is anything in the world particularly worth living for, it is freedom."

"Remember the Alamo!"

The defense of the Alamo was hopeless from the start against Santa Anna's superior force, but Travis, fighting back gamely, addressed a letter "To the People of Texas and all Americans in the world:

"I shall never surrender or retreat. I am determined to sustain myself as long as possible and die like a soldier who never forgets what is due to his own honor and that of his country. VICTORY OR DEATH."

By March 5 the inevitable slaughter of all the American defenders of the Alamo approached, but Crockett wrote cheerily into his diary that day: "Pop, pop, pop! Bom, bom, bom! throughout the day. No time for memorandums now. Go ahead! Liberty and independence forever!"

And Crockett was right — the independence of Texas, declared on March 2 at Washington-on-the-Brazos, did survive. Shouting "Remember the Alamo!" Texas troops under Sam Houston, retreating to the banks of the San Jacinto River, turned suddenly on Santa Anna. The Mexican army was crushed and a fourth flag flew over Texas — the banner bearing the lone star of the new Republic of Texas!

Under the Stars and Stripes

With Sam Houston as President, the young republic received quick recognition from the United States, Great Britain, France and Belgium. Continuing armed conflict with Mexico and Indian raids along the border beset the new country. High prices lessened the value of its currency. Since many southern families had settled in Texas, slavery was a serious handicap in efforts to effect American annexation, but on December 29, 1845 Texas finally was admitted to the Union as our twenty-eighth state. Three conditions governed the raising of a fifth flag — the Stars and Stripes — over the soil of Texas:

First, the state should keep its unappropriated and vacant land.

Second, no more than four new states (in addition to Texas) could be formed from its territory.

Third, all questions of boundaries with foreign countries must be settled by the United States.

After the War with Mexico, the Rio Grande became our southern boundary, and Texas laid claim to parts of Colorado, Wyoming, Kansas and Oklahoma — a dispute settled by the Compromise of 1850 when Texas surrendered this claim in return for a payment of $10,-000,000. Old Sam Houston fought bitterly against Texan secession, but slave-interests dominated the state and during the sad war years from 1861 to 1865 a sixth flag was raised over Texas — the banner of the Stars and Bars of the Confederacy. Between 50,000 and 60,000 Texans fought against the Union, and the port of Galveston, taken by the Federals in October, 1862 was recap-

tured the following January. Although Texas adopted a new constitution abolishing slavery in 1866, a military government was imposed and the state was not readmitted to the Union until 1870.

Texas Goes Ahead

Putting the scars of war aside, Texas began to stride forward. In 1850 its population had been 212,592, but by 1880 the figure rose to 1,591,749. Along the Chisholm Trail from San Antonio across Oklahoma to Abilene, Kansas, and over the Western Trail to Dodge City, Kansas, no sight became more commonplace than the dust clouds from moving herds of Texas longhorns — cattle descended from the stock left by Coronado. Eventually shorthorn cattle, crossed with Brahma cattle from India so they would be immune to tick fever, replaced the longhorn. By 1910 the population of Texas had leaped to 3,896,542, and part of the answer to that tremendous increase was in the discovery of oil and the opening of the Spindletop field in 1901. Later discoveries in north and central Texas, the Pan-

The
Lone Star
State

*The
Lone Star
State*

handle and the Pecos Valley kept the oil boom going, but the greatest discovery came in 1930 when the fields in East Texas were opened.

Today about one-third of the nation's oil supply comes from Texas, but the state possesses also other incredibly rich mineral resources — natural gas, natural gasoline, sulfur, salt, helium, gypsum, limestone and clays. Agriculture and livestock continue to add greatly to the wealth of Texas, with its chief crops including cotton, corn, wheat grain sorghums, oats, rice, fruits, vegetables, pecans, bees and honey. A state with sixteen port cities— Beaumont, Brownsville, Corpus Christi, Freeport, Galveston, Houston, Ingleside, Orange, Port Aransas, Port Arthur, Port Bolivar, Port Isabel, Port Lavaca, Port Neches, Sabine and Texas City — Texas has become a strong industrial state whose chief manufactures include petroleum products, lumber, peanut butter and oil, cottonseed, clay products, oil-field machinery, newspapers and periodicals, meats, flour, cement, chemicals, cotton textiles, airplanes, canned fruits and vegetables, brooms, sugar and lime.

Deep in the Heart of Texas

Open-hearted, proud of the wealth and expansiveness of his state, the modern Texan has become a national symbol. Tease him with the fact that Alaska is now a larger state, and he is likely to reply: "You just wait until the ice melts!" Varied scenes await the visitor deep in the heart of Texas — a mule-drawn chuck wagon coming down the road, the "Mosquito Fleet" setting off for a day's haul from Gulf ports, brand-ing cattle on the range, sheep herding in West Texas, sulfur mining in Freeport, fields of golden wheat in the Panhandle, a farmer chopping cotton near El Paso, towering oil derricks. Great Bend National Park in southwestern Texas offers, among other splendors, the spectacular canyons of Boquillas, Mariscal and Santa Elena, and the Alamo at San Antonio stands as a shrine to the last words of Davy Crockett and his fellow martyrs to Texan freedom: "Liberty and independence forever!"

"Friendship," declares the motto of Texas — and in spirit and deed Texans live up to that pledge. Among its distinguished citizens, over the years, have been Claire Lee Chennault, leader of the famous "Flying Tigers" during World War II; John Nance Garner, for two terms Vice President under Franklin D. Roosevelt; O. Henry, America's dean of short story writers; Samuel A. Maverick, a cattleman who added his name to the American language; Chester W. Nimitz, leader of our Pacific naval forces during World War II; and such modern statesmen and servants of government as Oveta Culp Hobby, Edward Mandell House, Vice-President Lyndon B. Johnson and Sam Rayburn. Irvin Cobb, the humorist, visited Texas and described it with complete humility. Here, he said, he had found "a timbered tract as large as Massachusetts, a cotton patch in the Black Waxy country as big as all Ohio, a grazing belt in the Panhandle as large as Pennsylvania, more wheatlands than in either of the Dakotas, and more corn fields than in Illinois."

OKLAHOMA
"The Sooner State"

THE FIRST white men to see Oklahoma were Spaniards in search of gold, silver and quick riches — the troops under Coronado, who crossed the western part of the state in 1541, and parties under Captain Francisco Leiva Bonilla in 1590, Governor Juan de Oñate in 1601 and Diego Castillo in 1650. Next came the French, dogged trappers and traders, who first heard of the country through followers of La Salle and who came by way of the Red and Arkansas rivers. In the international chess game that made Louisiana a possession of France, then Spain, then France, Oklahoma changed legal title until the Louisiana Purchase of 1803 brought it under the jurisdiction of the United States.

Jean Pierre Chouteau, who carried on an extensive trade among the Osages, received for his services in the Oklahoma country special recognition from President Thomas Jefferson, who also appointed Chouteau's son to West Point. Young Auguste Pierre Chouteau served the nation as captain of a militia company during the War of 1812, then, following in his father's steps, established in 1817 a trading post near the site of Salina on Grand River. This enterprise attracted some 2,000 hunters, including Frenchmen, other Europeans and Indians of many tribes.

From Chouteau's post an extensive trade was carried on with New Orleans and St. Louis — in bearskins, deerskins, beaver, otter, wildcat, raccoon, skunk hides and buffalo robes. To Chouteau's fine, two-storied home at Salina came visitors who learned at first hand the great promise of the Oklahoma country, among them the writer Washington Irving and Sam Houston, hero of Texan independence.

Indian Territory

Yet Oklahoma was, for decades to come, a kind of stepchild of the nation, governed as part of the Territory of Indiana, then included in the Territory of Missouri, and later in the Territory of Arkansas until, in 1834, most of the present state was set aside by Congress as Indian Territory for "The Five Civilized Tribes" — the Cherokee, Creek, Chickasaw, Choctaw and Seminole.

These homeless Indians, driven from the Gulf states, Tennessee and North Carolina, preyed on the nation's conscience. Yet they must live somewhere in peace and security, and so the Indian Territory in Oklahoma was created by a treaty that gave them title to the land "as long as grass shall grow and rivers run." Diligent farmers, good tradesmen, builders of churches and schools, these long-suffering Indians believed that at last they had found a home where, protected by the white man's laws, they could prosper.

The Civil War exploded that dream. The common belief that since some of the Indians were slaveholders they were drawn to the side of the Confederacy was only a partial truth. "Do nothing, keep quiet, comply with treaties," advised John Ross, chief of the Cherokees, but the circumstances prevented even this policy of neutrality.

The very position of the Indian Territory on the border of Confederate states like Arkansas and Texas, the preponderance of Southern agents on the scene, and the withdrawal of Federal troops from the territory all tended to compromise the Indians. Even so, a rather sizable band of loyal Indians under the leadership of Opothle Yahola, a Creek, consistently fought for the Union. But, politically, the damage had been wrought. After the war the pressure of land-hungry whites upon the National government led the United States to take the position that the Indians had lost their rights by fighting for the Confederacy. Other tribes were permitted to settle in the western half of their lands, and meanwhile, north, east and south of Oklahoma, settlements began pushing upon the Indian Territory.

The Wild Scramble

The "boomer" either ignored the law forbidding him to settle on the fertile ranges of Oklahoma, or secured a permit to do so from one of the tribal governments. For years such illegal settlers and Federal troops carried on a kind of hit-and-run warfare until finally the National government yielded to the homesteader's pressure. Nearly 2,000,000 acres of land in central Oklahoma were bought from the Indians and April 22, 1889 was selected as the day when the state would be opened to homesteaders (those who sneaked in *sooner* gave the state its nickname).

Among those who rode on the first train into the territory on the appointed day was a reporter for the St. Louis

Globe Democrat, who told what he beheld as the train approached the depot at Guthrie:

"What happened when the train began to slacken beggars all description. Boys, middle-aged men, and old fellows threw themselves off the platform and commenced a wild rush. They fell upon each other, scrambled to their feet, and made off, some carrying their grips and others dropping everything in the eagerness of the chase. As the train went on toward the depot the passengers kept jumping off. The town-lot craze seemed to lend speed even to cripples. A man with a wooden leg was among the first to make the dangerous jump, and he held his own in the race. Not a passenger by this first train went past Guthrie, so that the population of the new city was increased by this rush to the extent of nearly a thousand. All roads seemed to lead to the land office at which a line over one hundred yards

long was already formed. For a second the runners paused.

"Then they commenced a wild tear out east, and each man found an unclaimed lot, proceeded to stake it out and hold it down. The process of securing the lots, as in general adoption, is simple in the extreme. First of all a stake is driven in the ground, with or without a placer attached, setting forth the name of the claimant. Then the new owner paces off the ground he proposes to occupy for a residence or business house. There is at least a charm of variety about the laying out of Guthrie. Some people contented themselves with twenty-five feet frontage, others took forty feet, and others fifty. . . . Altogether ten trains got in before three o'clock, and making allowance for those who went on to Oklahoma City, there must have been at least six thousand people in Guthrie three hours after the Territory was legally opened

The
Sooner
State

*The
Sooner
State*

for settlement. . . . Hacks met the trains and drivers shouted, 'This way for lots at a dollar apiece!' For a dollar lot hunters were driven to vacant lots and left to get their dollar's worth themselves."

Toward Statehood

Within twenty-four hours, that April 22, 1889, about 50,000 settlers poured into Oklahoma. Another great "land run" came in 1893 and that year the Indian Territory was surveyed for townsites. First applying for admission to the Union in 1891, Oklahoma was forced to wait sixteen years before it became our forty-sixth state on November 16, 1907.

Oil wells on the grounds of the state capitol at Oklahoma City explain in large part why in succeeding years the "Sooner State" advanced rapidly. The Indians were familiar with the black liquid that oozed from Oklahoma's ground and believed that it could cure many illnesses. In 1889 — the year when the state was hopping with land-hungry homesteaders — Edward Byrd took petroleum from a well near Chelsea. Not until about 1910, however, were the great oil discoveries made — first on Osage land, then in Creek County in 1915 and in Oklahoma City in 1928. The Osage as a group today are probably the richest people in the world as a result of the oil on their property. Other natural resources that are found in Oklahoma include natural gas, lead and zinc, ceramic clay deposits and high-grade granite, copper, gold, iron and silver.

Agriculturally Oklahoma is one of

the nation's leading wheat producers, and other important crops are cotton, corn, oats, grain sorghums, barley, rye, hay, potatoes and peanuts. The state likewise supports prosperous poultry farms and livestock ranches. One of our foremost states in producing raw materials, Oklahoma's principal manufactures include petroleum and coal products, chemicals, metal products, machinery, printing and publishing and such food products as meat, grains and baked goods.

The Open-Hearted West

Labor Omnia Vincit, proclaims the state motto — "Labor Conquers All Things" — and Oklahomans, growing their corn "as high as an elephant's eye" and reaping a wealth from mineral and industrial resources that would have popped wide the eyes of Coronado, live by those words. Shaped like a saucepan, the state takes justified pride in such attractions as Boiling Springs near Woodward, old Fort Gibson that was once the steamboat terminal on the Arkansas River, beautiful Quartz Mountain near Altus and Robbers Cave near Wilburton, where, legend insists, a treasure in gold hidden by a highwayman remains to be found.

At Black Gum Mountain near Sallisaw the Cherokees hold their annual Sacred Fire Ceremony. Pow-wows of the Quapaw Indians near Quapaw and of the Ponca Indians at Ponca City are summer events and during the fourth week of every September Osage Indian dances are held at Pawhuska. At Claremore stands the memorial to Oklahoma's great humorist, Will Rogers.

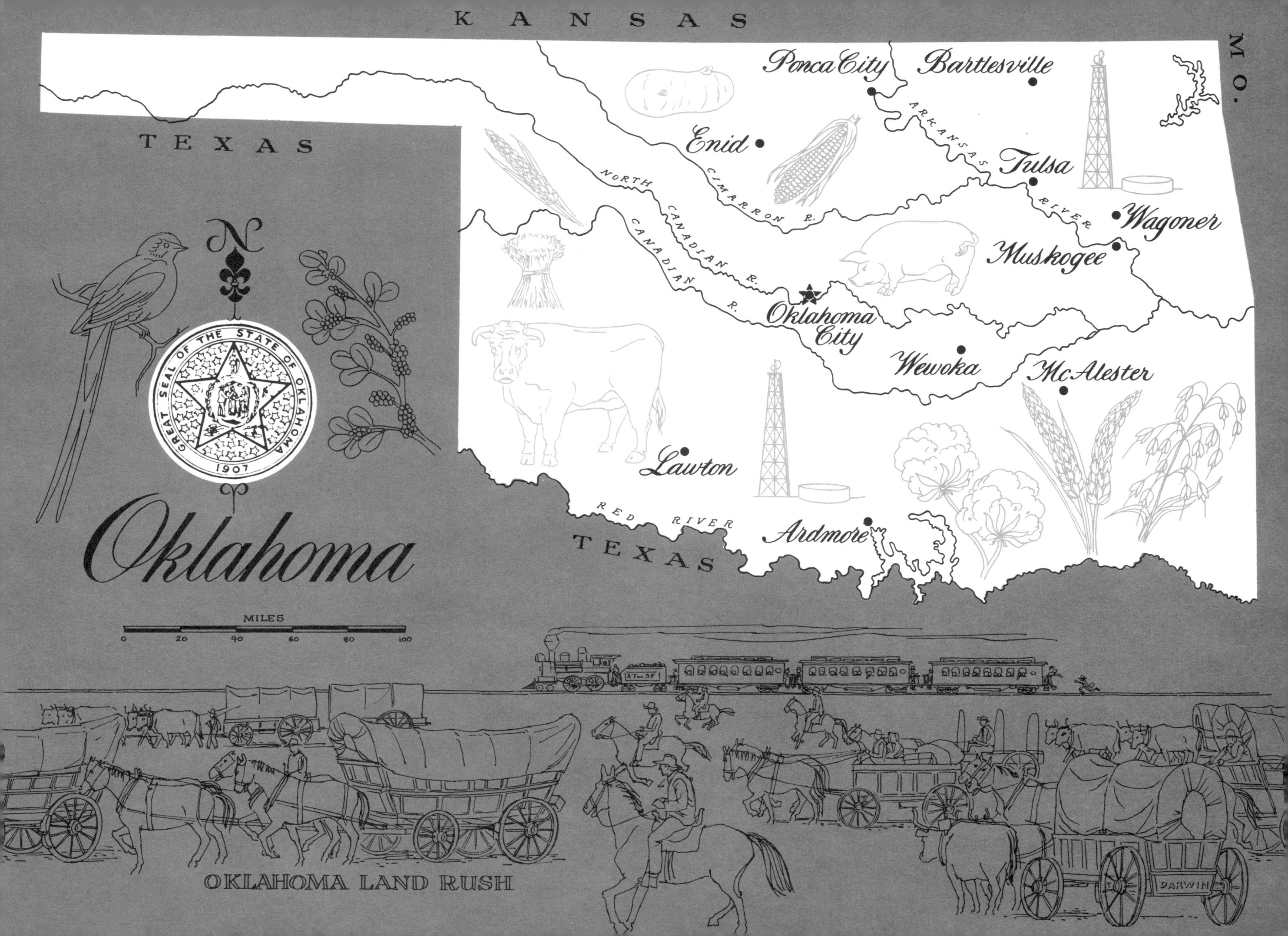

MO.

KANSAS

TEXAS

Ponca City

Bartlesville

Wagoner

Tulsa

ARKANSAS RIVER

Muskogee

McAlester

Enid

CIMARRON R.

NORTH CANADIAN R.

CANADIAN R.

Oklahoma City

Wewoka

Lawton

Ardmore

RED RIVER

TEXAS

GREAT SEAL OF THE STATE OF OKLAHOMA 1907

N

Oklahoma

MILES

0   20   40   60   80   100

DARWIN

A·T·&·SF

OKLAHOMA LAND RUSH

KANSAS

"The Sunflower State"

CORONADO'S search for the Seven Cities brought him in 1541 to the land of the Quivira people (Wichita Indians), where he found neither gold nor "any metal at all." Coronado stayed twenty-five days among the Plains Indians in their settlements northeast of the Great Bend of the Arkansas River, and reported afterward that "the land being very fat and black, and being well-watered by the rivulets and springs and rivers, I found prunes like those of Spain, and nuts and very sweet grapes and mulberries."

A century — perhaps a century and a half — passed before white men again appeared in this domain of the Plains Indians. French traders from Canada, traveling among the Osage and Missouri tribes, were probably the next

visitors, but the Frenchmen did not stay. American possession of present-day Kansas came about through two acts — the Louisiana Purchase in 1803 and a grant from Texas in 1850 — but in official Washington little value was placed on the new territory.

Expeditions by Lewis and Clark, Zebulon Pike and Major Stephen H. Long established the misconception that Kansas was part of the "Great American Desert, a useless waste of sand," and in 1824, when Congress heatedly debated the question of western development, Daniel Webster spoke with derision:

"What do we want with this vast and worthless area, of this region of savages and wild beasts, of deserts, of shifting sands and whirlwinds, of dust, of cactus and prairie dogs; of what use could we ever hope to put these great deserts, or those endless mountain ranges, impenetrable and covered to their very base with eternal snow?"

Bleeding Kansas

In 1821 Kansas was separated from Missouri and during the next thirty-three years existed as an unorganized territory. Various treaties with the Indian tribes stabilized the Kansas country — first with the Kansa, who gave their name meaning "People of the South Wind" to the land, and then with the Pawnee and Osage tribes. Of equal importance to the future of Kansas were the prairie schooners, rolling westward to California and Utah in the 1840's, for these wanderers dispelled the myth that Kansas was a useless wasteland.

The first permanent white settlement was established at Fort Leavenworth in 1827, and the first petition to organize a separate territory was sent to Congress in 1844. Ten years passed, however, before Senator Stephen A. Douglas of Illinois promoted the famous Kansas-Nebraska Bill that became a sputtering fuse in the powder keg ultimately called the American Civil War. This highly explosive legislation, which President Pierce signed on May 30, 1854, repealed the Missouri Compromise and created the Territories of Kansas and Nebraska on the understanding that the settlers could choose for themselves whether to become slave or free states.

The supporters of the Kansas-Nebraska Bill always had intended that Kansas should be a slave state and

Nebraska a free state, but they did not reckon with the militant New England Emigrant Aid Company, organized in 1854 by Eli Thayer of Massachusetts. This antislavery group sent Free Soilers and Sharp's rifles, popularly called "Beecher's Bibles," into Kansas. No less determined were proslavery advocates from Missouri, known as the "Border Ruffians," who invaded Kansas with the avowed intention of ridding the state of the abolitionist scourge. With a Free State capital at Lawrence and a Slave State capital at Lecompton, "Bleeding Kansas" became the first battleground of the tragic war soon to divide the nation.

The Sunflower State

Blood and Freedom

Border Ruffians, gathering on Wakarusa Creek, invaded Lawrence and sacked the town in 1856. The "Wakarusa War" now brought the vengeful abolitionist, old John Brown, to the fore and five reputedly proslavery men were executed by his followers along Potawatomi Creek. Thus began two years of open warfare, with the proslavery men or Border Ruffians meeting bitter opposition from the antislavery men or "Jayhawkers." Citizens were pulled from their beds and murdered on mere suspicion of taking one side or the other. Towns were burned, on no more than the same suspicion that their inhabitants supported the "wrong" side of this argument. Rival legislatures were formed and rival constitutions were drafted. Meanwhile the steady influx of antislavery settlers into Kansas began to tip the balance and in 1859 the Free Soilers won with the

The
Sunflower
State

adoption of a constitution prohibiting slavery.

On January 29, 1861, with civil war only weeks away, Kansas was admitted to the Union as our thirty-fourth state. The loyalty of Kansas to the National government could not be doubted, for in proportion to its population the number of soldiers it sent into the Union army was greater than that of any other state. Guerrilla warfare nibbled at Kansas and brought a terrible day on August 21, 1863, when the notorious bandit chief William Clarke Quantrill and his raiders rode into Lawrence. Dividing into squads of six or eight men, Quantrill's irregulars swept through the town, burning and slaying. Within four hours they left Lawrence in ruins and 150 persons dead in its streets.

"On the Lone Prairie"

In the years after the war, Kansas boomed — in part through the coming of the railroads, but also because of the great cattle drives up the Chisholm Trail to such cowboy towns as Great Bend, Hays and Dodge City. An annual drive would find as many as 300,000 head of cattle being moved to railroad centers for shipment to market.

The trailsman's life was seldom easy. A drover, ten or twelve cowhands, a couple of horse wranglers and the "old woman," or cook, would handle an average herd of 2,500 to 3,000 head. A good day's travel was twelve to fifteen miles, then a stop for flapjacks. Night horses were saddled before the cowboys bedded down, for a stampede could come at any time. Stormy nights,

with thunder and lightning, were most dreaded.

So it was small wonder when, at last reaching a cow town, the trailsman was ready to "bust loose." Gunmen, gamblers and other fakers drifted into Dodge City, Hays or Abilene, looking for trouble and sometimes finding it — *sometimes,* because Kansas made an art of finding frontier sheriffs who created their own legends.

Dandy Bat and Wild Bill

Dodge City, the cowboy capital of the Southwest, had its Bat Masterson, who strolled its streets in a pearl-gray bowler hat and diamond stickpin, twirling his cane like a city slicker from the East. Yet those who reckoned Bat was slow on drawing his six-shooter usually ended in Boot Hill cemetery. One day Bat left Dodge City, and when he was heard from again he was helping his old friend and former Dodge City peace officer, Wyatt Earp, clean out Tombstone, Arizona.

Abilene also had a celebrated marshal of the same dandified cut — Wild Bill Hickok, who walked its streets in a Prince Albert coat, checkered trousers and embroidered waistcoat. Yet those who doubted the efficiency of Wild Bill's fancy pearl-handled revolver changed their minds on the day when the sheriff drew on two murderers, fleeing in opposite directions, and brought them both down. Some say he only fired one shot, but that sounds a mite exaggerated!

How well Kansas managed to handle the lawless element was symbolized by the first school established in 1874 at

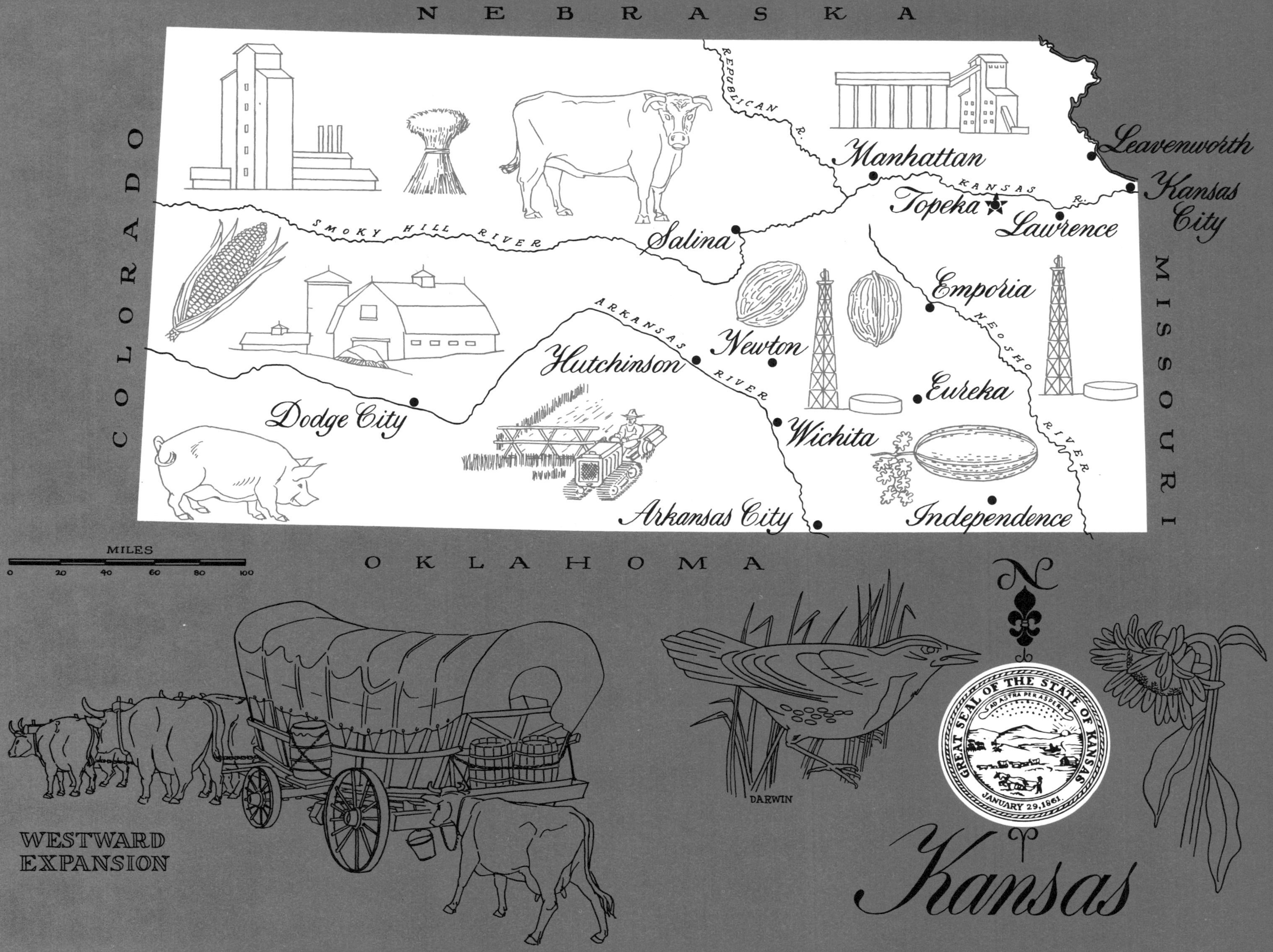

Kansas

MISSOURI

NEBRASKA

COLORADO

OKLAHOMA

Leavenworth

Kansas City

Lawrence

Topeka

Manhattan

Emporia

Eureka

Independence

Wichita

Newton

Salina

Hutchinson

Arkansas City

Dodge City

KANSAS R.

REPUBLICAN R.

NEOSHO RIVER

ARKANSAS RIVER

SMOKY HILL RIVER

GREAT SEAL OF THE STATE OF KANSAS · JANUARY 29, 1861 · AD ASTRA PER ASPERA

DARWIN

MILES

100
80
60
40
20
0

WESTWARD EXPANSION

*The
Sunflower
State*

Larned, in Pawnee County. Large red and yellow letters across the two front windows of the school spelled out S-A-L-O-O-N. The students sat on beer kegs. A bar was the teacher's desk.

The Farmers Take Over

The cattle boom had ebbed by 1885, and increasing numbers of farmers fenced in the range lands. Lean times often confronted these homesteaders in their sod houses, and none who were in Kansas in 1874 ever forgot that year of the grasshopper plague.

"I recall that when coming home late one afternoon for supper," wrote Stuart Henry, "I stepped back surprised to see what became known as Rocky Mountain locusts covering the side of the house. Already inside, they feasted on the curtains. Clouds of them promptly settled down on the whole country — everywhere, unavoidable. People set about killing them to save gardens, but this soon proved ridiculous. Specially contrived machines, pushed by horses, scooped up the hoppers in grain fields by the barrelfuls to burn them. This, too, was then nonsensical. Vast hordes, myriads. In a week grain fields, gardens, shrubs, vines, had been eaten down to the ground or to the bark. Nothing could be done. You sat by and saw everything go."

Yet stout was the heart of the pioneer, and afterward Kansans made jokes about the hoppers, telling their youngsters how the insects grabbed pitchforks and stood in the fence corners, fighting over the last ear of corn. In later years droughts tested the courage of the

Kansas farmer, and thousands moved away — but other thousands endured, and today they take pride in the fact that their state is known as "The Bread Basket of America."

To the Stars

Modern Kansas outranks all states in growing wheat, and as a corn producer and raiser of cattle has few peers. In flour milling, grist-mill products and meat-packing, Kansas likewise is a leader and is growing rapidly as a manufacturer of airplanes and aviation equipment. Mineral resources that add to Kansas's extremely sound economy are volcanic ash (used in making household cleaning compounds), zinc, salt, oil, gas, coal and helium.

Native Kansans have contributed a proud share to the life of the nation, including Dwight D. Eisenhower, thirty-fourth President of the United States; Walter P. Chrysler, automobile manufacturer; novelist Dorothy Canfield Fisher and poet Edgar Lee Masters; Carrie Nation, who used her hatchet to war on saloons, and editor William Allen White, who used his brain to war on intolerance.

Perhaps once it could be said of Kansas and the old Southwest that "there is no Sunday west of Newton and no God west of Pueblo," but Bat Masterson, Wild Bill Hickok, and the courage and common sense of Kansas homesteaders have left that age far behind. *Ad Astra per Aspera,* reads the state's motto, meaning "To the stars through difficulties."

And in Kansas, how close, how bright the stars appear!

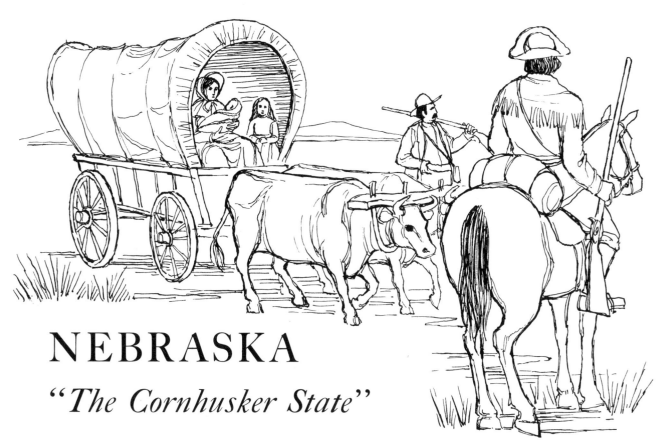

NEBRASKA

"The Cornhusker State"

IN NEBRASKA country, where the corn belt meets the plains of the cowboy, some historians believe that Coronado and his followers were the first white men to visit the region. Next on the scene were French traders, who were supplying Indians with guns, by the accounts reaching Spanish outposts in the Southwest, and in the early 1700's the Spanish sent punitive expeditions into the upper plains to deal with this problem.

Half-hearted efforts at best, the last of these expeditions in 1720 brought forty-five white soldiers, sixty Indian allies, a priest and an interpreter under Lieutenant Colonel Pedro de Villasur to the forks of the South Platte. The party camped within sight of a Pawnee village, occupying a poorly selected position in the tall grass beside the river. The Indians struck at daybreak.

Villasur was among the first to fall, and only thirteen of the white men ultimately stumbled back to Santa Fe. The massacre ended the poor influence of the Spanish in Nebraska, whose chief concern apparently had amounted to keeping others out of a country which they did not wish to occupy.

The French, however, maintained a lively interest. In 1714 Etienne Venyard de Bourgmont ascended the Missouri River to the mouth of the Platte, which he called the Nebraska after the Indian word *Nebrathka,* meaning "flat water," and in 1739 Pierre and Paul Mallet, journeying from French forts on the Illinois to Santa Fe, were probably the first white men to cross the state. Alternately the country belonged by treaty to France and Spain until in 1803 the Louisiana Purchase made most of it part of the United States.

The
Cornhusker
State

Under American Influence

Fur trappers like Manuel Lisa and William Ashley, explorers like Lewis and Clark, John C. Frémont and Stephen H. Long, Mormons in search of the Promised Land, and finally seekers after gold in California brought white men in increasing numbers into the fertile land of Nebraska. Indicative of some of the problems they also brought was the Indian Intercourse Act of 1834 which prohibited sale to the Indians of that peculiar brand of frontier liquor which at least one trader concocted from one gallon of raw alcohol, three gallons of water and a pound of chewing tobacco — enough to strain the sanity of any human! Yet by 1823 a permanent settlement at Bellevue was a center of the fur trade, missionary activity and Indian affairs, and by 1846 Fort Kearny was established.

The valley of the Platte was the secret of Nebraska's steady growth, for here was a natural highway to the Rocky Mountains and the Pacific Coast. When finally the Mormons no longer could supply wagons for the faithful, Brigham Young bade them to make handcarts and "foot it." The pluck and perseverance required to conquer a wilderness was in the picture of such a group of emigrants drawn by an eyewitness to their trek across Nebraska:

". . . The carts were generally drawn by one man and three women each, though some carts were drawn by women alone. There were about three women to one man, and two-thirds of

the women were single. It was the most motley crew I ever beheld. Most of them were Danes, with a sprinkling of Swedes, Welsh, and English, and were generally from the lower classes of their countries. Most could not understand what we said to them. The road was lined for a mile behind the train with the lame, halt, sick, and needy. Many were quite aged, and would be going slowly along, supported by a son or daughter. Some were on crutches; now and then a mother with a child in her arms and two or three hanging hold of her, with a forlorn appearance, would pass slowly along; others, whose condition entitled them to a seat in the carriage, were wending their way through the sand. A few seemed in good spirits."

Toward Statehood

When in 1821 Missouri became a state, Nebraska existed as a territory virtually without a government until 1834 when it was divided into three parts among Arkansas Territory, the Territory of Michigan, and Missouri. The country was thought of as strictly Indian land, yet white settlers continued to ignore the restrictions of a distant Federal authority. Many who went west remembered the sweeping plains of Nebraska, and, disappointed in California, returned to the pleasant valley of the Platte. By 1853 they organized a provisional government and the following year Congress passed the famous Kansas-Nebraska Bill [see Kansas, pp. 190-194] that became one of the climactic events propelling the country into civil war. The Territory of

SOUTH DAKOTA

WYOMING

IOWA

MO.

KANSAS

COLO.

MISSOURI RIVER

PLATTE RIVER

NORTH PLATTE RIVER

SOUTH PLATTE R.

Norfolk

Fremont

Omaha

Lincoln

Nebraska City

Beatrice

Grand Island

Hastings

North Platte

Alliance

Scottsbluff

Bridgeport

FLOUR

MILES
0 10 20 30 40 50

DARWIN

Nebraska

GREAT SEAL OF THE STATE OF NEBRASKA
EQUALITY BEFORE THE LAW
MARCH 1 1867

PLAINS SOD HOUSE

*The
Cornhusker
State*

Nebraska, as then defined, not only included the present state, but also parts of Montana, the Dakotas, Wyoming and Colorado, and not until 1863, with the organization of other territories, were the boundaries of Nebraska as they now exist more or less fixed.

At the outbreak of the Civil War the population of Nebraska had reached about 30,000, and 3,300 Nebraskans were counted in the ranks of the Union armies before the conflict ended. During these war years, the state's importance as the crossroads of the nation grew. Fort Kearny on the Platte was the meeting point for rival overland routes from Kansas City, St. Joseph, Leavenworth, Atchison, Nebraska City and Omaha. In 1865 — two years before Nebraska was admitted to the Union as our thirty-seventh state — as much as 200,000 tons of freight were carried over these trails.

Empire of Sod Houses

Once the Union Pacific Railroad extended across Nebraska, the rush of the homesteaders was on. There were few trees on the plains, and the sod house became the symbol of the Nebraska frontier. These homes, which early settlers insisted were constructed of "Nebraska marble," varied from simple caves to two-story structures. What little timber the plains provided was used for supports, and in most cases even the roofs were made of sod. Hard-packed earth served for floors. A cloth stretched across the top became a ceiling, and often old newspapers covered the walls. If the sod house seemed to offer dismal living quarters, driving to the point of despair the woman who tried to keep it clean, at least the sod house was cool in summer and warm in winter.

Cooking was always a problem on the Nebraska frontier, and the stoves of the pioneer burned buffalo or cow chips and even prairie hay. Many grew sunflowers as a substitute for wood. Osage orange hedges took the place of rail fences. Securing water frequently was the greatest difficulty. It had to be brought up from wells sometimes sunk to depths of six hundred feet, or hauled in barrels from miles away. Dry winds in summer, blizzards in winter added to the perils of the lonely Nebraska homesteader, who often gazed over a prairie that offered not even the sight of a tree.

To these normal troubles were added special bedevilments of nature — the great Grasshopper Plague of the 1870's [see Kansas, pp. 190-194], the devastating droughts of the 1890's. Many quit the apparently hopeless struggle, but others stayed, rooted by their own cussedness to the land. Quarrels with the railroads over shipping costs found human nature no less unfriendly than Mother Nature. Yet the hardy Nebraska pioneer surmounted all these obstacles by using his brain. His answer to the railroad was the organization of successful farmer cooperatives. Irrigation solved many of nature's hazards.

Modern Nebraska

Today the tractor, plow and harvester are the symbols of "The Cornhusker State," which proudly claims pre-eminence as one of the country's leading food producers. Not surprisingly, in view of Nebraska's nickname, corn is its leading crop, but it also provides the nation's tables and food-processing plants with great harvests of wheat, oats, barley, sorghum, rye, soybeans, potatoes, sugar beets, beans and fruits, while its vigorous livestock enterprises make Omaha a meat-packing center in a class with Kansas City and Chicago. Food products are its chief products of manufacture and among its mineral resources are limestone, pumice, clay, sand and gravel.

Nebraska has many characteristics that are strictly its own. Since 1875, for example, Nebraska has been a thrifty, debt-free state that took ten years to build the capitol at Lincoln rather than abandon its policy of pay-as-you-go. It had the first unicameral (one-chamber) legislature in the United States. Until 1945, Nebraska was known officially as "The Tree-Planters' State" in honor of the first Arbor Day, celebrated in 1872. From its soil have been dug fossils of prehistoric animals that lived in North America millions of years ago — a pig six feet tall, a dog the size of a bear, the skeleton of a mammoth over fourteen feet in height.

Upon the capitol is engraved these words: "Honor to pioneers who broke the sods that men to come might live." The summer sun, glistening upon fields of golden-ripe wheat in Nebraska, says the same thing.

The Cornhusker State

SOUTH DAKOTA

"The Sunshine State"

IN 1913 South Dakota school children found a lead plate buried on a hill overlooking the Missouri and Bad rivers. The story it told went back 170 years and began with an old Indian legend that the Missouri flowed into the Pacific Ocean. Fooled by this tale, two French explorers, François and Louis-Joseph La Vérendrye, were returning from a futile quest for the fabled ocean outlet of this muddy, crooked river when they came upon the country we now call South Dakota. The plate they buried claimed the region for France.

Others followed the beckoning Missouri — some lured on by the Indian legend that had attracted the Vérendryes, some in search of new sources of fur. Spaniards from the Southwest, French and Scots and Britons from Canada, American trappers and traders for a dozen companies penetrated the Dakota country, hoping for profits from the pelts of the animals that inhabited its "shining mountains." In 1804 Lewis and Clark, exploring the vast domain that came under the jurisdiction of the United States with the Louisiana Purchase, entered South Dakota along the Bad River. They visited the amiable Yankton Indians, feasted on roasted dog, pemmican and stewed prairie apples with the Tetons (a wily lot, who tried every trick from war threats to a day of pageantry to get more presents from Americans as "niggardly" as the Spaniards with their gifts), found the Arikaras "dirty, kind, poor and extravagant," and in a cottonwood grove built a winter post that they named Fort Mandan.

The First Election

Even then the Missouri River was becoming one of the most important waterways in America, linking the trading center at St. Louis with the beaver regions. No one, of course, could teach the fur trapper that greed would be his undoing. By 1831, when the fur trade was at its height, Pierre Chouteau churned up to Fort Pierre in a steamboat. Pelts from the "shining mountains" would last forever — or so everyone seemed to think, by the way their ruthless slaughter of the animals was carried on — but by 1855, when the Federal government bought Fort Pierre, the trappers had put themselves out of business.

An early traveler spoke of the black earth along the lower part of the Missouri in this land where "the sky is as clear as that represented in a Chinese painting" and "the flowery mead, the swelling ground, the romantic hill, the bold river, the winding rivulets, the groves, the shrubberies" were all arranged "in the most exquisite manner." The belief of early visitors that this country was likely always to belong to the Indians had been exploded by the mid-1800's. By then Norwegians from Minnesota and Wisconsin had established a string of communities along the rich river lowlands or "bottoms." French-Canadians were prospering on their farms at Elk Point, and in neighboring Vermillion Jacob Deuel operated a successful sawmill. Yankton grew to about 300 inhabitants, with a main street called Broadway and a lodging place called the Ash

Hotel where you could rent a bed if you didn't mind sharing it with two or three others.

Settlers in Dakota began petitioning Congress for separate territorial status in 1858, and that fall held their first election. Frontier politics, always a kind of fancy-free, devil-take-the-hindmost affair, lived up to its full reputation when settlers from Sioux City split into small groups and traveled the neighboring countryside. At every stop they took a drink, established a voting precinct, and voted in their own names, the names of their friends and all the relatives they could remember. Another halt and another drink meant a new voting precinct, so they all voted again. Apparently the process went on as long as the whiskey lasted and thus "suffrage" came to South Dakota.

Gold in the Black Hills

In 1861 the Dakota Territory was organized and included also Montana and part of Wyoming, but in 1869 the territory was reduced to present-day South Dakota and North Dakota. By 1870, however, the population in this extensive area had not reached 12,000, and the future looked bleak. Then, within a decade, the population skyrocketed to 135,000. The coming of the railroads and the development of large-scale farming were part of the answer to this sudden growth, but an equally significant part of the answer was to be found 400 miles west of the territorial capital at Yankton.

To the pioneer wandering across that curious, grayish stretch of ridges and mounds called the Badlands — the

The Sunshine State

haunt in prehistoric times of three-toed horses, camels without humps and saber-toothed tigers — the mountains that suddenly thrust upward tree-covered slopes appeared black in contrast and hence the pioneer called them the Black Hills. The Indians looked upon the region as sacred ground, but the rumor that gold was hidden in the Black Hills drew increasing numbers of prospectors despite orders forbidding them to invade this Indian Territory. Pressure kept mounting to open the territory to the gold-seekers and in 1874, wishing once and for all to verify or squelch the rumors, the Federal government sent an expedition of soldiers and scientists under General George Custer to explore the Black Hills. On August 22 Custer set the nation wild with his report — the gold was there!

A Wild Lot

The rush was on, attracting in many cases a wild and woolly lot. In Chicago, Charles Collins, who ran a newspaper in Sioux City, tried to rally 11,000 Irish volunteers to settle in the Hills so that with the wealth they found they could finance a private army to free Ireland from the British. By December, 15,000 persons already had entered the Hills and the Sioux and Cheyenne tribes rallied for the war they would unleash in the spring of 1876, a war

MILES
60
40
20
0

MINNESOTA   IOWA

NORTH DAKOTA

Watertown

Aberdeen

BIG SIOUX R.

Sioux Falls

Mitchell

MISSOURI R.

Pierre

Chamberlain

MISSOURI R.

CHEYENNE RIVER

Belle Fourche

Lead

Rapid City   Wall

Custer

MONT.

WYOMING

NEBRASKA

EARLY
TRANSCONTINENTAL
RAILROAD

DARWIN

STATE OF SOUTH DAKOTA · GREAT · SEAL · 1889

South Dakota

*The
Sunshine
State*

that cost Custer his life [see Montana, pp. 249-253]. But the gold rush in the Black Hills went on. When the first deposits in French Creek played out, the rush turned to the richer deposits discovered in the Deadwood area. Dakota's mining towns, wide-open and lawless, were peopled quickly with characters who forged a variety of legends — tough, buckskin-clad Calamity Jane and Poker Alice Tubbs; Wild Bill Hickok and the man who killed him, Jack McCall; Potato Creek Johnny Perrett, one of the last of the old prospectors, and "Deadwood Dick" Clark, a darling of the dime novels.

In time the gold rush ebbed and those two immortal gunslingers, Wild Bill Hickok and Calamity Jane, found their eternal rest in Deadwood's Mount Moriah Cemetery. The growth of the territory by 1889 led President Harrison to sign the proclamation of statehood for the nation's second set of twins — South Dakota and North Dakota.

The Modern State

Today South Dakota is one of the most prosperous agricultural states in the Union. Livestock and livestock products account for about seventy per cent of its farm income, with cash grain crops like oats, rye and alfalfa supplying the remainder. Mineral resources remain a vital part of South Dakota's economy, and the Homestake Mine at Lead, producing over twenty million dollars in gold each year, is the largest gold mine in North America. Other mineral products that have brought the Black Hills the nickname

of "the richest hundred-mile square on earth" include uranium, feldspar, mica, granite, gypsum, limestone and lithium (the softest metal known). Whereas South Dakota has been slow in developing industries, dams harnessing the power of the Missouri make the state's growth in manufactures only a question of time.

South Dakota has 8,400 square miles of Indian Reservation, 41 state parks and 4 state forests. Mount Rushmore National Monument in the Black Hills has cut into its 6,000-foot-high granite face the likenesses of George Washington, Thomas Jefferson, Abraham Lincoln and Theodore Roosevelt, and these sculptures by Gutzon Borglum compare with the great Sphinx of Egypt among the man-made wonders of the world. Badlands National Monument along White River offers spectacular scenery — and sometimes a glimpse of golden eagles that nest near Sheep Mountain. On the southeast flank of the Black Hills stands Wind Cave National Park, home of the buffalo and such animals of the plains as antelope, elk and prairie dogs. If you visit Wind Cave, remember that buffalo are wild animals — *stay in your car and do not go near them.*

The official seal of South Dakota depicts the variety of activities that have produced this great state — the plowman who is the symbol of its farming, its smelting and mining industry, cattle grazing on its plains, the steamboats that once plied its rivers, the trees that are cut for its lumber mills. Indeed, as South Dakotans insist, their state is a "land of infinite variety."

NORTH DAKOTA

"The Flickertail State"

LIKE its sister state to the south, North Dakota takes its name from the Dakota (or Sioux) Indians who inhabited this land when the white men first appeared, and its nickname from the flickertail gopher (or ground squirrel) that abounds in this country.

Among the fur traders who followed Pierre La Vérendrye into the Dakotas [see South Dakota, pp. 200-204] was Charles Chaboillez, representing the Northwest Fur Company, who established a trading post at Pembina in 1797. (Pierre La Vérendrye was the father of the La Vérendrye brothers who buried a lead plate near the site of Fort Pierre, South Dakota.) Scotch and Irish immigrants from Canada by 1813 had made Pembina the first permanent settlement in North Dakota. In their hooded blue capotes, their calico or painted muslin shirts, their moccasins and leather leggings, they gave Pembina the air of a Canadian frontier town.

When in 1823 Major Stephen H. Long led the first American expedition into the Red River Valley, the population of Pembina was about 350. The soil of the valley — rich and black — held the clue to the great, though still distant future of the region. During the Ice Age, an enormous lake (geologists call it Lake Agassiz) covered this part of North Dakota and much of Minnesota and Manitoba, Canada. In time the lake waters evaporated, leaving silt deposits that absorbed their dark color from decayed vegetation. What Major Long beheld in the Red River Valley was one of the most fertile areas in North America.

Territorial Troubles

But the fur trader still dominated life in the Northwest, and into the 1850's the famous Red River cart car-

ried on a brisk flow of trade between the posts at Fort Garry and Fort Snelling (St. Paul). Through the 1850's and '60's troubles with the Indians were almost constant and the Dakotas were not without justified complaint against the white man.

As a human specimen, the Dakota Indian, whose profile one day would be engraved on both the United States penny and nickel, was an imposing figure. Though tall, he usually possessed small hands and feet, and between his high cheekbones and above his beaked nose were dark eyes that burned with fierce pride. Once he had lived well, giving to our language his word for dwelling, or *tipi,* and now he not only had been driven from most of his lands in Minnesota, but also had seen white hunters wipe out his buffalo herds on the Dakota prairies. As an ally of the British during the War of 1812, he had amply demonstrated his qualities as a superb fighter and he would do so again in the face of the growing threats to his security. An uprising under Chief Little Crow in

1862 in Minnesota wiped out 400 white settlers, a link in a chain of bloody uprisings that quickened after the discovery of gold in the Black Hills [see South Dakota, pp. 200-204]. Custer and his soldiers all would perish in Montana as another link in that chain, and the end would not be reached until 1890 with the death of Sitting Bull at the Battle of Wounded Knee, South Dakota.

Yet history, rightly or wrongly, had turned against the Dakota tribes. The wave of white settlers into the Dakota Territory, organized in 1861, would swell with the end of the Civil War and the coming of the railroads. In 1870 present-day North Dakota counted its population at 2,405 and by 1890 the number of inhabitants had grown to 190,983. In another two decades the figure passed the half-million mark.

Role of the Railroads

By 1873 the rails of the Northern Pacific had reached Bismarck, a powerful stimulant to the settlement of western North Dakota. Though Norwegians constituted the largest group to settle in the territory, immigrants from more than forty foreign countries came into North Dakota. In 1889 North Dakota was divided from South Dakota and both were admitted to the Union as states. A factor thereafter in the development of the state was intense competition of the railroads. The Northern Pacific, beset with money problems, paid off stockholders in railroad lands, the beginning of many a large farm in North Dakota. Farming

North Dakota

MINN.

RED RIVER

Grand Forks

Fargo

Minot

Williston

MISSOURI RIVER

Mandan

Bismarck

LITTLE MISSOURI R.

MONTANA

SOUTH DAKOTA

DARWIN

MANDAN INDIANS

GREAT SEAL 1889 STATE OF NORTH DAKOTA LIBERTY UNITED OCTOBER

MILES
0 10 20 30 40 50

The
Flickertail
State

in turn brought prosperity to the state, which helped the railroads to struggle out of their financial troubles.

A progressive spirit in North Dakota politics was reflected as early as 1909 in the enactment of the first state Child Labor Law, and with the organization of the farmer-dominated Nonpartisan League six years later this spirit became the vital influence in increasing funds for rural schools, lowering tax assessments on farm improvements, and guaranteeing deposits in state banks.

As early as the 1870's great wheat farms — the "bonanza farms" — began to develop in the Red River Valley, and today North Dakota depends on its some 70,000 farms for the main source of its income. Wheat is still its chief crop, but it is also a large producer of oats, barley, corn, rye, flax, potatoes, sugar beets and hay. Livestock likewise contributes largely to the support of North Dakota farms, with cattle, sheep, hogs, chickens and turkeys yielding the largest production. The state's mineral resources include oil, lignite (a variety of coal), clay, sodium sulfate, shale, sand and gravel. Its manufactures, in addition to the food processing and meat packing natural to a predominantly agricultural state, are nonalcoholic beverages, printing and publishing, brick, tile and pottery.

Uniquely North Dakota

North Dakota's motto, "Liberty and Union Now and Forever, One and Inseparable" is nowhere better symbolized than in the International Peace Garden that spans our border with Canada. A bronze plaque pronounces:

TO GOD IN HIS GLORY

We Two Nations Dedicate This Garden and Pledge Ourselves That as Long as Men Shall Live, We Will Never Take Up Arms Against One Another

Nearby is the Monument to the Four Chaplains, Catholic, Protestant and Jewish, who, aboard the aircraft carrier *Dorchester* when it was torpedoed during World War II, gave up their own life jackets and were last seen in prayer, with arms linked, as the ship sank. The Theodore Roosevelt National Park honors the President who once was a rancher in the Little Missouri country. In Medora is the twenty-eight-room chateau built by the French Marquis de Mores, who set out in 1883 to build an empire in the Badlands. He planned to slaughter cattle on the range and ship his meat east in refrigerator cars, thus eliminating the expense of the packing plants. His ice was cut from the Little Missouri and three hundred persons were employed by his Northern Pacific Refrigerator Car Company before the enterprise failed in 1886. At Rugby stands the cairn that marks the geographical center of the North American Continent.

North Dakota calls itself not only "The Flickertail State" but also the "Land of New Frontiers," and its eighteen-story Capitol Building at Bismarck is known as "the skyscraper of the prairies." Its largest city, Fargo — named in honor of William G. Fargo of Wells-Fargo Express Company fame — stands on the site where, 10,000 years ago, the water melted from a glacier 200 feet deep.

Mountain States

NEW MEXICO
"Land of Enchantment"

FOR AT LEAST 10,000 years — some authorities believe for 15,000 years—man has inhabited New Mexico. Today ruins of the great cities he built more than 1,000 years ago contain dwellings of three, four and five stories and have as many as 1,200 rooms. These first apartment houses in North America, constructed of desert earth and desert rocks, were set on high cliffs as a protection from enemies. Neither doors nor windows were placed on the first floor, and the people entered the dwellings by ladders that could be drawn up in case of attack. The roof of each floor served as the yard for the rooms above.

A people of mysterious origin, these cliff-dwellers were short and black-haired and, since as babies they were carried on hard cradle boards, the backs of their heads became flattened. Peaceful farmers, they grew corn, beans, squash, tobacco and cotton, domesticated the turkey and hunted deer and mountain sheep. Dishes and bowls of clay, brightly and beautifully decorated, were widely used. The cliff-dwellers wove loincloths, shirts, sandals and headbands, and fur robes and blankets lined with rabbit skin or turkey feathers protected them in winter. Their descendants — the Hopi, Zuñi, Acoma, Taos and other tribes — be-

*Land of
Enchant-
ment*

came known as the Pueblos, after the Spanish word *pueblo* meaning "village."

Seen across the desert, with the sun shining on the colored earth and rock of which these cliff cities were constructed, the houses shone like structures made of precious metals.

The Fable of Tejo

One who repeated such a story was Tejo, an Indian in the service of Nuno de Guzmán, governor of New Spain. Tejo told of a journey northward he had made with his father to trade feathers for ornaments. After traveling "between the two seas" for forty days across "a grassy desert," Tejo claimed, he had beheld "seven towns so large that they could be compared in size to Mexico and its suburbs." Guzmán should see those cities—"whole streets" were "occupied by silversmiths." Guzmán wished to find nothing better and in December, 1529 set out with an army of 400 Spaniards and 20,000 Indians to reach this fabled paradise. In 1531 he was back in Mexico, no richer than when he had departed.

Five years later four survivors of a shipwrecked expedition from Spain to Florida staggered into the village of Culiacán, relating stories of their wanderings from the coast of Texas to Spanish settlements on the Gulf of California. New interest in the regions to the north, based on these accounts, encouraged officials of New Spain to send forth another party of explorers. A Franciscan friar, Marcos de Niza, who had marched with Pizarro in the conquest of Peru, was leader of this group

that included a Negro slave named Estevan. Like Tejo, Estevan spoke of the Seven Cities. Marcos came within sight of the Zuñi pueblo of Hawikúh, where Estevan was killed. The Zuñis would not permit the friar to enter their city. When Marcos returned to Mexico, the viceroy of New Spain reacted with typical high-handedness, sending an army under Francisco Vásquez Coronado to conquer the country.

In July, 1540 Coronado subdued Hawikúh, but found neither riches nor food. Still, tales of an unbelievably rich country far to the east, called Quivira, lured Coronado and his disgruntled soldiers to further explorations the following spring. When he had marched as far as the land of the Quiviras, or Wichita Indians, in eastern Kansas, without finding either cities or gold, Coronado turned back in discouragement. As far as he was concerned, this entire business was a fool's chase.

The First Colony

Franciscan missionaries entering the country in later years invariably were killed by the Indians. Others came to learn of the fate of the friars who had gone before, but New Mexico remained unsettled by the white man until a wealthy mine owner, Don Juan de Oñate, appeared in 1598. Four hundred soldiers and settlers traveled with Oñate. A supply train of 83 wagons and carts and 7,000 head of livestock raised a trail of dust as Oñate journeyed from Santa Barbara to a place on the Rio Grande below El Paso del Norte (Juárez, Mexico). Here Oñate took formal possession of New Mexico,

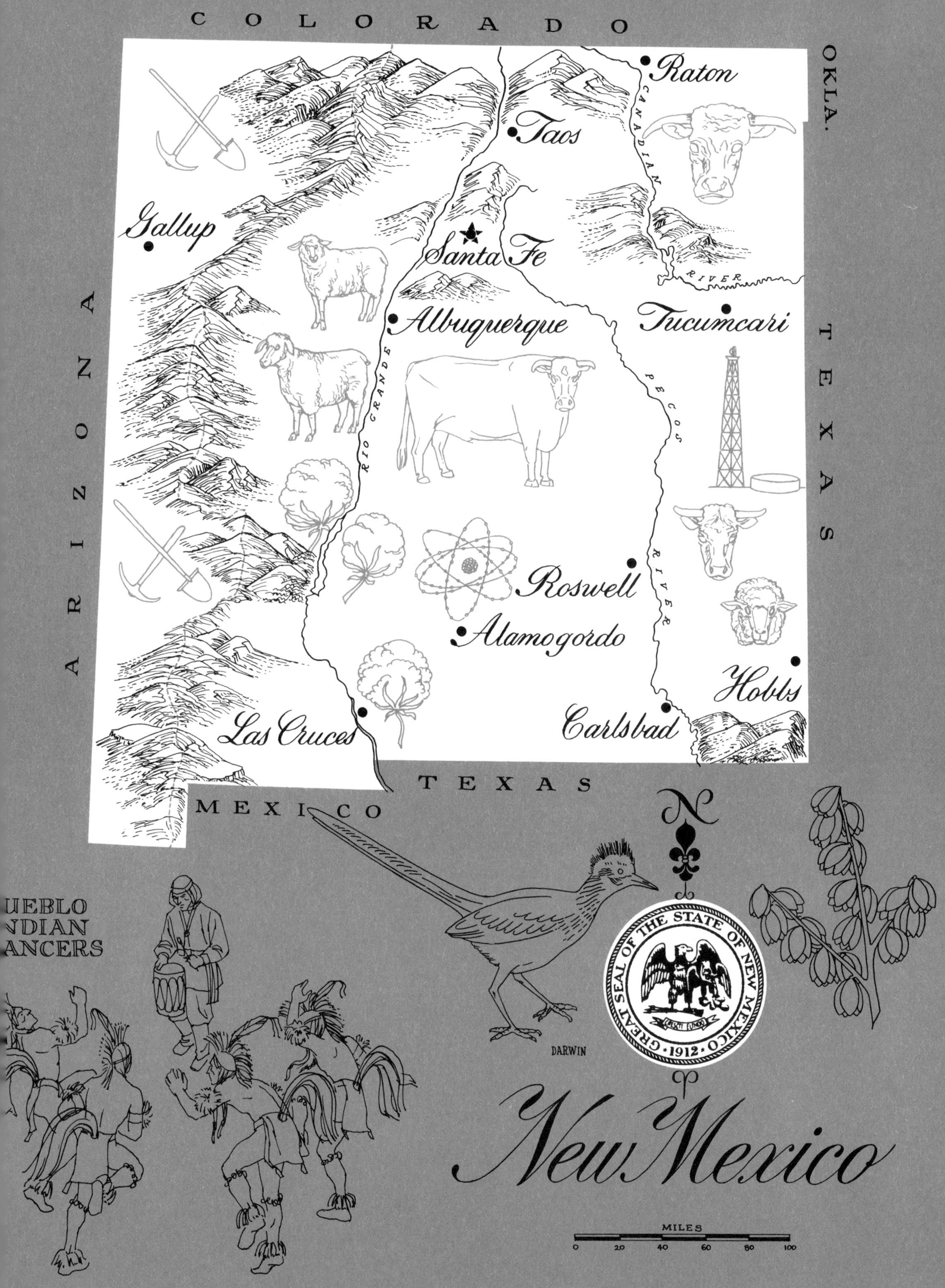

COLORADO

OKLA.

ARIZONA

TEXAS

• Raton

• Taos

CANADIAN

RIVER

Gallup •

Santa Fe

Tucumcari

Albuquerque •

RIO GRANDE

PECOS

RIVER

Roswell

Alamogordo

Hobbs

Las Cruces

Carlsbad

TEXAS

MEXICO

N

PUEBLO
INDIAN
DANCERS

DARWIN

· GREAT SEAL OF THE STATE OF NEW MEXICO ·
1912

New Mexico

MILES
0   20   40   60   80   100

Land of Enchant-ment

proclaimed himself governor, and established a permanent settlement on the Chana River that he called San Juan de los Caballeros — St. John of the Gentlemen — "in memory of those noble sons who first raised in these regions the bloody tree upon which Christ perished for the redemption of mankind." Within the boundaries of the United States only St. Augustine, established in Florida in 1565, antedated Oñate's colony.

Not only did Oñate bring the first mission system to New Mexico's Indians, but he also made extensive explorations of the Southwest, yet charges that he had ignored royal decrees, had acted disrespectfully toward the friars and had dealt too harshly with the Indians resulted in 1614 in his permanent banishment from New Mexico. Four years earlier a new governor, Don Pedro de Peralta, had moved the capital to Santa Fe, where it has since endured under four flags — of Spain, Mexico, the Confederacy and the United States.

Territorial Days

Spanish missions began to cover a wider area — to Pecos in the east and Zuñi and the Hopi pueblos in the west, to Taos in the north and El Paso del Norte in the south — and by 1626 forty-three churches ministered to 34,-000 Christian Indians. Civil and religious authorities quarreled constantly, however, and both in turn imposed forms of labor or tribute upon the Indians so that the region was harassed by sporadic Indian uprisings. Apache, Navajo and Ute Indians did not lose their distrust for the white man over

the next two centuries, accounting in no small measure for the fact that New Mexico remained so long a sparsely settled outpost of New Spain. With Mexican independence in 1821, the state became a province of Mexico, and was part of the territory that came to the United States after the close of the Mexican War.

Sections of the present states of Arizona and Colorado were included in the Territory of New Mexico, organized by Congress in 1850, and the region was further enlarged by the Gadsden Purchase four years later. Separate territories for Colorado (1861) and Arizona (1863) reduced the area of New Mexico. Briefly the Confederacy seized control during the Civil War, but in March, 1862, at the battles of Glorieta Pass and Pigeon's Ranch, sometimes called the "Gettysburg of the West," the Union regained control. Gold prospectors, down on their luck in California and Colorado, drifted into New Mexico in quest of happier days, and they were no small part of the movement that increased the population during these years.

"A Grand Necktie Party"

Another brand of "settler" also came into New Mexico, and this placard posted in Las Vegas on March 24, 1882 took heed of their presence:

"Notice to thieves, thugs, fakirs and bunko-seekers, among whom are J. J. Harlin, alias 'Off Wheeler,' Saw Dust Charlie, Wm. Hedges, Billy the Kid, Billy Mullin, Jack the Cutter, Pockmarked Kid and about twenty others; if found within this city after ten

o'clock p.m. this night, you will be invited to attend a grand necktie party, the expense of which will be borne by 100 substantial citizens."

Outlaws in New Mexico revealed their traits by their nicknames — Jackknife Jack, Web-fingered Billy, Splitnose Mike, Cold-deck George, Tommy the Poet. When the notorious Black Jack Ketchum was cornered after the Twin-Mountain Curve train robbery, he displayed the hard mettle of this breed as he watched a nervous hangman fumbling with the noose. "Hurry up," Black Jack snapped. "I'm due in hell for dinner."

The best known of this crew the Spanish-speaking people called "El Cabrito" or "Beely the Keed." Born in New York City in 1859 as William H. Bonney, Billy moved with his family to Kansas where, at the age of twelve, he stabbed a man who had insulted his mother, the first of a long line of murders. Thereafter the Kid drifted into Arizona, Mexico, Texas and finally New Mexico. Quick on the draw, Billy rode a horse with equal skill — "with no semblance of a rider," said Sheriff Pat Garrett, "save a leg thrown across the saddle and a head and arm protruding from beneath the horse's neck." Jailed, Billy starved himself for several days until he was skinny enough to shake off his handcuffs. He killed guard and jailer, danced a jig on the balcony of the jail, then rode off. The sheriff trailed him doggedly to a house in Fort

Land of Enchantment

Sumner where the following year, at the ripe old age (for an outlaw-killer) of twenty-three, the Kid's career ended under a rain of revolver shots.

Modern New Mexico

The coming of the railroads, cattle-ranching and a mining boom — and the collapse of Apache uprisings after the surrender of Geronimo in 1886 — found New Mexico growing steadily, and in 1912 it was admitted to the Union as our forty-seventh state. Its chief agricultural products, in addition to dairy and beef cattle, sheep and wool, and goats and mohair, include cotton, hay, wheat, peanuts, corn, alfalfa, sugar beets, sorghum, chickens and eggs, horses, fruits and vegetables. Among its mineral resources are petroleum, natural gas, natural gasoline, copper, coal, zinc, lead, manganese, potash, molybdenum (a metallic element of the chromium group), tungsten, gold and silver. The state's leading manufactures are pottery, iron and other metal products, chemicals, newspapers, flour, brick and tile, jewelry, leather goods and petroleum products.

Variously nicknamed "The Sunshine State" and "The Cactus State," it is as "The Land of Enchantment" that New Mexico is best described. Unique among the states, in that official business may be carried on either in Spanish or English, New Mexico's traditions may be traced in the language that has come down to us — in words like *chili, chocolate, coyote, mesquite* and *tamale* from Mexican-Spanish derivatives, in sayings like "all set" and "blaze away" from the era of the trad-ers and trappers, in the cattle raiser's *bronco* and *dogie*. The colorful terms of trailsmen enliven an American's speech — in phrases like "simple as a kit beaver" to denote stupidity, "hump yourself" to denote getting to work, "freeze on to it" to denote holding fast, or "feel like chawin'" to denote hunger.

On a broad sweep of the Rio Grande stands Albuquerque, founded in 1706, a city of streets lined with cottonwoods, tamarisks and poplars, one of New Mexico's proud towns. Santa Fe, the oldest capital in the United States, is the "Royal City" with a history that blends Indian, Spanish and American cultures. Taos, the British writer D. H. Lawrence once declared, possesses the most beautiful skyline in the world. But these places are only a few of the enchantments in this "Land of Enchantment." Stark and beautiful stands the mesa country — land of the Navajo Indian Reservation, the nation's largest, and famous El Morro with its Inscription Rock on which Oñate wrote *Paso por aqui* — "passed this way." The chants and drumbeats of Pueblo Indians, still living close to ancestral homes and hunting grounds, may be heard on ceremonial days. In southeastern New Mexico, once the haunt of Billy the Kid, are the famous Carlsbad Caverns, a wonderland of underground rooms and passages, and along the borderland deer, wild turkey, mountain lion and bear roam the forests of the Gila Wilderness Area. In this area one also finds a town named after a radio-television program — Truth or Consequences.

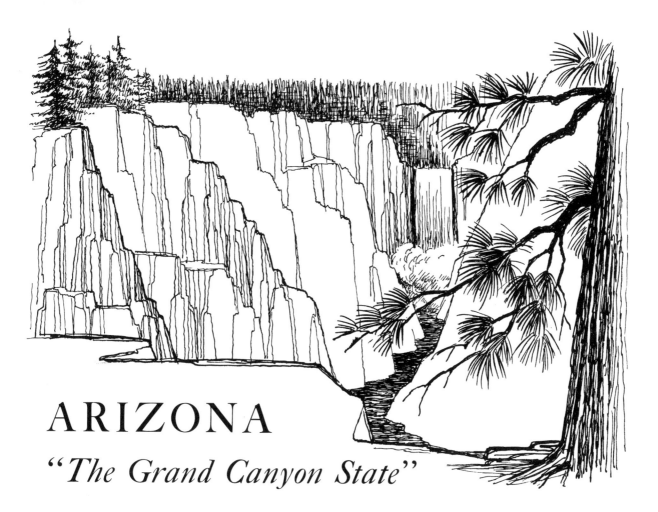

ARIZONA
"The Grand Canyon State"

UNTIL 1863 Arizona was included in the Territory of New Mexico, so it shares in common the history of its sister state. Probably the first inhabitant was Cochise Man, who may have lived in Arizona as long as 15,000 years ago, and so ancient is the land that dinosaur tracks found in the Painted Desert may date back 200 million years. In the valleys of the Gila, Colorado, Little Colorado, Verde and Salt rivers are the ruins of the cities of the cliff-dwellers that lured Coronado and his soldiers on their quest for gold.

A Franciscan friar, Marcos de Niza, passing through the San Pedro Valley in 1539 (the year before Coronado appeared), is the first white man known to have visited Arizona. Many Catholic priests came to preach among the Indians in the decades that followed, including Father Eusebio Kino who, in 1690, founded the mission of San Xavier del Bac near Tucson. After the Mexican War the region as far south as the Gila River became a possession of the United States. The Gadsden Purchase of 1854 extended the territory from the Gila River to its present boundary.

Early Territorial Days

Among those who visited Arizona in 1863, when it became a separate territory, was Daniel Conner, who pictured the typical town of adobe houses looking like small brick kilns:

"The alcaldes (mayors or judges) and padres (priests) are generally the

*The
Grand
Canyon
State*

only personages of any consequence in the whole country and are usually found about the little villages, lazily engaged in a game of cards, or else they are asleep. The houses seldom have other than a solidly beaten dirt floor and the major part of the people live and reside at their homes without a table or chair, knife or fork about the establishment. Their houses looked as void of comfort or conveniences or even of household plunder as a chicken-coop, and frequently [are] without a fireplace."

In this primitive country the universal vehicle was a two-wheel cart drawn by a small Mexican ox. Plows were made from the forks of trees, with one fork cut short and sharpened to go into the soil. Conner visited the territory's first capital, Tucson, then a village of some 300 inhabitants, where "the coyote wolves from the surrounding desert would come and howl at it all night and sneak about its suburbs all day." Father Kino's mission of San Xavier stood abandoned in the desert and was cared for by "a tribe of very black Indians, known as the Jacquois," who allowed no one to enter the cathedral without removing his shoes.

The Scourge of Geronimo

Without roads leading east or west in a country bristling with hostile Indians the future of the territory seemed bleak. Most feared of the warriors who opposed the white man was Geronimo, a medicine man and prophet of the Chiricahua Apache. Named Goyathlay, meaning "One Who Yawns," he was called Geronimo from the Span-

ish for Jerome. By his own account, he was born in June, 1829 in No-doyohn Canyon, Arizona, and as a boy "would practice stealing" and "feats of war."

When Mexicans killed his mother, wife and children in 1858, Geronimo vowed vengeance upon his enemies and thereafter his fame as a skillful, cunning leader of raids spread throughout the Southwest. Geronimo's last series of forays against settlements in New Mexico and Arizona began in 1884 and was provoked by the government's efforts to stop the Indians from making an intoxicating drink called *tiswin*. For three years, wherever Geronimo rode, he left a trail of death and destruction. In 1886 General George Crook captured the Indian terrorist, but Geronimo, agreeing to a truce, violated this promise and fled across the border. General Nelson A. Miles now led the pursuit. For five months Miles and his Federal soldiers searched the haunts of the Indian raiders and at last in the mountainous region of Skeleton Canyon, near the present town of Apache, cornered their prey. With his supplies gone, on September 3, 1886 Geronimo agreed to a surrender. He lived until 1909, accepting Christianity and dying peacefully.

With the scourge of Geronimo removed, Arizona began to develop rapidly. In 1870 its population was 9,658 and by 1900 the territory had grown to 122,931. Large deposits of gold, silver and copper were powerful incentives to settlement. Copper mining was in progress at Ajo as early as 1854, and silver mining began along the Santa Cruz River shortly thereafter. The first

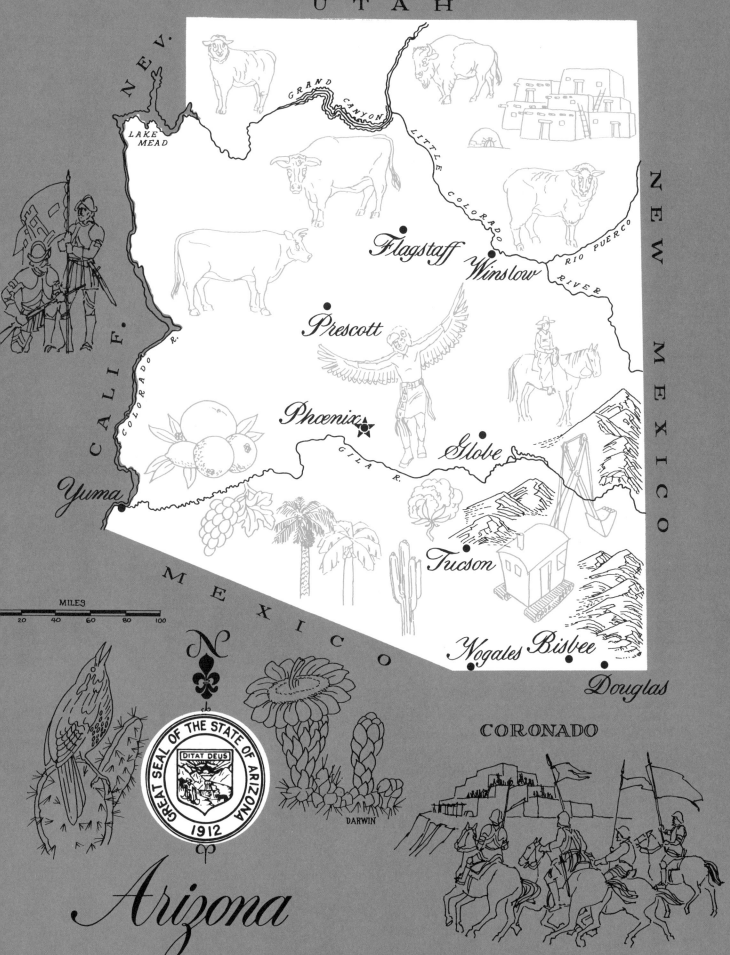

UTAH

NEV.

CALIF.

NEW MEXICO

MEXICO

LAKE MEAD

GRAND CANYON

LITTLE COLORADO

RIO PUERCO

RIVER

COLORADO R.

GILA R.

Flagstaff

Winslow

Prescott

Phoenix

Globe

Yuma

Tucson

Nogales Bisbee

Douglas

MILES
20 40 60 80 100

N

GREAT SEAL OF THE STATE OF ARIZONA
DITAT DEUS
1912

DARWIN

CORONADO

Arizona

Geronimo

until Wyatt Earp strode into town, with guns at his hips, determined to bring respect for the law to Tombstone.

This town, which in the boom years of the Schieffelin silver strike grew to 7,000 inhabitants, had 110 saloons where a man could find the courage for all kinds of deviltry. But it had also Boot Hill cemetery, where many a bad-man ended his career in desolate silence, although justice sometimes miscarried, as in the case of the tombstone reading "George Johnson, hanged by mistake." Floods began to ruin the mines in 1886 and by 1900 Tombstone was well on its way to becoming one of America's most celebrated "ghost" towns.

In 1912 Arizona was admitted to the Union as our forty-eighth state. In succeeding years irrigation and water-power projects, such as Coolidge Dam in 1930, the Yuma-Gila reclamation program begun in 1935, and Boulder Dam, dedicated the following year, have made desert lands flower. Long growing seasons combined with a semi-tropical climate today give Arizona an intensive, varied agriculture that includes such crops as dates, cotton, alfalfa, hay, barley, flaxseed, grain sorghums, potatoes, wheat, grapefruit and oranges.

But Arizona's leading industry is mining, and several of its copper mines are among the greatest in the world. Other mineral resources include gold and silver, wolframite (a source of tungsten), onyx marble and low-grade coal deposits, while among the fine gems found in the state are peridot (a deep yellowish-green variety of chryso-lite), garnet and turquoise. Smelting

gold placers were discovered on the Gila River in 1858, and in the late 1870's silver strikes were made near Superior and Tombstone.

"Hanged by Mistake"

All sorts followed the quest for quick wealth into Arizona, and with the plodding, ever-hopeful prospector came outlaws and gunfighters like Billy the Kid and the notorious Clanton brothers. The forbidding desert and arid gulches around Tombstone made it an ideal hideout for fugitives — that is, and sawmills provide Arizona's principal manufactures, and other products are brick and concrete blocks, cottonseed oil and cottonseed meal, flour, lime, canned and dried fruits, and mattresses.

"Amazing Arizona"

Ditat Deus reads the motto of Arizona, meaning "God enriches," and these words certainly ring true in this spectacular land in which seventeen national monuments and parks are situated. The most astonishing is Grand Canyon, a great gash in the earth 217 miles long, from 4 to 18 miles wide, and a mile deep to the Colorado River roaring through its multicolored walls. Among the other wonders of nature and the past preserved in Arizona are Wupatki National Park, northwest of Flagstaff, with 35,000 acres set aside for the preservation of Indian ruins; Chiricahua National Park, once the ancestral home of Geronimo and the nomadic Apaches, with its beautiful pinnacles of volcanic rock; Navajo National Monument, northeast of Flagstaff, with its cliff-dwellings dating back to A.D. 1300; the Petrified Forest, with the most colorful concentration of petrified wood to be found anywhere in the world; and Saguaro National Monument, east of Tucson, where cactuses bloom in a "forest without leaves."

The lakes and streams of Arizona tempt the angler with trout, bass and channel cat, and the hunter finds white-tailed deer, elk, antelope, bighorn sheep, javelina, bear, mountain lion, coyote, bobcat, quail and turkey. From March through August Arizona's sixteen Indian tribes hold various ceremonials — the Apache rodeo at San Carlos in late March, the Yaqui Ceremonials near Tucson during the Easter season, the All-Indian Powwow at Flagstaff in July and the Hopi Snake Dances and Smoki Ceremonials (at Prescott) in August. Land of breathtaking mountains and desert grandeur, of irrigated fields, orchards and grazing cattle, home of the cowboy and the miner with his pick — such is "amazing Arizona." Daniel Conner, among the first to explore this country in the middle 1860's, related:

The Grand Canyon State

". . . The Apaches do have one wonderful virtue of which we all might do well to consider, with a view to imitate it. They never fight amongst themselves and bruise one another's faces like enlightened people do. They never fly into a passion, and knock each other down, like we do in polished life. Nor do they become savage enough to kill a friend and say it was done under sudden heat and passion, like Christians do. All this is unknown amongst them. Even the children do not know how to become petulant and fight each other and to knock each other's teeth out. These customs seem to belong exclusively to the most polished races of mankind. And one other prominent charge I deem worth a single notice to wit: Their use of poisoned arrows. I do not suppose that there is one single instance of a responsible man ever charging an Apache Indian with ever having used a poisoned arrow or lance."

As a desert may be made to bloom, so, too, it seems, may the hearts of a primitive people.

COLORADO

"The Centennial State"

SINCE COLORADO was admitted to the Union in 1876, one hundred years after the adoption of the Declaration of Independence, it is known as "The Centennial State." Coronado, searching for his fabled Seven Cities in the early 1540's, led the first white men into Colorado country. Probably other Spaniards were in the territory in succeeding decades, and in 1776 two missionaries, Silvestre Vélez de Escalante and Francisco Atanasio Domínguez, exploring for a new route into northern California, visited western Colorado. The fur traders came next — among them an American, James Purcell, who operated in the Colorado region in 1803.

Three years later the young adventurer, Zebulon Montgomery Pike, set out from St. Louis to explore the country to the headwaters of the Arkansas and Red rivers. Descending the Arkansas through Royal Gorge, he beheld that towering mountain of the Rampart range of the Rocky Mountains that bears his name — Pike's Peak — although not until 1819 did a party under Major Stephen H. Long climb its forested slopes to the bare granite summit 14,110 feet above sea level. Long's journey through the valleys of the South Platte and Arkansas were responsible for the idea that only an uninhabited, uncultivable "Great American Desert" existed here. A waste of time to think of settling such a country, proclaimed Daniel Webster, who told the United States Senate: "I shall never vote one cent from the public treasury to place the Pacific Coast one inch nearer Boston than it is now."

"Pike's Peak or Bust"

In 1822 along the Santa Fe Trail the first wagons rolled dustily across Colorado. In the following decade fur traders strung private forts along the Platte, and in 1846-47 the Mormons settled briefly at Pueblo. The 1840's also brought the famous Pathfinder, John C. Frémont, into Colorado, and at last the nation was given accurate information about this vast domain. The year 1857 was one of gloom and financial depression in the East, and the movement westward was greatly accelerated.

But, generally, pioneers in search of brighter futures ignored, as among the wildest and most frightful of the unknown West, that part of the Kansas Territory now Colorado. Then, overnight, the situation changed as men read headlines such as appeared in the *Kansas Weekly Press* for September 4, 1858:

Gold! Gold!! Gold!!! Gold!!!!
Hard to Get and Heavy to Hold
California and Frasers river
"no whar!"...
Cherry Creek and Pike's Peak Ahead!!!
Great Excitement!! The Atlantic Cable
not Thought of!!!

Gold in Colorado had been discovered by the Cherokee Indians in 1850, but it was not until eight years later, when George Simpson took his breadpan and spade down to Cherry Creek near present-day Denver and "found the color" in the first panful he washed, that the country went wild with the Colorado gold fever. From all directions came the seekers of fortune, jogging over mountain trails in wagons

that had painted on their canvas covers: "Pike's Peak or Bust!"

A poet in the *Hannibal* (Missouri) *Messenger* caught the spirit of the times:

> *Take up the oxen, boys, and harness*
> *up the mules;*
> *Pack away provisions and bring*
> *along the tools;*
> *The pick and the shovel, and a pan*
> *that won't leak!*
> *And we'll start for the gold mines.*
> *Hurrah for the Peak!*

Another verse sang lustily:

> *Then ho! for the mountains, where*
> *the yellow dust is found,*
> *Where the grizzly bear, and buffalo,*
> *and antelope abound;*
> *We'll gather up the dust along the*
> *golden creek,*
> *And make our "pile," and start for*
> *home. Hurrah for Pike's Peak!*

Towns Grow Overnight

An estimated 100,000 persons poured into Colorado during the spring of 1859, and that year towns that sprang up almost overnight included Denver, Central City (which some called "the richest square mile on earth"), Mount Vernon and Nevada City. Still the miners came, and in 1860 and 1861 other new towns dotted the map of Colorado — Breckinridge, Empire, Gold Hill above Cripple Creek that prospectors dubbed a "$300,000,000 cow pasture," Georgetown and Mill City. Boulder and Golden were towns that came into being as places where miners stocked up before heading for "the hills." Some made fortunes, but many did not. In June, 1859 a reporter for the *Kansas Press* drew a picture of Pike's Peakers returning over the Santa Fe Trail:

". . . Hurrying into town, we found it jammed full of men, women, and children; within one hour we counted over one hundred wagons on their return. Never did our heart bleed for a set of people as it did for these men and women. . . . Mutterings, loud and deep, were heard against those who had humbugged them, as they said; men were swearing like pirates, who, from their awkward manner, in using the profane, had evidently been pious in the states. We should not wonder if we heard of terrible outbreaks, [and] when this emigration reaches the river towns, murders and robberies may become

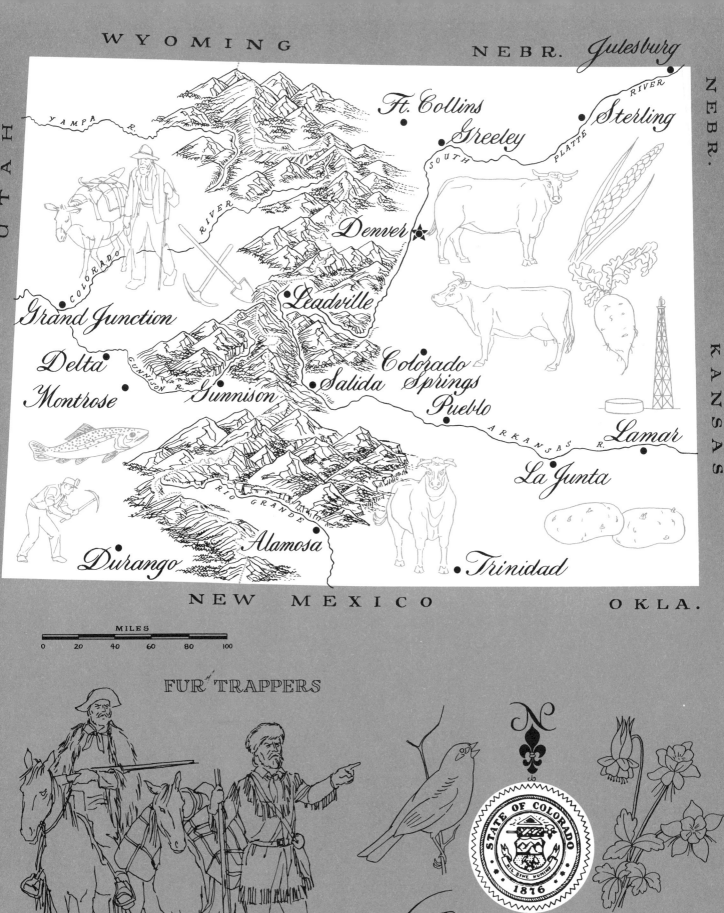

WYOMING   NEBR.   *Julesburg*

UTAH

Ft. Collins
Greeley
Sterling

NEBR.

Denver

Grand Junction

Leadville

KANSAS

Delta
Montrose
Gunnison
Salida
Colorado Springs
Pueblo
Lamar

La Junta

Durango
Alamosa
Trinidad

NEW MEXICO   OKLA.

MILES
0   20   40   60   80   100

FUR TRAPPERS

STATE OF COLORADO
NIL SINE NUMINE
1876

Colorado

The Centennial State

common. Great suffering, it was said, existed on the plains; men who had given out were, in many instances, left to starve. The wheel barrow, hand cart, and foot emigrant, were literally starving."

Toward Statehood

By 1860 the population of Colorado was 34,277. Two years earlier the state was included in "Arapahoe County," a part of Kansas Territory, and Congress was petitioned to create a separate "Jefferson Territory." The independent Territory of Colorado was formed in 1861, but the Civil War and conflict with the Cheyennes and Arapahoes held back the development of the country. In 1870 the railroads reached Colorado, new towns and farms spread across the region, and in 1876 Colorado was admitted to the Union as our thirty-eighth state. The mining booms, the removal of the Ute Indians from western Colorado, and the "wet" years of the 1880's that produced bumper crops on the eastern plains all stimulated growth, and by 1890 the state's population had risen to 413,249.

Then nature turned against Colorado. Years of dry weather wilted crops and 1893 brought a panic. Silver was dropped as a standard of United States currency. Strikes and lockouts in the mines produced unrest and martial law, and trouble between cattlemen and sheep raisers added to the general turmoil. With the turn of the twentieth century, however, a trend developed that found Colorado depending less on mining and more on agriculture, livestock raising and manufacturing.

Modern Colorado

Modern Colorado is a land where miracles possible through irrigation may be seen. Hay, sugar beets (especially in the valleys of the South Platte and Arkansas), grains, sorghum and broomcorn are the principal field crops. Vegetables and fruits are shipped to eastern markets, and the head lettuce grown in the high, cold mountain regions and cantaloupes from the Arkansas Valley are renowned for their fine flavor. Livestock raising today finds the rancher more concerned with better breeding than with maintaining wide open ranges, to make his profit.

Mining continues, of course, to contribute to Colorado's economic strength. Gold, copper, silver, lead and zinc are found in the mountain sections and many oil fields have been developed. Two-thirds of the world's supply of molybdenum, a metal used in hardening steel, comes from Colorado, and the state also possesses rich deposits of uranium. West of the Mississippi, Colorado is the nation's leading producer of coal, and its other natural resources include sandstone, granite, onyx, limestone, marble, alabaster and lava rock. With such raw materials available, Colorado quite naturally has become one of our most prosperous manufacturing states west of the Mississippi. Chief among its products are lumber products, processed meat, iron and steel, newspapers and periodicals.

"Nothing Without God"

Nil sine Numine, the motto of Colorado, means "nothing without God," and the words seem especially appropriate for this state situated in the heart of the Rocky Mountains. In the east are the hundreds of square miles of the Great Plains with grasses ideal for grazing cattle. In mid-state rise the mountains that are known as the "Roof of North America" and west of the Rockies lies the high Plateau region that becomes desert land as it approaches the boundary of Utah. Colorado's five majestic mountain ranges — San Juan, Park, Sangre de Cristo, Front and Sawatch — give the state an average height of 6,800 feet above sea level, and the chief peaks are Mount Elbert (14,431 feet), Mount Massive (14,481 feet), Blanca (14,390 feet), La Plata (14,340) and Uncompahgre (14,306). At the lowest elevation along the Arkansas River in Prowers County the state is 3,350 feet above sea level.

More than 14,000,000 acres of land in Colorado are national parks, forests and monuments, including Rocky Mountain National Park in north-central Colorado and Mesa Verde National Park in the southwest. The highest automobile road in the United States leads to the summit of Mount Evans, west of Denver, and near Colorado Springs stands the Garden of the Gods, where centuries of weathering have produced gorgeous pinnacles and spires of red sandstone. Into this beautiful country where once the miner came in covered wagon, visitors by the thousands come each year by plane, train and car to breathe Colorado's dry, invigorating air and to behold natural splendors that, indeed, do prove that there could be "nothing without God."

UTAH

"The Beehive State"

PERHAPS AS early as 1540, when Spanish *conquistadores* under García López de Cardenas discovered the Grand Canyon, white men looked upon southeastern Utah. Then 236 years passed before, in late July of 1776, two Franciscan priests, Father Escalante and Father Dominguez, seeking a direct route between Santa Fe, New Mexico, and Monterey, California, entered Utah along the White River, heard stories of the Great Salt Lake, and were treated kindly by bearded Utah Indians.

For the next half century, it was not missionaries but restless fur trappers who opened the territory to future settlers. Men who left their names in the histories of many mountain states appeared in Utah. Jim Bridger became the discoverer of the Great Salt Lake. Jedediah S. Smith, that devout Yankee Methodist who journeyed with a rifle in one hand and a Bible in the other,

was the first to cross the Salt Desert. From 1843 to 1845 John Frémont and Kit Carson explored and mapped the Utah country.

Yet the event that more than any other shaped the future of Utah occurred on a September day, 1823 in western New York State. On that day, said Joseph Smith, an ancient American prophet who gave his name as Moroni, appeared as a resurrected being and messenger from heaven. In a hill once called Cumorah and located between Palmyra and Manchester, New York, Moroni told Smith, was a record engraved upon gold plates. Here Smith would learn the stories and the prophecies of ancient Americans of Israelite origin who had lived in the western hemisphere from about 600 B.C. to A.D. 420. Later eleven witnesses testified that Joseph Smith had found the golden plates which he had translated "by the gift and power of God."

Thus came into being the *Book of Mormon,* upon which the religion of the Latter Day Saints was based. Among the tenets of the Mormons was this doctrine:

"We believe in the literal gathering of Israel and in the restoration of the Ten Tribes; that Zion will be built upon this [the American] continent; that Christ will reign personally upon the earth; and, that the earth will be renewed and receive its paradisical glory."

Wanderings of the Mormons

Smith's first converts were drawn from the rural districts of New England. Moving westward in search of the promised Zion, the Mormons settled in 1831 in Kirtland, Ohio. Other members of the church, reaching Jackson County, Missouri, believed that they had found the site for "Zion, the New Jerusalem," and were joined here in time by the Kirtland colony. Missourians of Jackson County favored slavery and the Mormons did not, an early seed of dissension between the two groups. Political tensions increased to the point where Missouri's governor, Lilburn W. Boggs, declared that the "Mormons must be exterminated or driven out of the state." At the Haun's Hill Massacre the militia killed seventeen Mormons and wounded many women and children.

Joseph Smith now led his followers on a new "exodus" to Hancock County, Illinois, and on swampy river land on the east bank of the Mississippi built Nauvoo, which, with a population of 20,000, quickly became the largest city in Illinois. Converts from Great Britain, won through the preaching of Brigham Young, swelled the Mormon ranks. A split in the church led Joseph Smith to high-handed action against his opponents in destroying their newspaper and calling out his own troops to patrol the city. Charged both with riot and treason, Smith was jailed in Carthage on the pledge of Governor Ford that he would not be harmed, but on June 27, 1844 an armed mob, their faces blackened, broke into the jail and murdered the Prophet.

Again the Mormons moved westward in search of Zion, this time under the leadership of Brigham Young, who "spoke with the voice of Joseph." In 1846 the first parties crossed the Mississippi and that winter quartered on the west bank of the Missouri, near present-day Omaha. Before leaving Nauvoo, Young had read Frémont's reports of the Great Salt Lake Valley, and a "vision" carried him irresistibly toward that goal. On July 21, 1847 the first Saints reached the promised land.

Miracle of the Gulls

The first act of the Mormons was to turn the waters of City Creek out of its bed to soften the land for plowing, and in this arid region an early knowledge of the miracles to be wrought by irrigation accounted for the survival of Young's followers. Land, water, timber were all owned by the community. The law of the land was the law of the church, while toward the Indians, Young proclaimed a simple policy: "It is better to feed the Indians than to fight them." By the end of August, that

The Beehive State

DARWIN

Mountain States

MONTANA
IDAHO
WYOMING
UTAH
ADA
COLORADO
ARIZONA
NEW MEXICO

The
Beehive
State

first summer, the Mormons "broke, watered, planted, and sowed upwards of 100 acres with various kinds of seed," stockaded nearly 10 acres, and constructed "one line of log cabins in stockade."

"Faith through works," the key to Mormon living, was severely tested in the spring of 1848. One of the settlers, John Steele, wrote in his journal that June: "Our wheat, corn, beans and peas are all up and looking grand and grass is 6 inches high. Sunday, June 4th, there is great excitement in camp. There has come a frost which took beans, corn and wheat and nearly every thing, and to help make the disaster complete the crickets came by the thousands of tons, and the cry is now raised, 'we can not live here, away to California,' and the faith of many were shaken." Then out of the skies, as though sent by God, appeared flocks of gulls to gobble up the crickets. By mid-July new wheat was through the ground. Wrote Steele in his journal: "God had sent us here, and here we are going to stay, come weal come woe."

The State of Deseret

The land the Mormons occupied belonged to Mexico, but with the treaty of Guadaloupe Hidalgo in 1848, terminating the Mexican War, the territory came under the jurisdiction of the United States. That December a memorial twenty-two feet long and bearing 2,270 signatures was sent to Congress, requesting admission to the Union for the "State of Deseret," a word that in the language of the *Book of Mormon* meant "honeybee." Not until Septem-

ber, 1850 did Congress act, granting territorial status and substituting for the Mormon "Deseret" the Indian name of "Utah," which, one historian has observed, hardly pleased those for whom it set up a vision of a "dirty, insect-infested, grasshopper-eating tribe of Indians." Young was named governor of the new territory, but unhappy times were ahead both for the Mormons and the Federal agents who dealt with them.

Three factors led to subsequent hostilities. For one, the Federal agents too often were either fools or outright scoundrels. For another, Young, as leader of the church, believed that he derived his authority directly from God, and the multiplication of Mormon settlements through Utah attested to the effectiveness of his administrative judgment. Finally, the Mormon doctrine of polygamy that allowed a man to take more than one wife was considered immoral by non-Mormons (or "gentiles"). Indian war in 1853, growing out of the Mormon government's prohibition of the slave trade among the Indians, and the grasshopper plague of 1855-56 were fleeting bedevilments compared to the continuing bickering with the Federal authorities.

President Buchanan, trying to keep the abolitionists from plunging the nation into a civil war, was easily convinced that the Mormons, who opposed slavery and favored polygamy, were in open rebellion against the United States Government. Federal troops were sent to Utah to curb the rebels. "We do not want to fight the United States," Young said grimly, "but if they drive us to it,

WYOMING

MILES
0 10 20 30 40 50 60 70

Logan
Brigham
Ogden

Salt Lake City

Vernal

GREEN RIVER

Moab

COLORADO

SAN JUAN RIVER

Provo

Price

JORDAN R.

Tooele

GREAT SALT LAKE

SALT LAKE DESERT

Nephi

SEVIER R.

Richfield

Cedar City

Kanab

ARIZONA

NEVADA

THE MORMON TREK

DARWIN

THE GREAT SEAL OF THE STATE OF UTAH
1896
INDUSTRY
1847

Utah

232

we shall do the best we can." And he added: "We have three years' provisions on hand, which we will cache, and then take to the mountains and bid defiance to all the powers of the government."

"Buchanan's Blunder"

The Utah War — sometimes called "Buchanan's Blunder" — followed. It does not make a pretty story. September, 1857 brought the frightful Mountain Meadows Massacre in southern Utah when men, women and children were led by whites into an ambush where a party of Indians and whites slaughtered them. Young's boast that he intended to rule Utah "until the Lord Almighty says, 'Brigham, you need not be governor any longer,'" convinced even the Federal authorities that they had best find a way to compromise their differences. The Federal troops were withdrawn, and many claimed they had been sent to Utah only as a ruse to get them out of the way until the plotters of the Confederacy could complete their conspiracy to secede from the Union. The Ute Black Hawk War, following in 1865-68, ended the conflict with the Indians and Utah since has existed in peace.

Triumph at Promontory

The occupation by Federal troops, the appearance of the Pony Express and finally the crews that came as the tracks of railroads east and west were pushed to a joining point doomed the isolated reign of the Mormons in Utah. Still, "gentiles" of a rowdier disposition coming into Utah soon learned to

Brigham Young

respect the Saints, and a popular song of pioneering days, sung to the tune of "Solomon Levi," advised the non-Mormon newcomer to Utah:

Have you heard of Porter Rockwell?
He's the Mormon triggerite.
They say he hunts for horse thieves
When the moon is shining bright.
So if you rustle cattle,
I'll tell you what to do,
Get the drop on Porter Rockwell,
Or he'll get the drop on you.

Meanwhile in Utah the tracks of the Central Pacific and the Union Pacific neared their point of joining at Promontory. On May 10, 1869 crowds gathered in an icy wind for the great event. Irish and Chinese railroad builders, statesmen and train crews, saloon-keepers and gamblers mixed in the waiting throng. Nevada had sent a silver spike, Arizona a spike "ribbed with iron, clad in silver, and crowned with gold." Gold and silver spikes came from Idaho and Montana. From Promontory the tracks of the Union Pacific ran 1,085.5 miles and the tracks of the Central Pacific 690 miles. At last the speeches were over, the last spike driven and the two locomotives touched their cowcatchers. To a country eager to celebrate this moment when East was linked with West by railroad, the telegrapher tapped out the message:

The last rail is laid.
The last spike is driven.
The Pacific railroad is finished.

"The Beehive State"

Utah applied for admission as a state in 1849, 1856, 1862, 1872, 1882 and 1887. Each time opposition to polygamy thwarted Utah's hopes. Finally in 1890 the Mormon Church outlawed plural marriages and on January 4, 1896 Utah was admitted to the Union as our forty-fifth state.

Utah is a natural wonderland. Mountains towering 13,000 feet, gorges that run to depths of 3,000 feet, the Great Salt Lake where a bather cannot sink — such are some of Utah's features. What geologists call Lake Bonneville was, in times when dinosaurs roamed this part of the world, a vast expanse of water covering 19,000 square miles, and Utah's principal cities are all built on terraces or "benches" of this enormous prehistoric lake.

"Dugway" is a Mormon word for a road or a deep rut scraped into the face of a hill, and today the word is applied to any road excavated around the side of a mountain. Eight mountain ranges — Wasatch, Oquirrah, Pine Valley, Raft River, Deep Creek, Uinta, La Sal and Henry — give Utah its full share of dugways. They give Utah as well considerable income from the mining of copper, silver, lead, gold and zinc.

Coal, salt, iron, gypsum and uranium also are mined. With seven national forests, Utah lists lumber among its income producers.

Where irrigation is possible, Utah's soil is rich and productive, and its most important crops are hay, wheat, potatoes, alfalfa seed, sugar beets, barley and corn. Food processing is its most important industry, then metal production, while other manufactures include petroleum and coal products, printing and publishing, chemicals, stone, clay and glass products, apparel and machinery.

Utah, "The Beehive State," is a series of happy images — the rocky pillars of the Temple of Queens in Bryce National Park, the Rainbow Natural Bridge in southeastern Utah, mining copper ore at Bingham, sheep on the range in Duchesne County, Great Salt Lake at sunset, the great Mormon temple built of gray granite six feet thick, the richly colored sandstone miracles of the Navajo Twins, Needle Rock, Ostrich Rock.

And Utah is a will, a spirit, a dedication — it is, perhaps above all else, a choir singing the words of "Come, Come Ye Saints," a Mormon hymn:

Come, come ye Saints, no toil nor labor fear.
But with joy wend your way;
Tho' hard to you this journey may appear,
Grace shall be as your day.
'Tis better far for us to strive
Our useless cares from us to drive;
Do this, and joy your hearts will swell —
All is well! All is well!

The Beehive State

NEVADA
"The Silver State"

IN NEVADA you can tell a man's occupation by the way he talks. In the mining regions a shovel is a *muck-stick,* a drill is a *steel,* a light hammer used in single-hand work is a *single-jack* and a heavier hammer used in double-hand drilling is a *double-jack. Hard-rock miners* work on a lode or underground, and the worker in gravel deposits is a *placer miner* or *gravel miner.* Shovelers are *muckers* and operators of drilling machines are *machinemen.* A miner who contracts tuberculosis from silica dust has *rocks on the chest.* Rich ore is *jewelry-store-ore* or *jewelry-ore.*

The ranch country of Nevada has another lingo. Cattle that require fattening are *feeders,* the oldest and poorest cattle are a *hospital bunch,* and strong cows and calves that require little special feed are a *dry bunch.* A group of saddle horses is a *cavy* or *remuda.* Branding irons are *stamp irons* or *running irons.* Men who ride the range are *cowboys* or *buckeroos, waddies, cow punchers, hands* and *cow pokes.* A saddle is a *cactus* or *rigging,* the horn of the saddle a *biscuit* or *old Susie.* A cowboy's guns are *smoke cannons, hip cannons* or *hog legs,* and the bed he carries is a *hot roll.* A saying among Nevada ranchmen insists that *riders* come from the north, *ropers* from the south.

Early Travelers in Nevada

The name Nevada is derived from a Spanish word meaning "snow-clad," and probably the first European to enter Nevada territory was a friar, Francisco Tomas Garcés, who may have crossed its southern tip when journeying from California to Mexico in 1775. The fur traders, undaunted by mountains, gorges and deserts, traveled through Nevada in the early 1800's — the Hudson's Bay Company's Peter Skene Ogden, Jedediah S. Smith, Joseph Walker and Captain Eulalie Bonneville, and those indefatigable explorers and mapmakers, John C. Frémont and Kit Carson. In 1830, striking out with a caravan from Santa Fe, William Wolfskill crossed Nevada near present-day Las Vegas on his way to Los Angeles, and this route became famous as the Old Spanish Trail.

When in 1849 Brigham Young organized Utah as the "State of Deseret," Nevada was included in the domain claimed by the Mormons. Then the gold rush of the Forty-Niners started a stream of wagon trains across Nevada, en route to California. That June, H. S. Beatie, a trader sent into the territory by Brigham Young, became Nevada's first settler when he built a stockade and corral in the valley of the Carson River that he called, not surprisingly, Mormon Station (its later name was Genoa). Soon from Mormon Station farmers sprinkled dwellings and plowed fields along neighboring Washoe and Eagle Valleys, and Pleasant, Steamboat, Jack and Pahranagat became names denoting new Mormon settlements.

In 1850 Congress organized Utah Territory, including most of Nevada as Western Utah, though part of southern Nevada was included in the Territory of New Mexico. Mail service by mule team and by men who traveled the Sierras on snowshoes led the way in 1854 to the establishment of a road between Salt Lake City and California. Non-Mormon settlers in the Carson Valley had reasons, both fancied and real, to complain over a government that had its seat five hundred miles away. When Federal authorities threatened war against the Mormons in 1857 [see Utah, pp. 226-233], Young recalled his Saints to Salt Lake City to mobilize for the conflict. As early as 1853, and again in 1856, non-Mormons in the Carson Valley had wanted to be annexed to California, but now the settlers tried to establish a provisional government at Carson City and to gain independent territorial status. Two years later, in 1859, they again petitioned Congress for recognition, but the reaction was entirely negative. What right had this wilderness with its sprinkling of settlers to the dignity of recognition as a territory?

The Comstock Lode

That year gold miners in Washoe were annoyed by "black stuff" that made the recovery of gold difficult, and finally sent a sample of the ore to be assayed. The "black stuff" was silver — the unbelievably rich Comstock Lode — and many who had rushed into California seeking quick riches rushed back into Nevada.

In a land where neither law nor authority existed, where a man's gun was his sole defense against rowdy and cutthroat, where Comstockers hired gunmen at twenty dollars a day to protect

The Silver State

Indian disturbances continued with raids on Pony Express and stage stations till after the Civil War.

The news of Abraham Lincoln's election as President was carried to Nevada by Pony Express riders, and Lincoln's wish in the closing months of the Civil War to gain another free state to support the amendment abolishing slavery greatly influenced Nevada's admission to the Union in 1864 as our thirty-sixth state. Nevada at the time had less than one-sixth of the population required for statehood, and in order to speed up its admission, the state's constitution was telegraphed to Washington — at a cost of $3,416.77!

Modern Nevada

The history of Nevada since statehood has been one of mining booms, depression, the discovery of other deposits and new booms. Thus Nevada divides its story of economic growth into distinct cycles — the Comstock Lode, the great silver discovery at Tonopah, the jewelry-ore gold strike at Goldfield, the copper mines at Ely, and finally the development of the cyanide process of recovery which makes possible the profitable working of low grade ores and the reworking of old tailings. Today, among the states, Nevada ranks first in the production of manganese and tungsten, second in mercury, fourth in copper, sixth in silver, seventh in gold and lead and eighth in zinc.

Ranching is the main support of Nevada's agriculture and a good part of the state's 110,540 square miles is devoted to the raising and grazing of

their claims and no saloonkeeper ever troubled to make change for a five-dollar gold piece, life was anything but even-tempered and easy-going. By 1861 the rush into mining camps around Virginia City had increased Nevada's population to the point where it was recognized as a territory (additions to its area in 1862 and 1866 brought the state to its present size). Indian uprisings, largely among the Paiutes, produced a three-hour battle at Pyramid Lake in May, 1860, and the casualties numbered forty-six Indians to three whites. The

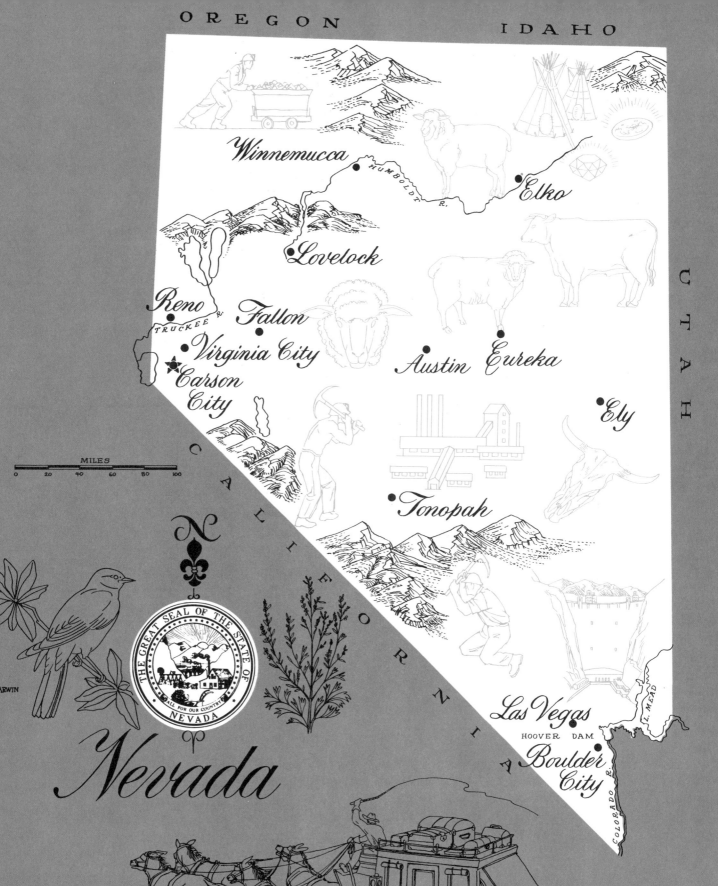

OREGON   IDAHO

Winnemucca

HUMBOLDT R.

Elko

Lovelock

Reno

TRUCKEE R.

Fallon

Virginia City

Austin   Eureka

Carson
City

Ely

C A L I F O R N I A

U T A H

MILES
0   20   40   60   80   100

Tonopah

N

THE GREAT SEAL OF THE STATE OF
ALL FOR OUR COUNTRY
NEVADA

DARWIN

Nevada

Las Vegas

HOOVER DAM

Boulder
City

L. MEAD

COLORADO R.

WELLS
FARGO
STAGE

The
Silver
State

cattle, sheep, hogs and horses and to the production of hay and forage. Farming is dependent on irrigation and each year arid land is being turned into verdant regions. Hearts of Gold cantaloupes and turkeys in the Fallon area and cotton near Pahrump are points of agricultural pride. Other leading crops include Irish potatoes, corn, wheat, oats and barley.

Manufacturing is just getting a start in Nevada, yet the state's industrial future is bright. Boulder Dam, the world's largest dam, is located about twenty-five miles southeast of Las Vegas. Lake Mead, the reservoir it has created, is the world's largest man-made lake, 115 miles long and 300 feet deep, with a capacity for storing 500 billion gallons of water. The generators operated by the dam supply half the power consumed in southern California, Arizona and Nevada, and can irrigate more than 800,000 acres of farm land in these same states. With Nevada's abundance of mineral resources, smelting and refining are, as one would expect, its chief industries, but the state is showing steady progress in meat packing and food processing, flour and grist milling, leather goods and glass, jewelry and clay products.

Take a Chance

Whirring roulette wheels and slot machines or "one-armed bandits" are a familiar part of the Nevada scene, for gambling long has been legalized. Reno, "the biggest little city in the world," and Las Vegas are gambling meccas that attract the larger part of the 12 million visitors who each year come to Nevada to take a chance on their luck.

Yet Nevada has much to offer the non-gambling visitor. The state is largely a vast tableland between 4,000 and 5,000 feet above sea level — part of what John C. Frémont named "the great basin" between the Wasatch Mountains and the Sierra Nevadas. It has many mountain ranges, rivers, lakes and deserts. Mountain-rimmed Pyramid Lake, Lake Tahoe — "the jewel in the sky" — scenic Wilson Canyon, the agricultural splendor of Paradise Valley, the "Singing Sand Mountain" near Fallon, the active geyser region near Beoawae, the Lehman Caves near Ely and the Joshua forests near Caliente suggest its variety of natural wonders.

And for the history-minded, Nevada comes close to making an industry of ghost towns, with Virginia City, "Queen of the Comstock," the most famous. Candelaria, Belmont, Rawhide, Round Mountain, Rhyolite, Aurora, Jumbo, Como, Austin, Eureka and Bullfrog are other ghost towns. Hamilton is another — once the first city in eastern Nevada, with 101 saloons.

Nevada, ninety-one times the size of Rhode Island, has one inhabitant to a square mile. Yet here is a state where anything can happen. Take, for example, that day in 1864 when Reuel C. Gridley brought a sack of flour to Austin to pay off an election bet. The sack was auctioned for the benefit of the United States Sanitary Commission, forerunner of the American Red Cross. That same fifty pounds of flour was sold and resold at auction until $275,-000 had been raised!

WYOMING

"The Equality State"

IF YOU would know how our nation developed west of the Mississippi River, turn to the history of Wyoming.

The Louisiana Purchase of 1803 secured that part of the state east of the Continental Divide except for a small part of Carbon and Albany counties. The remaining portion of southwestern Wyoming was included in the territory that came to the United States with the annexation of Texas in 1845. The following year the northwestern corner of the state was part of the "Oregon country" dispute settled by a treaty with Great Britain. At the close of the Mexi-

can War in 1848 Wyoming gained the final part of its land in the southwest.

For reasons no longer clear, the state is named after Wyoming Valley in Pennsylvania. The name is a corruption of a word of the Delaware Indians, *maughwauwame,* meaning "upon the great plain."

There are unverified legends of early Spanish expeditions reaching Wyoming, and still other authorities contend that the first white men in Wyoming were two French Canadians, François and Louis Joseph Vérendrye, who came overland from the Saskatchewan River in 1743. Another sixty

*The
Equality
State*

years were to pass, however, before that hardy group of trappers and explorers known as "the mountain men" began the enduring history of Wyoming.

A Land of Wonders

When the Lewis and Clark expedition was returning to its base in 1806, John Colter, a woodsman with the party, struck off into the wilderness to trap. He passed through the Big Horn Mountains, reached the headwaters of the Green River, and came at last upon the wonders of the Yellowstone country. He probably saw Lewis and Shoshone Lakes and the three falls at the head of the Grand Canyon. Hot pools, mud springs and small geysers were other marvels he encountered along the way. Skeptics doubted the stories he told afterward. Derisively they called this "fabled" region "Colter's hell."

But the wonders were there and elsewhere in Wyoming and later expeditions found them — the party under Wilson Price Hunt, who came into the northern part of the state for Astor's American Fur Company in 1811, and Robert Stuart who, returning with messages for Astor, crossed the Continental Divide in 1812. General William Ashley traveled up the Missouri and established a trading post on the Yellowstone in 1822. Other great explorers and trappers followed — among them the redoubtable Thomas Fitzpatrick, whom the Indians called "Broken Hand, Chief of the Mountain Men"; Robert Campbell and William L. Sublette, who founded the trading post that eventually was known as Fort Laramie; and the remarkable Jim Bridger, whose

three Indian wives included a Flathead, a Ute and a Shoshone.

Jim's life, like his stories, was almost unbelievable. Once, he claimed, he tried to jump across a gorge in a petrified forest and found he couldn't make it. "If the petrified air hadn't held me up," Jim said, "I would have been killed." You can believe the tale if you like, but there is more truth in the story of the officer at Fort Laramie who one day fired a six-pounder into a herd of bison and killed thirty with one shot.

Mountain Rendezvous

Until 1840, when the bottom fell out of the trade in beaver pelts, the rendezvous of mountain men along the Green River became the annual occasion when these fellows sought the enjoyments of "civilization." As many as 1,500 trappers attended a single rendezvous. Also, many Indian bands gathered for the festivities — Shoshones, Crows, Nez Percés, Flatheads, Bannocks.

Great trading sessions were held for sugar, coffee and clothing, whiskey, guns and ammunition. Rival trading companies bid for this business, and no one troubled over scruples in striking a bargain. Gambling and lusty brawls were numerous. Indians danced, chanted and beat their skin drums while squaws eagerly bought up beads and trinkets, and naked children raced around the grassy hillsides.

A sensation occurred at the rendezvous in 1836 when two missionaries, Dr. Marcus Whitman and the Reverend H. H. Spalding, arrived with their wives — the first white women to enter Wyoming! Bearded trappers cheered

MILES
0   20   40   60   80   100

MONTANA

S. DAKOTA

NEBRASKA

UTAH

COLORADO

SHOSHONE RIVER

•Sheridan

•Cody

Worland

Jackson

BIG HORN R.

WIND R.

BELLE FOURCHE R.

•Casper

Lander

GREEN R.

Kemmerer
Green River

Rock Springs

Evanston

•Douglas

N. PLATTE R.

Torrington

Laramie

Cheyenne★

N

FORT
LARAMIE

EQUAL RIGHTS

GREAT SEAL OF THE STATE OF WYOMING

Wyoming

DARWIN

*The
Equality
State*

the ladies and the Indians slaughtered their fattest dogs for a feast.

In the twenty years from 1848 to 1868 Wyoming came in turn under the jurisdiction of Dakota Territory, Nebraska Territory, Utah Territory, Idaho Territory and once more Dakota Territory. Yet Wyoming grew steadily toward becoming a territory in its own right, aided in no small part by the fact that the Oregon Trail, crossing Wyoming, brought some 300,000 persons westward during the period from 1840 to 1869. Free land was the promise of those who trudged the Oregon Trail. Those who plodded the Mormon Trail sought religious freedom, and those who traveled the California Trail dreamed of gold and quick riches.

Wyoming Gets Its Nickname

South Pass City, a town of placer ditches and sluice boxes on Big Hermit Creek, owed its origin to the rumor of a gold strike in 1842. Not until thirteen years later, however, was pay dirt taken from its streambeds, and even that find was not too promising. But later discoveries brought a stampede. False front stores and clapboard houses made from raw lumber sprang up. Two stage lines connected South Pass with the Union Pacific at Point of Rocks and by 1869 the town boasted of some 4,000 inhabitants, a weekly newspaper, a school system, five hotels and thirteen saloons.

That spring one of South Pass's leading citizens, William H. Bright, led the campaign for independent territorial status upon the basis that would earn Wyoming its designation as the "Equality State," for women were

given equal rights with men! The following year Esther Hobart Morris became America's first woman justice of the peace (and in 1924 Wyoming elected Nellie Tayloe Ross as the nation's first woman governor).

In the territorial years of Wyoming the bulk of settlers was found in the towns along the tracks of the Union Pacific. With the opening of the first land office in Cheyenne in 1870, the homesteaders began pushing in. But Wyoming's future in those years depended more on the discovery that cattle could be easily fattened on the bunch and buffalo grass covering the plains. Soon the depredations of the Shoshones and Sioux, who had ravaged the territory from 1862 to 1866, seemed mild beside the shootin' troubles that beset the cattlemen.

"Git Along, Little Dogies"

The farmer and his fences began the hostilities in the view of the cattlemen, who wanted free range for the herds they drove up from Texas. (In 1884 it was estimated that as many as 800,000 longhorns came up the Texas Trail, or Long Trail.) An unwritten law of the range that any unbranded animal over a year old — called a "maverick" — could be branded and claimed by the person who found it gave rise to a new breed of troublemaker in the rustler. Then the sheepherder added to the cattleman's bedevilments, for sheep nibbled the grass close and sharp hoofs dug up exposed roots. The hard winter of 1886-87 drove some ranchers out of business, and many unemployed cowhands turned to rustling. A symbol of the kind of bitterness brewing was the fact that the town of Buffalo, south of the Platte, became known as the "rustlers' capital" as Cheyenne in the north was called the "cowmen's capital."

The Johnson County Cattle War of 1892 was a classic example of the conflict. The way to cure rustling was to hang or shoot the men who practiced it, and to accomplish this end the cattlemen organized a society called the Regulators. Hired gunmen were brought from Texas, Idaho and Colorado. The objective was Buffalo — the Regulators aimed to clean out that rustlers' nest as often as necessary — but Buffalo was forewarned of the attack and the cattlemen were trapped on the T A ranch, fourteen miles south of town, and surrendered.

Knowing the temper of the Johnson County people, the government wisely sent the cattlemen to Cheyenne until peace could be restored. Ultimately the homesteaders won out over the cattle barons, yet as late as the early 1900's, sheepherders and camp tenders were shot by masked riders while their herds were "rimrocked" — that is, driven over cliffs by shouting raiders.

"There's a Growing, Splendid State"

Admitted to the Union in 1890 as our forty-fourth state, Wyoming advanced steadily toward its position today as a state where great herds of cattle graze on its mountain slopes and its sheep supply a good part of the nation's wool. As early as 1832, Captain B. L. E. Bonneville discovered oil in Wyoming, and travelers along the Oregon Trail once mixed it with flour as an axle grease for their wagons. Today twenty-two refineries in Wyoming process crude oil, and one well has been dug to a depth of 14,307 feet. The state is also a good coal producer. Englemann spruce and alpine fir form the backbone of Wyoming's lumber industry, but aside from petroleum refining and lumber products, the state's manufacturing is almost entirely designed for local consumption.

Wyoming truly has to be seen to be believed — this "cowboy's state" famous for rodeos, ghost towns, majestic dams, dude ranches, great national parks like Yellowstone and Grand Teton and a dozen mountain ranges. Its chief rivers are the Big Horn, Powder, Green and North Platte. Mountains look like *mountains* in Wyoming, and the state is a hunter's paradise, offering such game as bear, deer, elk, antelope, moose and mountain sheep. More than 5,000 lakes attract the fisherman. And for live Indians, who can beat the All-American Indian celebration held annually in Sheridan, the first week of August, when Indians from forty tribes and eighteen states gather to dance, display their crafts and pick an Indian Miss America!

A proud Wyomingite feels in his heart the words he sings when the band strikes up the official state song:

In the far and mighty West,
Where the crimson sun seeks rest,
There's a splendid, growing state that
  lies above;
On the breast of this great land,
Where the massive Rockies stand,
That's Wyoming young and strong,
  the state I love!

The Equality State

IDAHO
"The Gem State"

IDAHO, the most northern of the Rocky Mountain states, derives its name (or so the legend persists) from the Shoshone Indian words, *Ee da how,* meaning "the sun comes down the mountain" or "light coming down the mountain" or "it is morning." Part of the Oregon country claimed by Spain, Russia, Great Britain and the United States, Idaho was first visited by white men in 1805 when the Lewis and Clark expedition crossed the mountains from Montana. Four years later, two British traders — David Thompson and Finan McDonald — entered Idaho and the following spring they shipped out forty-six packs of fur, each weighing ninety pounds.

Hard on the heels of Thompson and McDonald appeared Andrew Henry, representing the Missouri Fur Company, and in 1811 William Price Hunt, who worked for John Jacob Astor's enterprises, led an expedition of fifty-six people through Idaho's overland trail to the mouth of the Columbia River. The War of 1812 brought Idaho under British control, and not for another thirty-five years, when Britain and the United States settled their border dispute along the forty-ninth parallel, did Idaho become indisputably an American possession.

A Noble Man

Ten years earlier — in 1836 — the Reverend Henry Spalding and his wife, sent into this wild region by the American Board of Foreign Missions, became the first white family to settle in Idaho. They built a school for Indians on Lapwai Creek, east of Lewiston, and here the following year their daughter, Eliza Spalding, became the first white child to be born and raised in Idaho.

A gentle, noble man, Henry Spalding planted corn, wheat and oats at his mission, and also the state's first apple and locust trees. From a granite cliff up the Clearwater River he quarried pieces suitable for a millstone and floated them on a raft to a site near his home. He built a mill wheel and dug a ditch from Lapwai Creek to carry the water to the wheel. Nez Percé Indians thus saw unfolding before their eyes a new kind of civilization. Later Henry Spalding built a sawmill and set up the first printing press west of the Rockies and north of California. A primer, a hymn book and the Gospel of Matthew in the Nez Percé language were among his publications.

Other missions came into Idaho — the Sacred Heart Mission among the Coeur d'Alene Indians, established in 1842 by Father Desmet, the great Catholic pioneer in the Northwest; and a Mormon mission and colony in the valley of the Lemhi River in 1855. Idaho remained, however, a lonely wilderness, without any real impulse to settlement, until 1860 when Captain E. D. Pierce discovered gold in "Canal Gulch," a tributary of Orifino Creek which in turn emptied into the Clearwater River. Reports published in Walla Walla and Portland newspapers set off a stampede.

"Houses Sprang Up Like Magic"

W. J. McConnell, who one day would serve as governor of Idaho, remembered the scene as thousands of prospectors rushed to Orifino Creek:

Chief Joseph

*The Gem
State*

"Houses had sprung up like magic in the town named 'Orifino,' and before the end of the summer of 1861, the newly fledged metropolis was supplied with stores, hotels and saloons, the last outnumbering the others. . . . The braying of the pack-mules, and the clatter of the carpenters' and the blacksmiths' hammers gave zest to the hundreds of pedestrians continually moving about the streets from one place to another as fancy or some excitement attracted them. Violin music was heard in most of the saloons, and gambling was an adjunct of them all. New arrivals were almost continuous and departures of prospecting parties were of daily occurrence. These parties usually consisted of from two to six, and up to ten men, all heavily armed and provided with pack animals to carry their supplies. In this manner the surrounding mountains were quite thoroughly explored during the summer of 1861, resulting in the discovery of many rich claims, including the placers adjacent to Pierce City, Elk City, Florence and Warrens.

"As each new discovery became known, a stampede from the first locations resulted, hundreds of men leaving fairly good claims, in many instances, to join the mad rush to the new Eldorado. Disappointment in many cases followed, for, while all the camps contained rich placer deposits, yet, as might have been expected, they were limited in area; it therefore happened that, of the thousands of gold seekers who followed each excitement, many were unable to secure claims. In fact, it mattered not how extensive the field might be, among such a number were always to be found many so-called men, who were merely grown-up boys, without sufficient experience or energy to locate a mining claim."

Others didn't try, preferring to depend on a gun or their luck at cards to wrest their riches. Quickly Idaho claimed its own special lot of cutthroats and thieves — its Henry Plummer and Matt Bledsoe and "Dutch Fred," among too many more. Another was "Cherokee Bob," a Georgian who commented on the style of two rival gunmen: "Jakey [Williams] always steps aside to get clear of the smoke of his revolver, while Rube [Robins] pushes through it and keeps on coming, getting nearer his adversary with each shot." But no matter what style an Idaho gunman used, his career almost invariably ended with a bullet or dangling from a rope!

Indian Uprisings

In 1862 at Lewiston the first newspaper in Idaho, appropriately titled the *Golden Age,* began publication. That same year gold was discovered in the Boisé basin of southern Idaho and in 1863 Idaho Territory was organized to include Montana (separated from the territory in 1864) and most of Wyoming (admitted to the Union in 1868).

Trouble with the Indians developed when the miners and ranchers who continued coming into Idaho tried first by treaty and then by coercion to seize the fertile valleys. A war with the Nez Percés broke out in 1877. These hardy Indians, whose name in French meant "Pierced Nose," were capably led by Chief Joseph. Federal troops were

CANADA

Sandpoint

Coeur d'Alene

WASH.

MONTANA

Lewiston

LEWIS and CLARK

MILES
0   10   20   30   40   50

N

GREAT SEAL OF
ESTO PERPETUA
THE STATE OF IDAHO

DARWIN

Idaho

SUGAR

Boise

Idaho Falls

WYOMING

SNAKE RIVER

Pocatello

OREGON

Twin Falls Burley

NEVADA

UTAH

The Gem State

roundly defeated in White Bird Canyon, and later the Nez Percés cleverly avoided a battle on the Clearwater. Surrounded at last near the Canadian border in Montana, Chief Joseph surrendered with a touching speech:

"I am tired of fighting. Our chiefs are killed. Looking Glass is dead. Toolhulhulsote is dead. The old men are all dead. It is the young men who say yes or no. He who led the young men are all dead. It is cold and we have no blankets. The little children are freezing to death. My people, some of them, have run away to the hills and have no blankets, no food. No one knows where they are — perhaps freezing to death.

"I want to have time to look for my children and see how many of them I can find. Maybe I shall find them among the dead. Hear me, my chiefs. I am tired. My heart is sick and sad. I will fight no more forever."

The Bannocks tried to carry on hostilities after the Nez Percés surrendered, but with the death of their great leader, Buffalo Horn, their cause was doomed. Idaho now was clearly the white man's domain. By 1890 its population had reached 88,548 and in the same year Idaho was admitted to the Union as our forty-third state.

Land of Mystery

Almost as large as England and Scotland combined, Idaho is a land where there are still regions that no one ever has explored. Its mountain ranges equal in beauty and majesty any range in America, with Mount Borah, the highest point in Idaho, towering 12,662 feet above sea level. Its Sho-

shone Falls are forty-three feet higher than Niagara Falls, and its Seven Devils Gorge is deeper than the Grand Canyon. Its Salmon River — "The River of No Return" — flows through one of the longest canyons in the world and is the longest river entirely within one state, while in its Craters of the Moon National Monument are more than sixty volcanic craters, lava and cinder cones. Its Warm Springs, in Boisé, maintain a temperature of 170° Fahrenheit, and it has caves where the ice never melts.

Yet amid all this beauty, grandeur and mystery, Idaho today remains a place where people live well and work hard. Agriculture and livestock are its main income producers, and principal crops include hay, wheat, barley, oats, corn, alfalfa, potatoes, sugar beets, fruits and vegetables. In the production of antimony, cobalt, silver and zinc, Idaho has become the nation's leader, and it also ranks high in lead and cadmium, and in the production of elemental phosphorus. Forests that are rich in pine, spruce, cedar, white fir, larch and red fir make shingles and other lumber products the bulwark of its industrial enterprises, but other manufactures include beet sugar, canned goods, flour and meat products.

Esto Perpetua — "Be Forever" — reads the motto of Idaho, where such natural wonders as the Bitterroot and Wasatch ranges, great waterfalls and health-giving mineral springs promise to endure as long as man. An effort failed in 1921 to create a new state, to be called Lincoln, from parts of Idaho, Montana and Washington.

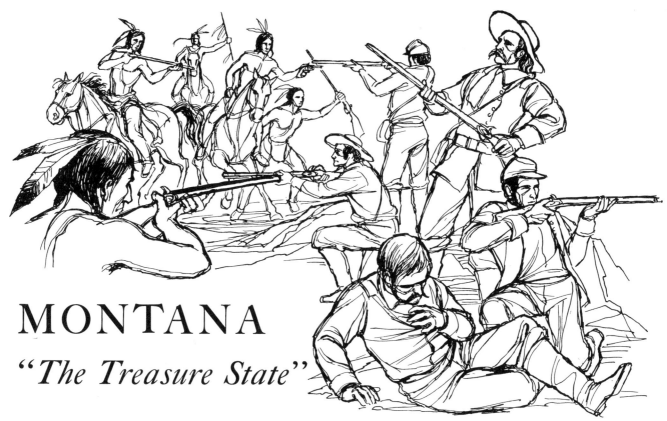

MONTANA
"The Treasure State"

POSSIBLY an expedition under the French trader, Pierre Vérendrye, reached Montana, though the evidence is not clear, and the first white men known definitely to have visited this country were the party that followed Lewis and Clark across the continent in 1805. Ascending the Missouri River to the confluence of the three streams that form it, they named the main fork Jefferson, after the President who had sponsored their expedition, and the other forks Madison and Gallatin, in honor of his Secretaries of State and the Treasury.

Around the voyagers towered the wilderness — awesome and lonely, for even the Indians seemed to have dropped out of sight. The explorers passed through canyon walls that rose twelve hundred feet overhead and whose projecting rocks appeared ready to tumble on them. They saw mountain sheep on a nearly perpendicular cliff and these big-horned animals, Lewis wrote in his diary, "walked about and bounded from rock to rock with apparent unconcern where it appeared to me that no quadruped could have stood." They saw herds of buffalo, and Lewis estimated their number at not less than ten thousand within two miles.

By late July, Clark suffered with torn feet that had ulcerated, so Lewis and three companions struck out with Sacajawea, their Shoshone guide, to explore the region. On August 12 they came to a little rivulet that was part of the great Columbia and they had crossed the Continental Divide — the first Americans ever to do so. Later they led their party across the Divide, near the vicinity of Dillon, Montana, through Lemhi Pass into Idaho. When they returned the next year, they re-entered Montana by the same pass.

*The
Treasure
State*

Traders and Miners

Fur traders came next into Montana — Manuel Lisa in 1807 to construct the first building on the Yellowstone at the mouth of the Big Horn, John Colter who, that same year, lost his trail and stumbled on what is today Yellowstone Park, David Thomas of the Northwest Company who, in 1808, built a trading post on the western slopes of the state at Kootenai Falls. For the next half century the fur trade in Montana was a seesaw, with the Americans holding the eastern half and the British controlling the western.

Only a few white settlers had trickled into the valley of the Bitterroot when in 1858 James and Granville Stuart found the first gold, yet a full-fledged rush into the Montana

country did not develop until three years later with the rich strike on Grasshopper Creek in the country of the Beaverhead. Other strikes by 1864 at Alder Gulch, and later at Confederate and Last Chance Gulches, soon made Bannack, Virginia City and Helena the names of mining camps known across the United States.

Montana's mining boom attracted the same motley crew that appeared in all gold fields. Weather-beaten prospectors, using the sharpened prongs of elk horns for picks, came over the western mountains, and from the east came former Confederate soldiers who, stumbling in their broad-toed army boots as they traveled the rocky land, gave Montana the nickname of "The Stubtoe State." Outlaws and murderers came like rodents out of the hills, and in a country where neither courts nor sheriffs existed, local vigilantes brought their own brand of justice into Montana — the hangman's noose without the nuisance of a trial.

These were lively times in old Montana. Georgia-born John M. Bozeman brought the first party in 1863 over the famous trail he opened from Fort Laramie, Wyoming, to Virginia City. Jim Bridger, the renowned wilderness scout, favored a pass to the north and in 1864 raced Bozeman to see who had the better route. Making from fifteen to twenty miles a day, they reached Virginia City only hours apart. Eleven miles south of Dillon, the historical highway marker tells the story of an age when men tried to rule by a .45 Colt: "Henry Plummer, sheriff and secret chief of the road agents, was

NORTH DAKOTA

Montana

THE GREAT SEAL OF THE STATE OF MONTANA

DARWIN

WYOMING

IDAHO

Miles City

RIVER

YELLOWSTONE

FORT PECK RES.

MISSOURI R.

Billings

BIG HORN

Great Falls

Bozeman

Livingston

Helena

Butte

Missoula

Anaconda

CLARK FORK RIVER

Polson

Kalispell

BLACKFOOT
INDIANS

MILES
0   20   40   60   80   100

*The
Treasure
State*

hanged at Bannack in '64 by the Vigilantes. It tamed him down considerably."

Disaster at the Little Big Horn

Montana was moving toward future empire. At Virginia City in 1864 *The Montana Post* became the state's first newspaper. Hitherto part of the territories of Missouri, Nebraska, Oregon, Washington and Idaho, the Territory of Montana was organized that same year with the capital at Helena, where Last Chance Gulch ran down what is now its main street. In round figures, gold taken from Montana by 1876 was valued at $144,400,000 — and the flow of miners into the territory quickened. But so, also, did the tempers of the Cheyennes and the Sioux.

General George A. Custer, who at the age of twenty-three had been the youngest brigadier general in the Union armies, led the Federal troops against the Indians in 1876. A tough, wiry man, Custer did not disguise his sympathy for his foes, declaring: "If I were an Indian, I often think that I would greatly prefer to cast my lot among those of my people who adhered to the free open plains, rather than to submit to the confined limits of a reservation."

In late June of 1876, Custer and his six hundred troops pushed cautiously along the Rosebud, where scouts brought reports of Indian trails turning westward toward the Little Big Horn River. Custer made two mistakes: he refused to wait for reinforcements and, in sighting the Indian encampment two miles from the river, he underestimated

its size. Dividing his company into two attacking columns, he gave the order to charge. The Indians, however, were everywhere. They overwhelmed the Federal troops, throwing them in panic against the bluffs of the river. Custer waved his hat in encouragement, the last time he was ever seen alive. Only one survivor, a mute witness, lived through the disaster on the Little Big Horn — Comanche, Custer's horse.

"The Richest Hill on Earth"

Yet the following year, with the surrender of the rebellious Nez Percés under Chief Joseph [see Idaho, pp. 244-248] the Indian troubles in Montana largely ended. Already cattle drives from Texas had reached western Montana, where they were trailed to Ogden, Utah, for shipment on the Union Pacific, and now with the Indians subdued and the rails of the Northern Pacific creeping through the state, the cattle business flourished. The sheepherder, shipping his wool by flatboat to New Orleans via the Missouri and the Mississippi, also was becoming a substantial figure in Montana.

But Montana's future was still as "The Treasure State," especially when metalliferous quartz taken from the hills at Philipsburg and Butte revealed rich veins of silver. Even so, "the richest hill in the world" remained to be discovered. Marcus Daly, who liked to boast that he had landed in America at the age of fifteen with nothing to his credit except his Irish smile, changed Butte from a dying mining camp into an Eldorado. As manager and owner of a mine named by whim after a phrase in a newspaper that said Grant's army was encircling Lee's "like a giant anaconda," Daly began with a discouragement. Three hundred feet down the silver played out and a red metal appeared. But Daly's Irish smile flashed where others turned away, and today the Anaconda Copper Mine, one of the richest in the world, is a monument to his faith.

Oro y Plata

Oro y Plata — "Gold and Silver" — proclaims the motto of Montana, but copper also dominated the story of the territory, the more so, really, after Montana was admitted to the Union in 1889 as our forty-first state. The "Wars of the Copper Kings" between Marcus Daly and W. A. Clark — reputedly growing out of an injury to Daly's thin-skinned Irish pride when Clark insisted the success of the Anaconda Mine was simply "dumb luck" — so rent Montana with political animosities that the state's development was handicapped for a decade.

Death finally ended the Daly-Clark feud. Montana's farming grew, its railroads expanded, and sugar refining and flour milling developed into stable industries. Oil and natural gas, discovered in the 1920's, and Federal irrigation projects later, explain also why Montana's population, slightly more than 20,000 in 1870, had passed the half-million mark by 1940.

Farm crops in Montana today include wheat, oats, barley, hay, corn, seeds, flax, sugar beets, potatoes, peas and fruits. Cattle and sheep, horses and swine are the bulwarks of its livestock enterprises, but poultry and dairy products each year are growing in importance. Mining comes next to farming and livestock in Montana's economic resources, and in addition to petroleum, natural gas, coal, gold, silver, copper, zinc, manganese, phosphate rock and granite, jewels are cut from sapphires found in Rock Creek, Cottonwood Creek, Yogo Gulch and Judith Basin. Softwood dominates Montana's lumbering. Smelting and the refining of ores are the leading industries.

The Treasure State

A wide, high and handsome state, say many of Montana — and so indeed is this state that includes seventeen national forests in addition to Glacier National Park. Along with spectacular scenery, rodeos and Indian ceremonial dances await the visitor to Montana, and in honor of one large group of hardy pioneers, Norwegian Independence Day is observed in Sheridan County on each May 17. The Indians, who gave the state its name, called Montana "the land of the shining mountains," and all agree when they behold such towering mountains as Granite Peak (12,799 feet), Mount Powell (12,000 feet), Mount Douglas (11,300 feet), Mount Cowen (11,190 feet) and Crazy Peak (11,178 feet).

Think of a wheat pile a mile high, or a stack of lumber that size, or a million Christmas trees, or a silver dollar, or trout in a stream and elk in a forest, or row upon row of haystacks, or a miner panning a creek, or a cowboy chasing a dogie, or the crater of an old volcano, or a geyser spouting into the air. These thoughts could only mean you were thinking about Montana!

Pacific Frontier

HAWAII
"Paradise of the Pacific"

EVEN among gods of legend, life is no bed of roses. Maui, the Polynesian demigod, suffered far more than anyone suspected. As the youngest in the family, he was a pesky tag-along to his brothers. Once in a fit of impatience his mother threw Maui into the sea, where he might have perished had not a kindly jelly-fish befriended him. And his sister complained that she would not feel so hungry if Maui were a better fisherman.

Weary of such ridicule, Maui set out to prove he was not a shiftless no-account. He descended into the underworld, and from the jawbone of an ancestor fashioned a fishhook. For bait he took one of his mother's sacred birds. With his brothers paddling the canoe, Maui demanded that they row farther and farther into unknown seas before he consented to cast his line.

When the canoe lurched, Maui's brothers could tell that the hook had caught the greatest fish they ever had seen. Quietly Maui smiled to himself, relishing the prospect of their astonishment when he hauled from the water the catch he knew was there — the islands of Niihau, Kauai, Oahu, Molokai, Lanai, Kahoolawe, Maui, and Hawaii.

The Fall of Mighty Lono

How many thousands of years passed before the white man stumbled upon Maui's fabulous haul, no one can say. The eight islands that comprise our fiftieth state cover an area of 6,439 square miles, but so vast is the Pacific Ocean that for centuries they remained tucked away like forgotten pennies in a pocketbook. Some believe that Juan de Gatan, a Spanish navigator, discovered these islands and called them the Islas de Mesa, or Table Land.

So you can take a choice, but in January, 1778 — a year and a half after we adopted the Declaration of Independence — Captain James Cook either discovered or *re*discovered the Hawaiian Islands when, searching for the mythical Northwest Passage between Europe and Asia, he found Maui's legendary island-fish. Cook named them the Sandwich Islands, after Britain's corrupt old First Lord of the Admiralty who, it is said, wouldn't stop gambling even for meals and so invented a luncheon specialty that made his name world-famous.

The natives believed Captain Cook to be their god-king Lono, who long years ago had wandered off in a fit of madness after killing his wife. They lavished favors and comforts upon the explorer. But acts of cruelty by some of Cook's crew aroused resentment. The Britishers, staying on and on, threatened to eat the natives out of their recent harvests. One of Cook's sailors died, proving that these fair-skinned men were less than gods.

The bitterness deepened. Quarrels multiplied. Then one day angry Hawaiians fell on Captain Cook, and whether he died from stabbing or drowning is not clear. In 1928 — two hundred years after Cook's birth—a tablet was placed at the spot in Kealakekua Bay where he died, and the memorial may be the

only one of its kind, for it cannot be seen except at low tide. Still, such a watery monument may not be strange for a man who, although he revealed the mysteries of the seven seas, never learned how to swim.

Life in the Island Paradise

What a wonderful land Cook, and those who quickly followed him, found in this "Paradise of the Pacific!" Trade winds and sea breezes cooled the land so that the climate remained mild the year round. Tropical flowers covered the lowlands with dazzling colors. Hillsides glistened with forests of the *koa* tree (candlenut), the *ohia* (mountain apple), slender palms and bushy ferns. The volcanic fires of mighty Mauna Loa (elevation 13,680 feet) and Kilauea (elevation about 4,000 feet) reddened the night sky. The coasts of the islands varied from the rugged slopes of Diamond Head, an extinct crater, to the gentle beach at Waikiki.

From grass huts, to welcome Cook and his sailors, came people of medium size with bright copperish skin, short heads, large eyes, and teeth like pearls. Still so close were they to the Stone Age that they would barter anything for the marvel of an iron nail to fashion into a fishhook! Captain George Vancouver, another explorer, brought cattle and sheep from California to the islands between 1792 and 1795 — but Hawaiians had small reason a few years later to thank the crew of the *Wellington* who, snubbed by the ladies of the islands, let loose the larvae in their water casks and deliberately in-

Paradise of the Pacific

troduced mosquitoes to this island paradise.

A pleasure-loving people fond of sailing, fishing, swimming and dancing, early Hawaiians lived under a system resembling feudalism in Europe during the Middle Ages. The chiefs owned everything and the people were their followers in war and their servants in peace. The law was the *tabu,* and violations were punished with instant death. Tabus forbade women to eat cocoanuts, to take meals with men or to marry before a proper age. Some fish could not be caught nor birds of certain bright plumage hunted. These belonged exclusively to the chiefs.

Kings and Missionaries

A legend predicted that one day a king would be born who would slay all the chiefs and rule supreme over the islands. As though to fulfill this promise, on a stormy November night in 1758, Kamehameha I — "The Lonely One" — was born beneath a blazing light in the sky that was probably Halley's comet. Somewhat like Herod, the local chief ordered the baby slain, but the child was spirited away into the mountains and reared by foster parents. And before the century ended, by 1795, "The Lonely One" *did* rule all the islands, as his descendants would continue to rule for almost a hundred years!

Kamehameha I was a shrewd, dignified ruler over both his own people and the ship crews that soon made his island paradise a favorite way station in the China trade. The first American ship

to visit the shores of our fiftieth state (1789) — indeed, the first American ship to sail around the world — was the 220-ton, two-decked, full-rigged *Columbia Rediviva* under the command of Robert Gray, a navigator who is also famous as the discoverer of the Columbia River. Yet perhaps a more important day in Hawaiian history was October 23, 1819, when at the Long Wharf in Boston the first missionaries boarded the brig *Thaddeus* for the long voyage to bring the blessing of the white man's civilization to semi-naked natives.

How well the missionaries succeeded in the years that followed could be seen in more than well-covered bodies. Wooden houses replaced grass huts, schools and churches sprang up — all looking as though they had been lifted off a New England town square and dropped into this tropical paradise! Whatever was good and sufficient in Massachusetts, reasoned the missionaries, would be equally good and fit in any part of the world. They brought the first printing press to the islands and by 1845 published an English-Hawaiian dictionary, opening to native minds the world's store of knowledge.

Sugar, Pineapples and "Old Lil"

Missionaries, traders in sandalwood, hard-bitten harpooners from New Bedford whalers — each left his mark here. The islands prospered and in 1850, under Kamehameha III, Hawaii adopted its national motto: "The life of the land is perpetuated in righteousness." Also during the reign of Kamehameha III, three New Englanders, operating as

Paradise of the Pacific

Hawaii

KAUAI
Lihue
NIIHAU
Kekaha

OAHU
Kahuku
Waipahu
Honolulu

MOLOKAI
Lahaina
Wailuku
MAUI
LANAI
KAHOOLAWE

HAWAII
Hilo
Keaau
Kapaau

MILES
0 10 20 30 40 50

KING KAMEHAMEHA

STATE OF HAWAII 1959

DARWIN

*Paradise
of the
Pacific*

Ladd & Company, gave the islands their first successful sugar plantation. The presence of pineapples in Hawaii was first recorded in 1813, but not until seventy-three years later did Captain John Kidwell, an English horticulturist, bring from Jamaica in the West Indies plants of the "Smooth Cayenne" pineapples for which Hawaii is now world-renowned.

These two crops, sugar and pineapples, became Hawaiian gold growing on stalks and trees. They changed history in Maui's islands-fished-from-the-sea, and proved anew the strength of the American influence in Hawaii planted by a generation of hard-working, hard-thinking Yankee missionaries. A war for power between the sugar growers and native rulers reached a climax when Queen Liliuokalani ascended to the throne in 1891. Determined to wrest absolute power by breaking the tie between the islands and America, "Old Lil's" policies could lead only in the direction that Hawaiians called *pilikia*. That word meant trouble.

A bloodless, American-inspired revolution forced Queen Liliuokalani to surrender her authority. President Cleveland offered to restore the monarch to power if she would spare the heads of the American "conspirators," but "Old Lil's" stubborn, somewhat bloodthirsty streak lost her a kingdom forever. A republic under a constitution authorizing annexation by the United States as soon as practicable flourished briefly. Its first — and only — president was Sanford B. Dole, son of a missionary, who was also the first

of the twelve governors to serve Hawaii after it became a territory in 1900.

All That the Heart Wishes

When on March 12, 1959 a bill to make Hawaii our fiftieth state was passed, many Americans remembered another day — December 7, 1941 — when Japanese planes, dropping their bombs on our naval base at Pearl Harbor, plunged the United States into World War II. Since that earlier day, islands and mainland clearly had embraced a common destiny.

Modern Hawaii — land of wild orchids and the beautiful hibiscus — mixes automobiles, buses and the conveniences of the twentieth century with mystery and charms unknown to the mainland. Here coconut shells are polished for food bowls to hold exotic native fruits like mangoes, golden papaya, avocadoes and bananas. Here the traditional staff of life is taro, a tuberous plant which is steamed, peeled and pounded into *poi,* a pastelike pudding. Here the hula is danced, and hand movements tell the story of the song or chant while hips and feet provide the rhythm. Here many races live in happy harmony, and nothing that the heart wishes seems unattainable.

Remember Maui, who fished the islands from the ocean? One day Maui asked the sun to slow down its race across the sky to help his mother dry some tapa cloth. At first the sun refused to help, so Maui lassoed some of its rays and broke off a few — just to teach the sun a lesson. And that is why the rays of the sun appear irregular and we have night and day.

CALIFORNIA

"The Golden State"

Oh! Californy!
That's the land for me!
I'm bound for Sacramento
With the washbowl on my knee.

SO SANG that reckless breed of men — the Forty-Niners — as dreams of a gold strike drew them across the high Sierras. Not one of these rough, bearded fellows ever guessed that, like a puppet dangled on a string by history, he was playing a part in a legend already centuries old.

The first mention of California in a Spanish book, published in 1510, described an "island" where "a great abundance of gold and precious stone is found." To reach California, a traveler must sail "on the right hand of the Indies" and when "very near to Terrestrial Paradise" he would behold this wondrous land — "peopled with black women" whose "arms were full of gold!"

Is it great wonder, hearing such tales, that the first white men came to California as adventurers and plunderers? In place of fortune, what they usually discovered were mysteries that belonged to a time beyond memory.

Indian Days

Shell mounds left by early Indian inhabitants give evidence of settlements in California three or four thousand years before the appearance of the white man. Walled off by deserts and mountains, Indians growing up within a few miles of one another often remained strangers.

Each tribal village, a world unto itself, taught its own language, its own customs. Thus the dome-shaped huts in

*The
Golden
State*

one region would be built of planks, bark-covered in another district, perhaps made of sod in a valley village. Where the oak forests grew, the staple food was acorn-meal, either baked in unleavened cakes or boiled in a gruel. Desert Indians lived on mesquite beans. Inland the Colorado River tribesmen were skilled farmers, and the Canalino Indians, living along the Santa Barbara Channel, were great fishermen whose boats of lashed planks were a type of craft found nowhere else in North America.

Yet one thing Maidu and Hupa Indian, Mojave and Yuma and Canalino shared in common — life passed happily. Basket weaving supplied the utensils he needed. Bone, shell or stone gave him arrowheads, pestles and mortars, pots, charms, beads. Clamshells were used for money. Rattles made of clapsticks filled with gravel, bone whistles, musical bows and drums enlivened his dances. Snares, nets, bows and arrows caught the game to fill his larder.

"It Pleased God"

The first white man to behold this Indian paradise was Juan Rodríguez Cabrillo, a Portuguese navigator employed by Spain, who in 1542 sailed into San Diego Bay. Cabrillo explored much of the California coast, also discovering Santa Monica Bay and the three large islands of the Santa Barbara group, before an illness caused by the suffering from a broken arm resulted in death. Cabrillo's crew brought back no proof of the romantic tales about the island of black women whose arms were covered with gold. Spanish au-

thorities sorted fact from fancy — obviously north of Mexico the New World was not worth the trouble of a second thought.

The English took another view, and in 1579 "it pleased God" for the hundred-ton schooner *Golden Hind,* under Sir Francis Drake, to sail into San Francisco Bay. The Indians, bearing gifts of feathers and tobacco, greeted Drake and his sailors as gods. Singing and dancing put everyone in a good mood, and the English supplied the Indians with "necessary things to cover their nakedness." Finally (or so Drake claimed) the natives begged him to "take their province and kingdom into his hand and become their king."

When Spain learned that Drake had claimed California for England, the interest of Spain in the New World north of Mexico quickly revived. An expedition led by Sebastián Vizcaíno in 1602 sent the Spanish king an enthusiastic report on the land, urging him to colonize California at once.

The Sword and the Cross

More than a century and a half passed, however, before in 1769 an expedition led by Captain Gaspar de Portolá established forts at the sites of San Diego and Monterey. Spain's formula for establishing a colony — bring the sword, then the cross — found Franciscan priests establishing a mission between the two forts. During the next half century, twenty more missions were built from San Diego to Sonoma.

The "heathen" Indians in all regions except the mountain country were quick

The Golden State

to choose the cross over the sword. Although an Indian could not be sold, his life in the mission amounted to slavery. If he ran away or was disobedient, he could be whipped and jailed. So the freedom-loving Indian learned to tend the mission's herd of cattle and to hoe its gardens. He built its irrigation system. As a weaver, mason, carpenter, blacksmith, he filled its many needs.

Near the mission stood the fort, or *presidio,* often with a town like San Diego or San Francisco, Santa Barbara or Monterey sprouting up on the fringes of these military outposts. Yet Spain's military strength in the New World was only skin-deep. Russian fur traders, building their own stockade (Fort Ross) less than a hundred miles north of San Francisco, proved that point. Vessels from Britain, France, South America — even *Yanqui* ships from New England — entered and left Spanish-dominated ports as they pleased. In 1821 Mexico broke away from Spain, bringing the first measure of self-government to California.

Lone Star and Grizzly Bear

Up from the stony soil of Mexico moved a new kind of colonist, drawn by stories of how herds of cattle thrived on the virgin pastures of California. After 1825 his plain, comfortable ranch house, built of sun-dried adobe brick, became a familiar sight. The *ranchero,* by nature a hard-working, good-humored person, was influential in organizing California as a province of Mexico. He made Indians free citizens and in other ways established an en-

lightened government. Unhappily, many of the governors sent up from Mexico were mean-tempered, short-sighted dictators. A spirit of rebellion grew. Los Angeles and Monterey bickered constantly over which should be the capital, and jealousy began to wear many faces.

Meanwhile, Americans grew more numerous in California. Yankee traders and whalers in the North Pacific made its seacoast towns regular ports of call. American fur trappers climbed the barrier of the Sierras and descended into the Sacramento and San Joaquin Valleys — men like Jedediah Strong Smith, discoverer of the Great Salt Desert, and James Ohio Pattie, who

John C. Frémont

*The
Golden
State*

brought smallpox vaccine into California. Finally, Kit Carson guided the three expeditions under an army engineer, Captain John C. Frémont, whose scientific explorations won him justified fame as "The Pathfinder."

Moreover, Frémont was conveniently on hand when in 1846 in the pueblo of Sonoma a band of Yankee rebels surrounded the Mexican military commander and seized the ungarrisoned *presidio.* A farmer, William B. Ide, hauled down the Mexican flag and raised one the Americans had brought — a banner of homespun with a strip of red flannel on which appeared a star, a grizzly bear and the words "California Republic."

The idea of an independent republic was abandoned, however, when the settlers learned that the United States had declared war on Mexico. The Treaty of Guadalupe Hidalgo, which formally ended that conflict on February 2, 1848 made California an American territory.

"Gold!"

In 1839 Captain John A. Sutter built the first white man's post in inland California. He named the place New Helvetia, but nine years later the town there was called Sacramento. Nearby, at Sutter's Fort, the captain operated a sawmill. One day in 1848 an employee, John Marshall, rushed into Sutter's private rooms.

"Look!" he said in a hushed voice.

Staring down, Sutter whispered: "Gold!"

Thus was triggered the famous Gold Rush of 1849 that changed California forever. By land, by sea, within twelve years 260,000 fortune-seekers poured into the territory. A boisterous, devil-may-care lot, their spirit was reflected in the names they gave their shanty towns — Git-up-and-git, Bogus Thunder, Angel's Camp, You Bet, Shinbone Creek, Lazy Man's Canyon. Soon a shack rented for one hundred dollars a week, an old New York newspaper sold for one dollar a copy.

In ragged shirt and scrubby beard, the Forty-Niner trudged off behind his mule, hoping to "hit a strike" and become rich. A few did. Sometimes they even kept their fortunes. But gamblers and desperadoes followed the easy money. Often a rope dangling from a tree bespoke the only justice fit for a claim jumper or horse thief.

Land of Contrasts

And what of the Forty-Niners who did not hit a strike? Some, of course, were incurable seekers after quick riches who could be found in Colorado when gold was discovered there in 1858 or who, at news of the great silver strike at the Comstock Lode in 1859, followed the rush into Nevada. But the great many who were not lucky in the gold fields drifted down into the Great Valley where as farmers and ranchers they brought strength and wealth to California.

Nor was that all. The cry of "Californy or bust" kept the prairie schooners rolling westward until a continent had been conquered. Scraggly towns like San Francisco and Sacramento almost overnight became flourishing young cities, so that by 1850 when California was admitted to the Union as

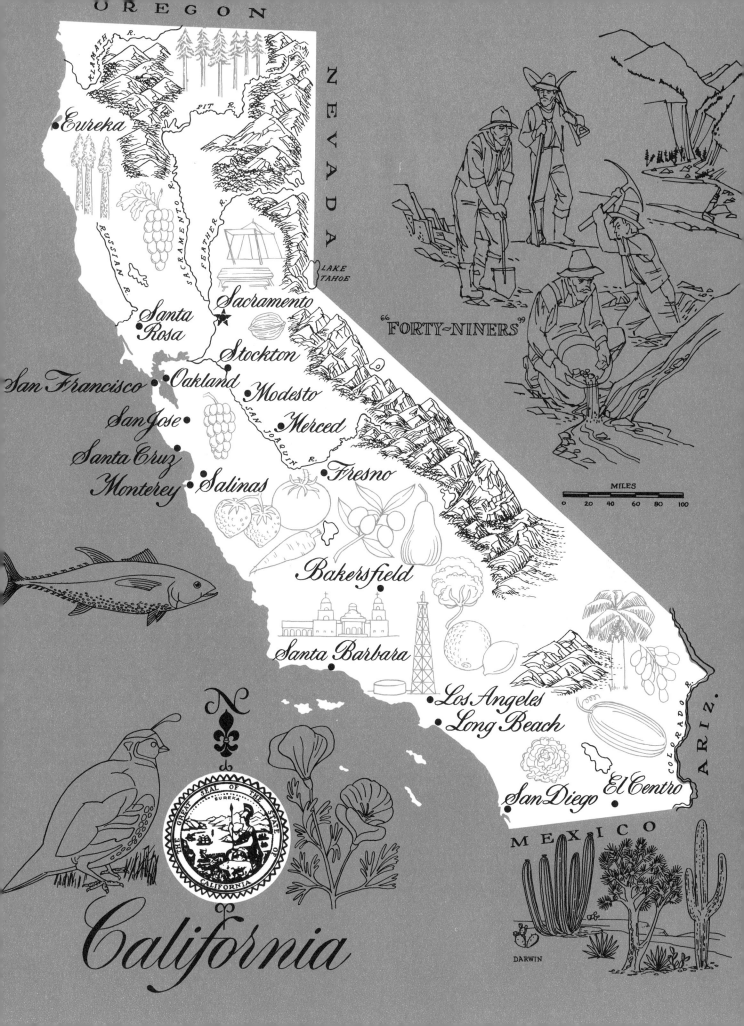

OREGON

NEVADA

KLAMATH R.

PIT R.

Eureka

RUSSIAN R.

SACRAMENTO R.

FEATHER R.

LAKE TAHOE

Sacramento

Santa Rosa

Stockton

San Francisco

Oakland

Modesto

SAN JOAQUIN R.

San Jose

Merced

Santa Cruz

Monterey

Salinas

Fresno

Bakersfield

Santa Barbara

Los Angeles

Long Beach

San Diego

El Centro

COLORADO R.

ARIZ.

"FORTY~NINERS"

MILES

0   20   40   60   80   100

N

THE GREAT SEAL OF THE STATE OF
EUREKA
CALIFORNIA

California

MEXICO

DARWIN

*The
Golden
State*

our thirty-first state — on the provision that slavery would be forever prohibited — the years ahead were filled with bright promise.

A land boom followed the Civil War. Then, with a large influx of Chinese and Japanese labor, a serious depression held back the state's development until the turn of the twentieth century. But California, with an area greater than that of Illinois, Iowa and Ohio combined, in time forged ahead.

Few states can equal California as a land of contrasts. Here Mount Whitney towers 14,495 feet above sea level and desert wastes like Death Valley lie 276 feet below sea level. Here, where both the palm tree and pine tree flourish, the temperature at Greenland Ranch in Inyo County may soar to 134°F. (July, 1913) or at Boca fall to –45°F. (January, 1937).

California ranks among our foremost states in agriculture, canning, livestock, mineral resources, fisheries. Only Texas surpasses California in supplying petroleum, natural gas and gasoline. The state's extensive forests of pine and redwood make it a leader in lumbering. Los Angeles and San Francisco are two of the world's busiest seaports.

And, of course, in one industry it is without equal anywhere on the globe.

"We Want Action!"

Yet that industry began three thousand miles away, on April 14, 1894, when in New York City spectators dropped a nickel into a slot to look into Thomas Edison's kinetoscope or "peepshow." Two years later a screen was used so that larger audiences might view moving pictures of a policeman chasing a tramp. To Edison's cameraman, Edwin S. Porter, belongs the credit for deciding that these pictures also should tell a story. Porter's first story on film, "The Life of an American Fireman," proved a smash hit, and led to an epic event in Pittsburgh, Pennsylvania, when on Thanksgiving Day, 1905 a converted storeroom became America's first motion picture theater!

Imitators rushed into the field, and Edison pursued them all for infringing on his patents. To escape Edison and the law, these producers fled to Florida, Chicago, and even Cuba before in 1911 David Horsely brought his Nestor Film Company of New Jersey to a studio at Sunset Boulevard and Gower Street and made Hollywood's first movie. The rush was on. Films and more films were made. Hollywood's early motto was: "Never mind the acting — we want *action!*"

And action it got — in cowboys chasing Indians, cattle rustlers and train robbers, or in comedians ducking custard pies. Then in Gladys Smith — "the cute little girl with curls" — Hollywood discovered the movie "star." Gladys became Mary Pickford and earned $10,000 a week, one of a long line of Hollywood "celebrities" who belonged in a twentieth century fairytale world.

In time great acting produced great pictures. A big fad became a big business. When the bills for a modern first-rate motion picture are totaled up, any Hollywood producer can give you *one* reason why California still is called "The Golden State."

Captain Robert Gray

OREGON

"The Beaver State"

EARLY IN THE 1800's the national craze was that of wearing fur hats made of beaver skin. A prime pelt brought from four to six dollars a pound, and an experienced trapper, finding a new beaver colony, sometimes took two hundred skins in a single day. High profits in the beaver trade drove trappers over mountains and plains, across turbulent rivers and through virgin forests, until their camps, trading posts and forts lined a path to the Pacific Ocean.

Among the adventures related by these lonely wanderers, none surpassed the tales of those who had been to "Old Oregon." The term designated a vast domain that included the present states of Oregon, Washington and Idaho and parts of Montana, Wyoming and the Canadian province of British Columbia.

"O! the Joy!"

A Spaniard, Bartolome Ferrelo, sailing along the Oregon coast in 1543, encouraged a succession of his country's navigators to explore the waters of the Northwest and to claim the land for Spain. Russian fur traders considered the territory part of the czar's realm on three continents. Sir Francis Drake, touching the southern coast in 1579, and Captain James Cook, sighting Alsea Bay in 1778, established a British claim, while the discovery of the mouth of the Columbia River in 1788 by a Boston mariner, Robert Gray, gave the United

The
Beaver
State

States a toehold in the four-nation scramble for the land [see Washington, pp. 270-274].

When President Thomas Jefferson consummated the Louisiana Purchase, no one was more in his thoughts than Robert Gray. What lay beyond the mouth of the river Gray had seen? Was the Columbia the "Great River of the West" that was part of Indian legend? When the expedition under Meriwether Lewis and William Clark set out to explore the territory Jefferson had secured through the Louisiana Purchase, of first importance was finding the answers to these questions.

In mid-October of 1805, following the swirling course of the Snake River, Lewis and Clark at last attained the goal Jefferson had set for them. Across a rippling sand bar they saw flowing through a desert plain cut off east and west by low hills a larger river — the Columbia! Through canyons whose walls were covered with dark lava, they journeyed into a country of breathtaking beauty. When they portaged at Clelilo Falls, they looked upon the snow-covered peak of majestic Mount Hood. The Dalles and the Long Narrows were passed by late October and they slipped through the Cascades on November 2. Fog at night and cold, wet mornings told the voyagers then that they were nearing the coast, and on November 7 an exuberant William Clark wrote in his notebook: "Ocean in view! O! the joy."

But part of the exultation rubbed off when the party discovered that the Northwest Indians were not only acquainted with the white man, but could even speak a few words of English. The natives possessed the goods of the white man's trade — woolen clothing, muskets, axes, wire. Five miles from Astoria, Oregon, Lewis and Clark built Fort Clatsop, and here Americans spent their first Christmas Day in the Northwest. Clark described that occasion: "After breakfast we divided our Tobacco which amounted to 12 carrots, one half of which we gave to the men of the party who used tobacco. To those who do not use it we made a present of a handkerchief." Christmas dinner, Clark admitted, consisted of a "poor Elk, so much Spoiled" that it was eaten through "mere necessity."

Founding the Territory

Six years later, trappers working for John Jacob Astor founded the first American settlement in the territory. Spain relinquished her claims in 1819 and a few years later Russia decided to surrender its interest in any land south of 54°40′ north latitude. In the resulting struggle between Great Britain and the United States for control of the territory, the zeal of missionaries, settling in the region, finally turned the tide in favor of the Americans [see Washington, pp. 270-274]. By 1846, Americans outnumbered the British in the territory, 6,000 to 1,000!

For the most part, these hardy settlers made their way over the Oregon Trail where hardship and heatbreak waited around every turn. The jumping-off point was the River Platte in Nebraska. Ten miles a day was a wonderful pace for a wagon train rumbling up the North Platte into Wyoming.

COLUMBIA RIVER

W A S H I N G T O N

Astoria

Portland

Salem

MOUNT HOOD

The Dalles

Pendleton

Baker

SNAKE R.

I D A H O

Corvallis

Bend

WILLAMETTE RIVER

Eugene

Coos Bay

Medford

Klamath Falls

C A L I F O R N I A

MILES
0   20   40   60   80   100

N

STATE OF OREGON
THE UNION
1859

DARWIN

WILLAMETTE
HOMESTEADERS

Oregon

Sometimes the summer heat shriveled the wood on the rims of the wagon wheels and the alkali dust of the trail made every breath a misery. But the pioneers pushed on, along the Sweetwater in Wyoming, looking for their first glimpse of the snow-capped Rockies. Days piled into weeks and months. Those who died of natural causes, or were killed by Indians, were buried beside the wagon ruts. The others pressed forward — through South Pass and down the western slope of the continent to Fort Bridger.

On the trail, a wagon train was a world in its own right. Sometimes a thousand persons with all their livestock and personal belongings traveled together — they were like a whole town on the move. Sixty wagons might make up the train, usually divided into platoons of four wagons each. The pilot was a fellow who had grown up on the edge of the wilderness, and who could sniff a hostile Sioux miles off. Ten or fifteen young men usually rode off in a pack hunting buffalo, and they might travel twenty miles off the trail before they found their game. At night there were four watches, from 8 P.M. to 4 A.M., and anybody able to bear arms put in his lick. Before bedtime the kids got a chance to romp and play games. From one tent might come the sound of a violin or a flute, and for all the day's hard labor the young men found the energy to give their girls a dance. By ten o'clock, though, everyone was asleep, knowing that before dawn the camp would be stirring and "On to Oregon" would be the answer to every muscle ache.

In 1848 Oregon was organized into an American territory, and two years later Congress passed the Donation Land Law, giving free land to every American who would live on and cultivate his tract for four years. After that, traffic quickened on the Oregon Trail, for all its hardships — 15,000 making the long haul overland in 1852, another 8,000 in 1853. Washington territory was separated from Oregon that year, and a decade later Idaho was made a separate territory.

Symbols of Oregon

The state seal carries the date 1859, the year that Oregon entered the Union as our thirty-third state. Mountains and an elk with spreading antlers, a covered wagon, a sailing schooner at anchor, a sheaf and plow and pickax — these symbols on Oregon's seal tell a story of the principal forces behind the state's steady growth. A series of Indian uprisings — the Rogue River Wars of the '50's, the Madoc War and Nez Percé War in the '70's — marked the struggle of the red man to hold onto his beautiful homeland. But still the settlers came. Of all the pioneers who pushed across the continent, these settlers had come the farthest and despite famine or bad weather or Indians with their feathers up, they had traveled the Oregon Trail meaning to stay put once they made it!

In the same spirit, in the 1890's, Oregonians added a number of amendments to their state constitution, and, as a group, these changes became known as the "Oregon Plan." Other states would copy such Oregon contributions to popular government as the initiative and referendum — measures which give voters control over the making of laws.

Future Unlimited

Shimmering waterfalls, sparkling rivers, snow-capped mountains and rolling coast, lake country to the southeast and high, dry plains in the west ideal for cattle raising — ask any Oregonian and he'll tell you that his state has anything, *everything*. Even allowing for local pride, he won't be too far wrong, either. Oregon's mines produce gold, silver, coal, mercury. The state is one of the country's leading wheat producers. To the Lewelling brothers and William Meek, who in 1847 brought eight hundred fruit trees from Iowa, Oregon remains indebted for fruit crops known around the world.

Lumbering is another industry in which Oregon excels, principally because the Douglas fir, growing to heights of from 180 to 200 feet, produces more lumber per acre than any other tree in North America. In addition, Oregon's forests support the furniture factories that center around Portland and the paper mills in the Willamette Valley. When in 1937 Bonneville Dam was completed forty miles east of Portland and the Columbia River became navigable for seagoing vessels as far as The Dalles, Oregon turned a new chapter in its history that might well begin with the words: "Future unlimited." At Bonneville special fish ladders help Columbia River salmon go upstream to their spawning grounds. Even for fish, Oregon is an easy-to-live-in state!

The Beaver State

WASHINGTON

"The Evergreen State"

WHAT ARE the human forces that transform a wilderness into a great, prosperous state? Washington, the forty-second member of the Union and today the most thickly populated state in the Pacific Northwest, is proof that many forces may be needed.

Timber, free land, minerals, railroad construction, fishing — each of these economic attractions brought its wave of settlers to Washington.

But there were other influences. Some folk, who had tried their luck in older states and were restless and dissatisfied, came just to try something different. Southerners, ruined and uprooted by the Civil War, turned westward in quest of a brave, new world. Immigrants from Europe and the Orient added to the march of settlers. Later, from the worn-out lands of the Middle West, came discouraged farmers.

Together, they forged the state named in honor of the Father of our Country.

Discovering America's Switzerland

As long ago as 1578, when Sir Francis Drake glimpsed Puget Sound, the white man must have drawn a quick breath at the astonishing beauty of this land. Sometimes called the "Switzerland of America," Washington offers gentle coastal plains, mountains towering 14,000 feet above sea level, rain-drenched forests. Great glaciers and snowfields, unmelted for centuries, exist in its mountains. Yet the climate along the coast is so mild that flowers bloom the year round.

Still, for two hundred years after Drake sailed his *Golden Hind* along its coast, this vast region remained the undisturbed domain of some seventy Indian tribes, who were divided between the Horse Indians of the coastal

The Evergreen State

plains and the Canoe Indians living west of the Cascade Mountains. True, in 1592 a Greek navigator named Apostolos Valerianos, who worked for Spain, sailed along these same coasts, and by the early 1700's Russian fur traders must have known this country. Even so, the first landing by a white man on the soil of Washington was not recorded until 1775, when Bruno Heceta and Juan Francisco de la Bogeda y Quadra stepped ashore near present-day Point Grenville and claimed the land for Spain.

Captain James Cook, in quest of the Northwest Passage, arrived in 1778 to establish British claims in the region and later English navigators — notably Charles William Barkley and George Vancouver — strengthened the British foothold. In 1788 the *Washington* and *Columbia,* captained by Robert Gray and John Kendrick, carried the American flag into the waters of the Northwest. Spain and England settled their differences by negotiation in 1793, but the "Oregon Question" remained a recurring point of bitter dispute between Britain and America for the next half century.

A Bloodless War

The claim of the United States to the territory rested largely on Robert Gray's discovery of the Columbia River in 1792, for international practice gave to the nation finding the entrance of a river sovereignty over its valley and watershed as well as over the adjacent coast. England sneered at the claim, insisting Gray had come on a commercial rather than an official voyage. The Louisiana Purchase and the Lewis and Clark Expedition in 1805 [see Oregon, pp. 265-269] added to America's claim.

Stories told to a twenty-year-old Briton sailing to America to make his fortune selling musical instruments worked next in America's favor. The young man whose ears perked up at tales of the profits to be made in the Indian fur trade was John Jacob Astor. Years later, as Astor's fortune from furs grew, so did his dreams, and about 1809 he conceived the idea of establishing a chain of trading posts not only from the Great Lakes to the Pacific, but on to the Sandwich Islands and China! Thought and act became one to Astor with the organization of the Pacific Fur Company and two expeditions — one by sea, one by land — were dispatched to the mouth of the Columbia River. On April 10, 1811, Astor's men pounded their hammers building Astoria, a trading post. Later that year at Fort Okanogan the American flag was raised for the first time over territory now within Washington.

The British, however, were not idle. The War of 1812 gave them an excuse they hardly required for forcing American competitors out of the Oregon fur trade and in 1813 Astoria was sold to the British. Although the Treaty of Ghent restored Astoria to the Americans in 1814, the spirit of an undeclared war in no way diminished. In 1818, and again in 1827, an agreement was reached that the country "westward of the Stony Mountains" should be open to the "vessels, subjects and citizens" of both nations. But Britain's powerful Hudson's Bay Company was on the

*The
Evergreen
State*

spot, controlling the principal trading posts and forts, and claiming in John McLoughlin, its chief factor, a leader of iron will and clear judgment. The odds seemed a hundred to one that in time Britain would win this struggle for territorial control.

"The Oregon Fever"

McLoughlin had emerged as virtual czar of the Hudson's Bay enterprises west of the Rockies when he met his match in an unexpected quarter. One

day in 1834 a most unalarming missionary, Jason Lee, arrived with his party at Fort Vancouver. Obligingly McLoughlin helped Lee establish a mission in Willamette Valley. Two years later Marcus Whitman and Henry Spalding appeared and again McLoughlin helped to establish a mission, this time near Fort Walla Walla. In 1839 Fathers Blanchet and Demers set up a Roman Catholic mission at Cowlitz.

Too late, McLoughlin saw what was happening. In 1839 Jason Lee reckoned that Americans in the Oregon country numbered about 150 persons. Steadily thereafter the number multiplied. In 1843 — the year of the "Great Migration" — about 900 persons arrived! The "Oregon Fever" had caught on, spread by the letters, speeches and pamphlets of the missionaries and by Washington Irving, whose tale of "Astoria" romanticized Astor's overland expedition of 1811. The "Oregon Fever" reached Congress and produced a militant slogan, "54-40 or fight!" that helped elect James K. Polk to the Presidency, though it was happily in a more reasonable mood that in 1846 Britain and the United States finally settled their boundary dispute along the forty-ninth parallel.

Lincoln Turns Down a Job

In 1848 Congress approved the bill creating the Oregon Territory, of which Washington was a part. The governorship was offered to Abraham Lincoln, but he decided to stay in Illinois where he knew his way around! Five years later Washington was organized as a

IDAHO

CANADA

OREGON

COLUMBIA RIVER

SPOKANE R.

Spokane

SNAKE R.

Walla Walla

YAKIMA R.

COLUMBIA RIVER

Yakima

MOUNT RAINIER

Olympia

Hoquiam

Vancouver

Bellingham

Everett

Seattle

Tacoma

Port Angeles

PUGET SOUND

MILES

0   20   40   60   80   100

EARLY LOGGING

THE SEAL OF THE STATE OF WASHINGTON · 1889

Washington

DARWIN

The
Evergreen
State

separate territory, and when in 1863 the Idaho Territory was formed, Washington acquired its present boundaries. Despite a series of small Indian wars, settlers continued to pour into the Northwest country, probably drawn in no small measure by the discovery of gold in Idaho, Oregon and British Columbia. A special attraction to cattle raisers was the fine open range in eastern Washington.

Statehood was bestowed in 1889, and although among western states Washington is smallest in size west of Iowa, it is still larger than the New England states and Delaware combined. Wheat fields and apple orchards, replacing the old cattle ranges, give Washington a profitable agriculture. Aluminum production, aircraft manufacture, atomic energy, forest products, and mineral resources have been mainly responsible for the state's tremendous industrial growth, and, as the world-wide fame of Columbia River salmon should suggest, no state surpasses Washington in its output of canned salmon. The first canneries along the Columbia were built in 1860, and shortly thereafter the industry began to boom. Doubtless a good Californian, proud of his state's great native product, can list its movie stars, but a good Washingtonian likewise can name his state's five great stars — Chinook or King Salmon, Chum or Dog Salmon, Silver or Coho, Pink or Hump Back and Sockeye or Blueback.

Man's Biggest Job

Washington has many wonders bestowed by nature — the rain forest with trees growing to heights of two hundred feet, Beacon Rock rising nine hundred feet above the Columbia River so that only the Rock of Gibraltar in the Mediterranean is larger, Ginkgo Petrified Forest near Ellensburg — yet Washington's greatest wonder is man-made.

Even the Great Pyramid of Egypt cannot compare as a mighty piece of masonry to Washington's Grand Coulee Dam. Begun in 1933 and completed in 1941, this "biggest job on earth" is higher than a forty-six-story building and longer than twelve city blocks. The dam's central spillways create a waterfall half as wide as Niagara Falls and twice as high, and the power it controls runs turbines capable of producing more electricity than any other turbines in the world. Franklin D. Roosevelt Lake, formed by Grand Coulee, is 151 miles long. The waters from this lake one day will irrigate more than a million acres of land, an area three-fourths the size of the state of Delaware.

The spirit of Washington as a state is reflected in the events that make headlines in its home town newspapers — the Treaty Day Powwows on the Indian Reservations in January, the stock show at Spokane in February, the ski patrol race in Snoqualmie Pass in March, the rhododendron and daffodil festivals in April, the apple blossom festival at Wenatchee in May, the strawberry festival at Bellevue in June, the rodeo at Chelan in July, the air show at Seattle's Boeing Field in August, the salmon fishing derby in September, State Day in November.

As elsewhere, Washington reserves December for Kris Kringle — and, if necessary, it can supply the reindeer!

ALASKA
"The Last Frontier"

IN ST. PETERSBURG in the early 1700's, the Czar of All the Russias listened to tales that had traveled five thousand miles. Along the frozen coasts of Siberia, these stories said, storms in the Pacific often washed up timber unlike the wood of native trees, as well as the bodies of strange beasts with spears in them. To the east there must be inhabited land, perhaps connecting the continents of Asia and America. Scholars of the Russian Academy of Science, believing there must be some truth in these tales, urged the Czar to join the quest for the fabled Northwest Passage.

Two expeditions under the Danish navigator, Vitus Jonassen Bering, ultimately were sanctioned. The first carried Bering through the straits that now bear his name, but when he had sailed as far north as latitude 67°18′ without sighting new land, he decided that an arm of the Pacific Ocean separated Asia and America. Neither the officers of the Court nor the scholars of the Academy of Science were satisfied by these discouraging conclusions, and so in 1784 Bering returned to the shores of the Pacific for his second voyage into the waters of the icy north.

ALASKA

Pacific Frontier

HAWAII

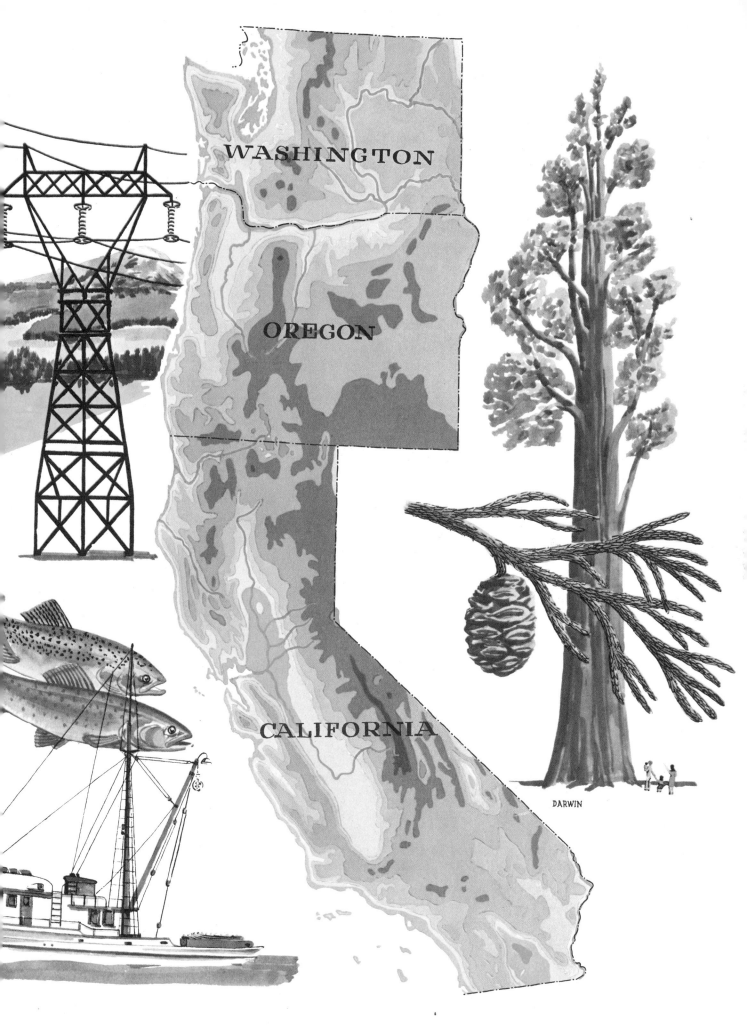

WASHINGTON

OREGON

CALIFORNIA

DARWIN

The Last
Frontier

Mystery and Disaster

The expedition sailed in two vessels, the *St. Peter* under Bering's command and the *St. Paul* under another experienced navigator, Alexei Chirikof. Storms at sea separated the two ships.

On July 15, 1741 Chirikof's *St. Paul* sighted through the mist the west side of Prince of Wales Island near what is now called Cape Addington. Two days passed before he found the entrance to a bay (probably Sitka) and here he sent a longboat with ten men and his trusted mate to explore the harbor. The Russians, singing as they swung their oars, disappeared around an arm of land. A day went by, but the longboat did not reappear. A second day slipped by, a third, a fourth, a fifth. Chirikof sent his boatswain and six sailors in the remaining longboat to find the first party.

They also sailed around the arm of land — and vanished forever! That night smoke could be seen rising from fires within the harbor. And next morning natives rowed out in canoes, jabbered at the Russians in a strange language, then hastened off. Chirikof would never solve the mystery. Had both parties drowned in a treacherous riptide or had both been captured and murdered by the natives? Chirikof was more than willing to leave this cursed land!

Where Forget-me-nots Bloom

And what luck had Bering? On July 16, 1741, from aboard the *St. Peter* he sighted the majestic peak of Mount St. Elias on the Alaskan mainland and four days later landed on Kayak Island.

Though the natives had vanished, Bering's party found huts of logs and rough planks roofed with bark and dried grass. They found also copper instruments, a whetstone, a rattle made of clay, some broken arrows, dried fish, a rope made of seaweed, and various cooking utensils. Vast forests with impassable thickets covered the mountainsides. In the meadows bloomed the beautiful forget-me-not, Alaska's state flower.

Bering became oddly stubborn in this strange land, as though premonitions of impending disaster haunted him, and he sailed away before his crew secured sufficient fresh water for the journey home. That voyage carried Bering by the Sea Otter Rocks, along the eastern side of Kodiak Island, through Douglas Pass and on past Chirikof Island. Scurvy ran rampant through the ship, killing many of the crew. Bering, ill, took to his cabin. The steersman staggered to the helm, held up by sailors who supported him under the arms. The winter was spent in the Commander Islands where in early December Bering was laid to rest on a sandy hillside. A plain Greek cross marked his grave.

Settling Alaska

Again, Bering seemed to have failed. Yet his crew, returning to the Asiatic mainland the following summer, brought stories of the animals they had seen — the docile sea cow, the sea otter, seals and sea lions, the red fox. Local fur trappers set off in their wooden shallops to ascertain if these tales were so and soon every Siberian owner of a

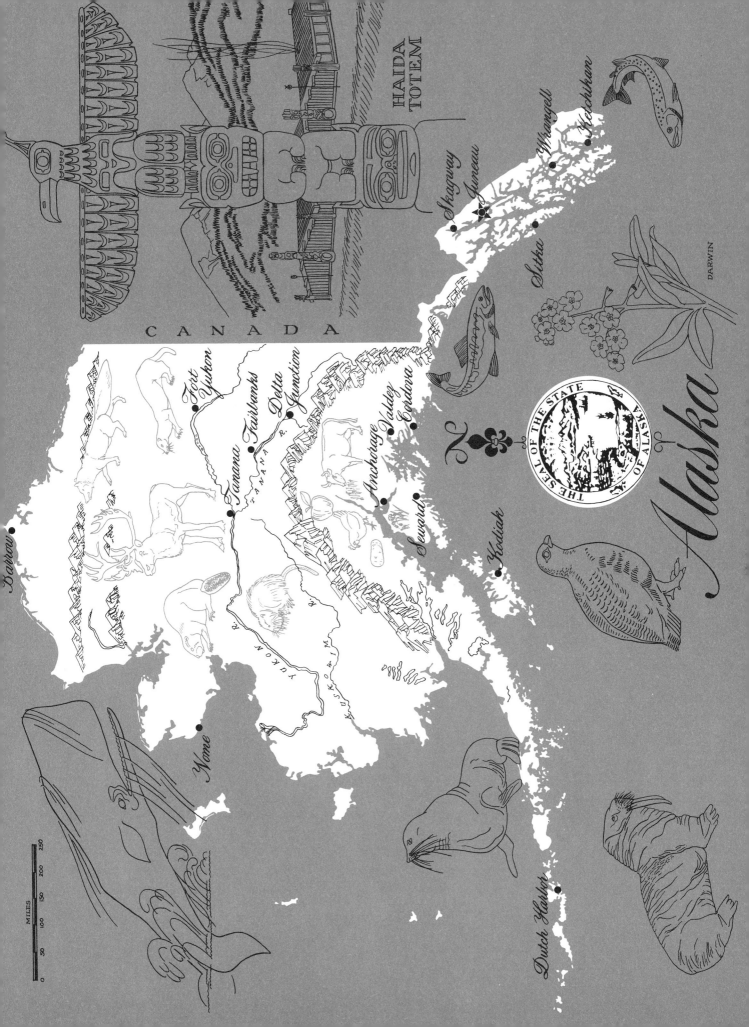

HAIDA
TOTEM

CANADA

DARWIN

Ketchikan

Wrangell

Juneau

Skagway

Sitka

THE SEAL OF THE STATE OF ALASKA

Alaska

Fort Yukon

Tanana

Fairbanks

Delta Junction

Valdez

Cordova

Anchorage

Seward

Kodiak

Barrow

YUKON R.

TANANA R.

KUSKOKWIM R.

Nome

Dutch Harbor

MILES

0 50 100 150 200 250

The Last Frontier

sailing craft who could engage a crew on shares rushed into the Alaska fur trade. They were a rough, quarrelsome lot, these tireless Cossacks and Muscovites, who robbed and killed as they conquered Alaska. Some natives, it is claimed, committed suicide to escape from Russian barbarities, and under the reign of the Russians the population of the Aleutians dwindled from 25,000 to less than 1,000!

Other nationalities arrived to stake their claim in Alaska — the Spanish in 1773, the English under Captain James Cook in 1778, the French under La Pérouse in 1786 — but none could compete with the Russians, who approached colonizing and fur-hunting with the hard-headedness of men organizing a big business. And the Russian American Company, set up by the Imperial Government in 1799, was a big business. Managed by the extremely capable Alexander Baranof, Russian profits bounded upward, and the fortunes of the natives steadily worsened, for Baranof was a harsh master.

The First Alaskans

The first Russian invaders found the gentle Aleuts, who inhabited the Aleutian Islands and the western part of the Alaskan Peninsula, living in large subterranean houses covered with sod, dirt and driftwood which they entered through a hole in the roof. A hoodless skin parka reaching to the knees was the principal article of clothing for both men and women, and since there was no timber on their islands, weapons and implements were fashioned from driftwood, bone or stone. Related to

the Eskimos, who frequented the Arctic and Bering Sea coasts, the Aleuts were boatmen of unsurpassed skill as they skimmed the waves in their skin boats.

The Eskimos — about one-half the population of pre-Russian Alaska — revealed in their flat, broad faces and coarse black or dark brown hair characteristics of both the American Indians to the south and the Mongolians of northeastern Asia. A maritime people, they settled where they could find good landings for their boats and defenses for their semi-subterranean homes. Trousers, boots and parkas were their common articles of dress, the kayak their favorite means of transportation. Objects made of walrus ivory attest to the skill they achieved as carvers.

The Indians of Alaska — the Thlingits and the Haidas—may have seemed more primitive in their simple garb of skin loincloths and aprons made of bark fibers, but appearances were deceiving. These tribesmen could build canoes that would carry forty or fifty men, and the houses they constructed on two or three levels revealed a skill in carpentry unequaled by other tribes of North American Indians. Nor were the red men of Alaska inclined to accept docilely Russian mistreatment. The Thlingits were especially savage in their rebellion and in 1802 massacred the white settlers at Sitka.

"Seward's Folly"

Yet quickly, after the Thlingit uprising, New Sitka was built upon the ashes of the old town, and crowded streets by day and gay parties and balls at night gave proof of Russia's growing prosperity in Alaska. Then with the death in 1819 of Alexander Baranof, the dynamic leader of the Russian American Company, the Czar's fortunes in Alaska seemed to tumble as rapidly as they had soared. In time, Russia not only had to reckon with dwindling profits from her American enterprises, but also with a rising threat of war with England. Self-interest shaped Russian policy — if Alaska belonged to the United States, it would act as a buffer state between Russia's Asiatic holdings and British possessions in Canada. Almost out of a clear sky — or so it seemed to the public — William H. Seward, our Secretary of State, announced the purchase of Alaska for $7,200,000. On October 18, 1867, the American flag was raised at Sitka.

Many Americans refused to take seriously the purchase of this vast empire in the Arctic, calling it "Seward's Folly." Then the discovery of gold on the Klondike River in Yukon Territory in 1897 started a human stampede into Alaska. The discoveries of gold continued — at Nome in 1899, at Fairbanks in 1903. When Alaska's territorial legislature was established nine years later, the gold fever had subsided and thousands had left the region to seek quick riches elsewhere. Those who remained found in Alaska a promise for the future in the scene depicted on the territorial seal where the sun, rising over the mountains, revealed the resources upon which the territory depended for its growth and prosperity — forests, a lake, fishing and shipping, farming and mining.

Modern Alaska

Alaska, our forty-ninth state, is a magic land to visit, with its hundreds of mountains, green forests, glaciers, the volcanoes of the Valley of Ten Thousand Smokes, and long winter nights when the skies are brilliant with the aurora borealis. Mount McKinley, 20,320 feet above sea level, is the tallest peak in North America, and the glacier, Malaspina, is the largest ice mass on the continent. To be sure, Alaska gets cold. Its lowest temperature on record is −75°F. at Fort Yukon, where incidentally, 100°F. is also its warmest temperature on record.

The Last Frontier

Alaska's mines produce gold, silver, copper, platinum, oil, coal. Its fisheries catch and process salmon, herring, halibut, shrimp, crabs, cod. Its manufactures, other than processed foods, include lumber and wood products, ships and plywood. Its farms grow wheat, barley, oats, hay, vegetables, fruits, and raise sheep, cattle, hogs and poultry.

But the first resource of Alaska — furs — remains still a chief resource. Fishermen and miners who find that they can only work at these jobs in summer turn in winter to their traplines. Marten, muskrat, white fox, land otter, wolf, lynx, beaver and bear are among the pelts they ship to market. Sealskins, sold by the government, may run to 100,000 annually. Ranches in the Aleutians and on the islands of Prince William Sound raise blue fox. Silver fox are ranch-grown on the Kenai Peninsula.

Al-ay-ek-sa, said the Aleutians, meaning "great land." It surely is!

INDEX

BRIEF FACTS ABOUT THE STATES

NOTE — *Statehood:* date of admission to statehood in the Union and numerical order of admission. *Population:* represents figures reported in the 1960 census. *Area:* in square miles and includes inland water. *Highest elevation:* altitude, in feet, above sea level. *U.S. Government* (Congress): first number indicates U.S. Senators (2 for each state); second number indicates U.S. Representatives. *State Government:* (Legislature): first number indicates State Senators; second number indicates State Representatives or Assemblymen.

ALABAMA
Capital: *Montgomery;* Statehood (and rank): *Dec. 14, 1819 (22);* Population (and rank): *3,266,740 (19);* Area (and rank): *51,609 (29);* Highest Elevation: *Cheaha Mountain (2,407);* U.S. Government: *2/9;* Electoral Votes: *11;* State Government: *35/106;* Counties: *67;* Flower: *Camellia;* Tree: *Southern Pine;* Bird: *Yellowhammer;* Fish: *Tarpon;* Song: *"Alabama";* Motto: *Audemus jura nostra defendere (We dare defend our rights).*

ALASKA
Capital: *Juneau;* Statehood (and rank): *Jan. 3, 1959 (49);* Population (and rank): *226,167 (50);* Area (and rank): *586,400 (1);* Highest Elevation: *Mount McKinley (20,-320);* U.S. Government: *2/1;* Electoral Votes: *3;* State Government: *20/40;* Boroughs: *16;* Flower: *Forget-me-not;* Bird: *Willow Ptarmigan;* Song: *"Alaska's Flag."*

ARIZONA
Capital: *Phoenix;* Statehood (and rank): *Feb. 14, 1912 (48);* Population (and rank): *1,302,161 (35);* Area (and rank): *113,909 (6);* Highest Elevation: *Humphreys Peak (12,670);* U.S. Government: *2/2;* Electoral Votes: *4;* State Government: *28/80;* Counties: *14;* Flower: *Saguaro;* Tree: *Paloverde;* Bird: *Cactus Wren;* Song: *"Arizona";* Motto: *Ditat Deus (God enriches).*

ARKANSAS

Capital: *Little Rock;* Statehoood (and rank): *June 15, 1836 (25);* Population (and rank): *1,786,272 (31);* Area (and rank): *53,104 (27);* Highest Elevation: *Magazine Mountain (2,823);* U.S. Government: *2/6;* Electoral Votes: *8;* State Government: *35/100;* Counties: *75;* Flower: *Apple Blossom;* Tree: *Pine Tree;* Bird: *Mockingbird;* Song: *"The Arkansas Traveler";* Motto: *Regnat populus (The people rule).*

CALIFORNIA

Capital: *Sacramento;* Statehood (and rank): *Sept. 9, 1850 (31);* Population (and rank): *15,717,204 (2);* Area (and rank): *158,693 (3);* Highest Elevation: *Mount Whitney (14,495);* U.S. Government: *2/30;* Electoral Votes: *32;* State Government: *40/80;* Counties: *58;* Flower: *Golden Poppy;* Tree: *California Redwood;* Bird: *California Valley Quail;* Animal: *California Grizzly Bear;* Fish: *California Golden Trout;* Song: *"I Love You, California";* Motto: *Eureka (I have found it).*

COLORADO

Capital: *Denver;* Statehood (and rank): *Aug. 1, 1876 (38);* Population (and rank): *1,753,947 (33);* Area (and rank): *104,247 (8);* Highest Elevation: *Mount Elbert (14,431);* U.S. Government: *2/4;* Electoral Votes: *6;* State Government: *35/65;* Counties: *63;* Flower: *Rocky Mountain Columbine;* Tree: *Blue Spruce;* Bird: *Lark Bunting;* Song: *"Where the Columbines Grow";* Motto: *Nil sine Numine (Nothing without God).*

CONNECTICUT

Capital: *Hartford;* Statehood (and rank): *Jan. 9, 1788 (5);* Population (and rank): *2,535,234 (25);* Area (and rank): *5,009 (48);* Highest Elevation: *Mount Frissell (2,380);* U.S. Government: *2/6;* Electoral Votes: *8;* State Government: *36/294;* Counties: *8;* Flower: *Mountain Laurel;* Tree: *White Oak;* Bird: *Robin;* Motto: *Qui transtulit sustinet (He who transplanted, sustains).*

DELAWARE

Capital: *Dover;* Statehood (and rank): *Dec. 7, 1787 (1);* Population (and rank): *446,292 (46);* Area (and rank): *2,057 (49);* Highest Elevation: *Ebright Road (442);* U.S. Government: *2/1;* Electoral votes: *3;* State Government: *17/35;* Counties: *3;* Flower: *Peach Blossom;* Tree: *American Holly;* Bird: *Blue Hen Chicken;* Song: *"Our Delaware";* Motto: *Liberty and Independence.*

FLORIDA

Capital: *Tallahassee;* Statehood (and rank): *March 3, 1845 (27);* Population (and rank): *4,951,560 (10);* Area (and rank): *58,560 (22);* Highest Elevation: *(in) Walton County (345);* U.S. Government: *2/8;* Electoral Votes: *10;* State Government: *38/95;* Counties: *67;* Flower: *Orange Blossom;* Tree: *Sabal Palm;* Bird: *Mockingbird;* Song: *"Swannee River";* Motto: *In God we trust.*

GEORGIA

Capital: *Atlanta;* Statehood (and rank): *Feb. 2, 1788 (4);* Population (and rank): *3,943,116 (15);* Area (and rank): *58,876 (21);* Highest Elevation: *Brasstown Bald (4,784);* U.S. Government: *2/10;* Electoral Votes: *12;* State Government: *54/205;* Counties: *159;* Flower: *Cherokee Rose;* Tree: *Live Oak;* Bird: *Brown Thrasher;* Song: *"Georgia";* Motto: *Wisdom, justice and moderation.*

HAWAII

Capital: *Honolulu;* Statehood (and rank): *July 4, 1960 (50);* Population (and rank): *632,772 (44);* Area (and rank): *6,439 (47);* Highest Elevation: *Mauna Kea (13,796);* U.S. Government: *2/1;* Electoral Votes: *3;* State Government: *25/51;* Counties: *5;* Flower: *Red Hibiscus;* Tree: *Kukui;* Bird: *Nene (Hawaiian Goose);* Song:

"Hawaii Ponoi"; Motto: *The life of the land is perpetuated in righteousness.*

IDAHO

Capital: *Boise;* Statehood (and rank): *July 3, 1890 (43);* Population (and rank): *667,191 (42);* Area (and rank): *83,557 (13);* Highest Elevation: *Borah Peak (12,662);* U.S. Government: *2/2;* Electoral Votes: *4;* State Government: *44/59;* Counties: *44;* Flower: *Syringa;* Tree: *White Pine;* Bird: *Mountain Bluebird;* Song: *"Here We Have Idaho";* Motto: *Esto perpetua (Be forever).*

ILLINOIS

Capital: *Springfield;* Statehood (and rank): *Dec. 3, 1818 (21);* Population (and rank): *10,081,158 (4);* Area (and rank): *56,400 (24);* Highest Elevation: *Charles Mound (1,241);* U.S. Government: *2/25;* Electoral Votes: *27;* State Government: *58/177;* Counties: *102;* Flower: *Violet;* Tree: *Oak;* Bird: *Cardinal;* Song: *"Illinois";* Motto: *State sovereignty, national union.*

INDIANA

Capital: *Indianapolis;* Statehood (and rank): *Dec. 11, 1816 (19);* Population (and rank): *4,662,498 (11);* Area (and rank): *36,291 (38);* Highest Elevation: *Franklin Township (1,253);* U.S. Government: *2/11;* Electoral Votes: *13;* State Government: *50/100;* Counties: *92;* Flower: *Peony;* Tree: *Tulip Tree;* Bird: *Cardinal;* Song: *"On the Banks of the Wabash";* Motto: *The crossroads of America.*

IOWA

Capital: *Des Moines;* Statehood (and rank): *Dec. 28, 1846 (29);* Population (and rank): *2,757,537 (24);* Area (and rank): *56,290 (25);* Highest Elevation: *(in) Osceola County (1,675);* U.S. Government: *2/8;* Electoral Votes: *10;* State Government: *50/108;* Counties: *99;* Flower: *Wild Rose;* Bird: *Eastern Goldfinch;* Song: *"The Song of Iowa";* Motto: *Our liberties we prize and our rights we will maintain.*

KANSAS

Capital: *Topeka;* Statehood (and rank): *Jan. 29, 1861 (34);* Population (and rank): *2,178,611 (29);* Area (and rank): *82,276 (14);* Highest Elevation: *(in) Wallace County (4,135);* U.S. Government: *2/6;* Electoral Votes: *8;* State Government: *40/125;* Counties: *105;* Flower: *Sunflower;* Tree: *Cottonwood;* Bird: *Western Meadow Lark;* Animal: *American Buffalo;* Song: *"Home on the Range";* Motto: *Ad astra per aspera (To the stars through difficulties).*

KENTUCKY

Capital: *Frankfort;* Statehood (and rank): *June 1, 1792 (15);* Population (and rank): *3,038,156 (22);* Area (and rank): *40,395 (37);* Highest Elevation: *Black Mountain (4,145);* U.S. Government: *2/8;* Electoral Votes: *10;* State Government: *38/100;* Counties: *120;* Flower: *Goldenrod;* Tree: *Tulip Poplar;* Bird: *Kentucky Cardinal;* Song: *"My Old Kentucky Home";* Motto: *United we stand, divided we fall.*

LOUISIANA

Capital: *Baton Rouge;* Statehood (and rank): *April 30, 1812 (18);* Population (and rank): *3,257,022 (20);* Area (and rank): *48,523 (31);* Highest Elevation: *Driskill Mountain (535);* U.S. Government: *2/8;* Electoral Votes: *10;* State Government: *39/101;* Parishes: *64;* Flower: *Magnolia;* Bird: *Eastern Brown Pelican;* Song: *"Song of Louisiana";* Motto: *Union, justice and confidence.*

MAINE

Capital: *Augusta;* Statehood (and rank): *March 15, 1820 (23);* Population (and rank): *969,265 (36);* Area (and rank): *33,215 (39);* Highest Elevation: *Mount Katahdin*

(5,268); U.S. Government: 2/3; Electoral Votes: 5; State Government: 33/151; Counties: 16; Flower: *White Pine Cone and Tassel;* Tree: *White Pine;* Bird: *Chickadee;* Song: *"State of Maine Song";* Motto: *Dirigo (I direct).*

MARYLAND
Capital: *Annapolis;* Statehood (and rank): *April 28, 1788 (7);* Population (and rank): *3,100,689 (21);* Area (and rank): *10,577 (42);* Highest Elevation: *Backbone Mountain (3,360);* U.S. Government: 2/7; Electoral Votes: 9; State Government: 29/123; Counties: 23; Flower: *Black-eyed Susan;* Tree: *White Oak;* Bird: *Baltimore Oriole;* Song: *"Maryland, My Maryland";* Motto: *Fatti maschii, parole femine (Deeds masculine, words feminine).*

MASSACHUSETTS
Capital: *Boston;* Statehood (and rank): *Feb. 6, 1788 (6);* Population (and rank): *5,148,578 (9);* Area (and rank): *8,257 (45);* Highest Elevation: *Mount Greylock (3,491);* U.S. Government: 2/14; Electoral Votes: 16; State Government: 40/240; Counties: 14; Flower: *Mayflower;* Tree: *American Elm;* Bird: *Chickadee;* Motto: *Ense petit placidam sub libertate quietem (By the sword we seek peace, but peace only under liberty).*

MICHIGAN
Capital: *Lansing;* Statehood (and rank): *Jan. 26, 1837 (26);* Population (and rank): *7,823,194 (7);* Area (and rank): *58,216 (23);* Highest Elevation: *(in) Baraga County (1,980);* U.S. Government: 2/18; Electoral Votes: 20; State Government: 34/110; Counties: 83; Flower: *Apple Blossom;* Tree: *White Pine;* Bird: *Robin;* Animal: *Wolverine;* Song: *"Michigan, My Michigan";* Motto: *Si quaeris peninsulam amoenam, circumspice (If you seek a pleasant peninsula, look about you).*

MINNESOTA
Capital: *St. Paul;* Statehood (and rank): *May 11, 1858 (32);* Population (and rank): *3,413,864 (18);* Area (and rank): *84,068 (12);* Highest Elevation: *Misquah Hills (2,230);* U.S. Government: 2/9; Electoral Votes: 11; State Government: 67/131; Counties: 87; Flower: *Lady's-slipper;* Tree: *Norway Pine;* Bird: *Goldfinch;* Song: *"Hail! Minnesota";* Motto: *L'Etoile du Nord (The Star of the North).*

MISSISSIPPI
Capital: *Jackson;* Statehood (and rank): *Dec. 10, 1817 (20);* Population (and rank): *2,178,141 (28);* Area (and rank): *47,716 (32);* Highest Elevation: *Woodall Mountain (806);* U.S. Government: 2/6; Electoral Votes: 8; State Government: 49/140; Counties: 82; Flower: *Magnolia;* Tree: *Magnolia;* Bird: *Mockingbird;* Song: *"Way Down South in Mississippi";* Motto: *Virtute et armis (By valor and arms).*

MISSOURI
Capital: *Jefferson City;* Statehood (and rank): *Aug. 10, 1821 (24);* Population (and rank): *4,319,813 (13);* Area (and rank): *69,674 (19);* Highest Elevation: *Taum Sauk Mountain (1,772);* U.S. Government: 2/11; Electoral Votes: 13; State Government: 34/157; Counties: 114; Flower: *Hawthorn;* Tree: *Dogwood;* Bird: *Bluebird;* Song: *"Missouri Waltz";* Motto: *Salus populi suprema lex esto (The welfare of the people shall be the supreme law).*

MONTANA
Capital: *Helena;* Statehood (and rank): *Nov. 8, 1889 (41);* Population (and rank): *674,767 (41);* Area (and rank): *147,138 (4);* Highest Elevation: *Granite Peak (12,799);* U.S. Government: 2/2; Electoral Votes: 4; State Government: 56/94; Counties: 56; Flower: *Bitterroot;* Tree: *Ponderosa Pine;* Bird: *Western Meadow Lark;* Song: *"Montana";* Motto: *Oro y plata (Gold and silver).*

NEBRASKA
Capital: *Lincoln;* Statehood (and rank): *March 1, 1867 (37);* Population (and rank): *1,411,330 (34);* Area (and rank): *77,227 (15);* Highest Elevation: *Johnson Township (5,424);* U.S. Government: 2/4; Electoral Votes: 6; State Government: *43 senators (unicameral legislature);* Counties: 93; Flower: *Goldenrod;* Tree: *American Elm;* Bird: *Western Meadow Lark;* Song: *"My Nebraska";* Motto: *Equality before the law.*

NEVADA
Capital: *Carson City;* Statehood (and rank): *Oct. 31, 1864 (36);* Population (and rank): *285,278 (49);* Area (and rank): *110,540 (7);* Highest Elevation: *Boundary Peak (13,145);* U.S. Government: 2/1; Electoral Votes: 3; State Government: 17/47; Counties: 17; Flower: *Sagebrush;* Tree: *Single-leaf Piñon;* Bird: *Mountain Bluebird;* Song: *"Home Means Nevada";* Motto: *All for our Country.*

NEW HAMPSHIRE
Capital: *Concord;* Statehood (and rank): *June 21, 1788 (9);* Population (and rank): *606,921 (45);* Area (and rank): *9,304 (44);* Highest Elevation: *Mount Washington (6,288);* U.S. Government: 2/2; Electoral Votes: 4; State Government: 24/400; Counties: 10; Flower: *Purple Lilac;* Tree: *White Birch;* Bird: *Purple Finch;* Song: *"Old New Hampshire";* Motto: *Live free or die.*

NEW JERSEY
Capital: *Trenton;* Statehood (and rank): *Dec. 18, 1787 (3);* Population (and rank): *6,066,782 (8);* Area (and rank): *7,836 (46);* Highest Elevation: *High Point (1,803);* U.S. Government: 2/14; Electoral Votes: 16; State Government: 21/60; Counties: 21; Flower: *Violet;* Tree: *Red Oak;* Bird: *Eastern Goldfinch;* Motto: *Liberty and prosperity.*

NEW MEXICO
Capital: *Santa Fe;* Statehood (and rank): *Jan. 6, 1912 (47);* Population (and rank): *951,023 (37);* Area (and rank): *121,666 (5);* Highest Elevation: *Wheeler Peak (13,160);* U.S. Government: 2/2; Electoral Votes: 4; State Government: 32/66; Counties: 32; Flower: *Yucca Flower;* Tree: *Piñon;* Bird: *Road Runner;* Fish: *Cutthroat Trout;* Song: *"O, Fair New Mexico";* Motto: *Crescit eundo (It grows as it goes).*

NEW YORK
Capital: *Albany;* Statehood (and rank): *July 26, 1788 (11);* Population (and rank): *16,782,304 (1);* Area (and rank): *49,576 (30);* Highest Elevation: *Mount Marcy (5,344);* U.S. Government: 2/43; Electoral Votes: 45; State Government: 58/150; Counties: 62; Flower: *Rose;* Tree: *Sugar Maple;* Bird: *Bluebird;* Motto: *Excelsior (Ever upward).*

NORTH CAROLINA
Capital: *Raleigh;* Statehood (and rank): *Nov. 21, 1789 (12);* Population (and rank): *4,556,155 (12);* Area (and rank): *52,712 (28);* Highest Elevation: *Mount Mitchell (6,684);* U.S. Government: 2/12; Electoral Votes: 14; State Government: 50/120; Counties: 100; Flower: *Dogwood;* Bird: *Cardinal;* Song: *"The Old North State";* Motto: *Esse quam videri (To be, rather than to seem).*

NORTH DAKOTA
Capital: *Bismarck;* Statehood (and rank): *Nov. 2, 1889 (39 or 40);* Population (and rank): *632,446 (43);* Area (and rank): *70,665 (17);* Highest Elevation: *White Butte (3,530);* U.S. Government: 2/2; Electoral Votes: 4; State Government: 49/113; Counties: 53; Flower: *Wild Prairie Rose;* Tree: *American Elm;* Bird: *Western Meadow Lark;* Song: *"North Dakota Hymn";* Motto: *Liberty and union, now and forever, one and inseparable.*

OHIO
Capital: *Columbus;* Statehood (and rank): *March 1, 1803 (17);* Population (and rank): *9,706,397 (5);* Area (and rank): *41,222 (35);* Highest Elevation: *Campbell Hill (1,550);* U.S. Government: *2/23;* Electoral Votes: *25;* State Government: *38/139;* Counties: *88;* Flower: *Scarlet Carnation;* Tree: *Buckeye;* Bird: *Cardinal;* Motto: *With God, all things are possible.*

OKLAHOMA
Capital: *Oklahoma City;* Statehood (and rank): *Nov. 16, 1907 (46);* Population (and rank): *2,328, 284 (27);* Area (and rank): *69,919 (18);* Highest Elevation: *Black Mesa (4,978);* U.S. Government: *2/6;* Electoral Votes: *8;* State Government: *44/121;* Counties: *77;* Flower: *Mistletoe;* Tree: *Redbud;* Bird: *Scissor-tailed Flycatcher;* Song: *"Oklahoma!";* Motto: *Labor omnia vincit (Labor conquers all things).*

OREGON
Capital: *Salem;* Statehood (and rank): *Feb. 14, 1859 (33);* Population (and rank): *1,768,687 (32);* Area (and rank): *96,981 (10);* Highest Elevation: *Mount Hood (11,245);* U.S. Government: *2/4;* Electoral Votes: *6;* State Government: *30/60;* Counties: *36;* Flower: *Oregon Grape;* Tree: *Douglas Fir;* Bird: *Western Meadow Lark;* Song: *"Oregon, My Oregon";* Motto: *The Union.*

PENNSYLVANIA
Capital: *Harrisburg;* Statehood (and rank): *Dec. 12, 1787 (2);* Population (and rank): *11,319,366 (3);* Area (and rank): *45,333 (33);* Highest Elevation: *Mount Davis (3,213);* U.S. Government: *2/30;* Electoral Votes: *32;* State Government: *50/210;* Counties: *67;* Flower: *Mountain Laurel;* Tree: *Hemlock;* Bird: *Ruffed Grouse;* Motto: *Virtue, liberty and independence.*

RHODE ISLAND
Capital: *Providence;* Statehood (and rank): *May 29, 1790 (13);* Population (and rank): *859,488 (39);* Area (and rank): *1,214 (50);* Highest Elevation: *Jerimoth Hill (812);* U.S. Government: *2/2;* Electoral Votes: *4;* State Government: *44/100;* Counties: *5;* Flower: *Violet;* Tree: *Maple;* Bird: *Rhode Island Red;* Song: *"Rhode Island";* Motto: *Hope.*

SOUTH CAROLINA
Capital: *Columbia;* Statehood (and rank): *May 23, 1788 (8);* Population (and rank): *2,382,594 (26);* Area (and rank): *31,055 (40);* Highest Elevation: *Sassafras Mountain (3,560);* U.S. Government: *2/6;* Electoral Votes: *8;* State Government: *46/124;* Counties: *46;* Flower: *Carolina Jessamine;* Tree: *Palmetto;* Bird: *Carolina Wren;* Song: *"Carolina";* Motto: *Dum spiro, spero (While I breathe, I hope)* and *Animus opibusque parati (Prepared in mind and resources).*

SOUTH DAKOTA
Capital: *Pierre;* Statehood (and rank): *Nov. 2, 1889 (39 or 40);* Population (and rank): *680,514 (40);* Area (and rank): *77,047 (16);* Highest Elevation: *Harney Peak (7,242);* U.S. Government: *2/2;* Electoral Votes: *4;* State Government: *35/75;* Counties: *67;* Flower: *Pasqueflower;* Tree: *Black Hills Spruce;* Bird: *Ring-necked Pheasant;* Animal: *Coyote;* Song: *"Hail! South Dakota";* Motto: *Under God the people rule.*

TENNESSEE
Capital: *Nashville;* Statehood (and rank): *June 1, 1796 (16);* Population (and rank): *3,567,089 (17);* Area (and rank): *42,244 (34);* Highest Elevation: *Clingman's Dome (6,642);* U.S. Government: *2/9;* Electoral Votes: *11;* State Government: *33/99;* Counties: *95;* Flower: *Iris;* Tree: *Tulip Poplar;* Bird: *Mockingbird;* Song: *"My Homeland, Tennessee"* and *"When It's Iris Time in Tennessee";* Motto: *Agriculture and commerce.*

TEXAS
Capital: *Austin;* Statehood (and rank): *Dec. 29, 1845 (28);* Population (and rank): *9,579,677 (6);* Area (and rank): *267,339 (2);* Highest Elevation: *Guadalupe Peak (8,751);* U.S. Government: *2/22;* Electoral Votes: *24;* State Government: *31/150;* Counties: *254;* Flower: *Bluebonnet;* Tree: *Pecan;* Bird: *Mockingbird;* Song: *"Texas, Our Texas";* Motto: *Friendship.*

UTAH
Capital: *Salt Lake City;* Statehood (and rank): *Jan. 4, 1896 (45);* Population (and rank): *890,627 (38);* Area (and rank): *84,916 (11);* Highest Elevation: *Kings Peak (13,498);* U.S. Government: *2/2;* Electoral Votes: *4;* State Government: *25/64;* Counties: *29;* Flower: *Sego Lily;* Tree: *Blue Spruce;* Bird: *Gull;* Song: *"Utah, We Love Thee";* Motto: *Industry.*

VERMONT
Capital: *Montpelier;* Statehood (and rank): *March 4, 1791 (14);* Population (and rank): *389,881 (47);* Area (and rank): *9,609 (43);* Highest Elevation: *Mount Mansfield (4,393);* U.S. Government: *2/1;* Electoral Votes: *3;* State Government: *30/246;* Counties: *14;* Flower: *Red Clover;* Tree: *Sugar Maple;* Bird: *Hermit Thrush;* Song: *"Hail, Vermont";* Motto: *Freedom and unity.*

VIRGINIA
Capital: *Richmond;* Statehood (and rank): *June 26, 1788 (10);* Population (and rank): *3,966,949 (16);* Area (and rank): *40,815 (36);* Highest Elevation: *Mount Rogers (5,720);* U.S. Government: *2/10;* Electoral Votes: *12;* State Government: *40/100;* Counties: *98;* Flower: *Dogwood;* Tree: *Dogwood Tree;* Bird: *Cardinal;* Song: *"Carry Me Back to Old Virginia";* Motto: *Sic semper tyrannis (Thus always to tyrants).*

WASHINGTON
Capital: *Olympia;* Statehood (and rank): *Nov. 11, 1889 (42);* Population (and rank): *2,853,214 (23);* Area (and rank): *68,192 (20);* Highest Elevation: *Mount Rainier (14,410);* U.S. Government: *2/7;* Electoral Votes: *9;* State Government: *49/99;* Counties: *39;* Flower: *Coast Rhododendron;* Tree: *Western Hemlock;* Bird: *Willow Goldfinch;* Song: *"Washington, My Home";* Motto: *Al-Ki (Bye and bye).*

WEST VIRGINIA
Capital: *Charleston;* Statehood (and rank): *June 20, 1863 (35);* Population (and rank): *1,860,421 (30);* Area (and rank): *24,181 (41);* Highest Elevation: *Spruce Knob (4,860);* U.S. Government: *2/6;* Electoral Votes: *8;* State Government: *32/100;* Counties: *55;* Flower: *Rhododendron;* Tree: *Sugar Maple;* Bird: *Cardinal;* Animal: *Black Bear;* Song: *"West Virginia, My Home Sweet Home";* Motto: *Montani semper liberi (Mountaineers always free).*

WISCONSIN
Capital: *Madison;* Statehood (and rank): *May 29, 1848 (30);* Population (and rank): *3,951,777 (14);* Area (and rank): *56,154 (26);* Highest Elevation: *Rib Mountain (1,941);* U.S. Government: *2/10;* Electoral Votes: *12;* State Government: *33/100;* Counties: *71;* Flower: *Violet;* Tree: *Sugar Maple;* Bird: *Robin;* Animal: *Badger;* Fish: *Muskellunge;* Song: *"On Wisconsin";* Motto: *Forward!*

WYOMING
Capital: *Cheyenne;* Statehood (and rank): *July 10, 1890 (44);* Population (and rank): *330,066 (48);* Area (and rank): *97,014 (9);* Highest Elevation: *Gannett Peak (13,785);* U.S. Government: *2/1;* Electoral Votes: *3;* State Government: *27/56;* Counties: *23;* Flower: *Indian Paintbrush;* Tree: *Cottonwood;* Bird: *Meadow Lark;* Song: *"Wyoming";* Motto: *Equal rights.*

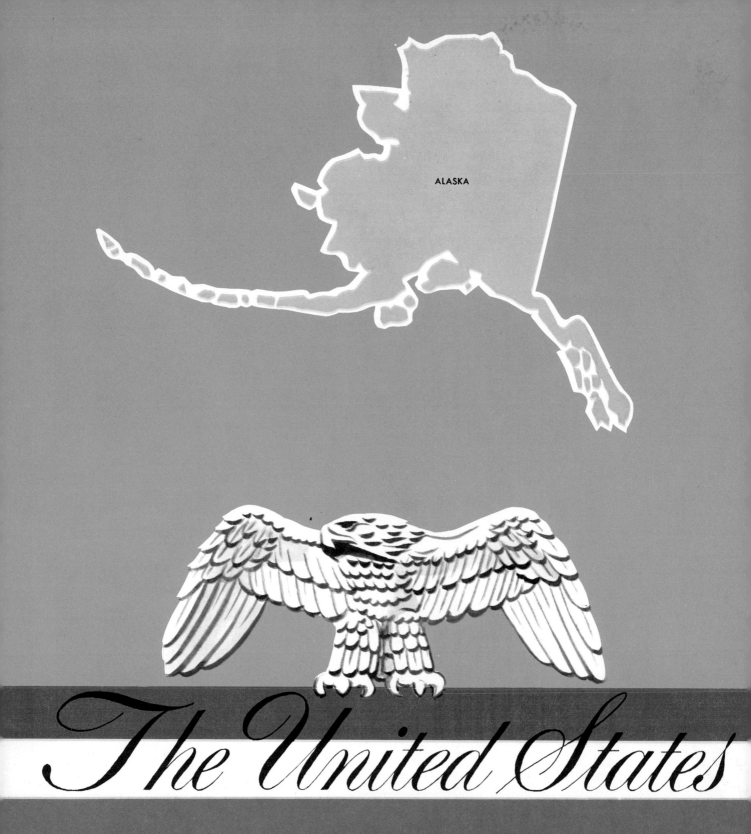

ALASKA

The United States

HAWAII